Introduction to
SOLID STATE PHYSICS

Introduction to
SOLID STATE PHYSICS

Charles Kittel

PROFESSOR OF PHYSICS
UNIVERSITY OF CALIFORNIA
BERKELEY, CALIFORNIA

CHARLES KITTEL

New York · JOHN WILEY & SONS, Inc.
London · CHAPMAN & HALL, Ltd.

Library of Congress Catalog Card Number: 53-7203
Printed in the United States of America

Preface

This volume is intended as an introductory textbook in solid state physics for senior and beginning graduate students in physics, chemistry, and engineering. My object has been to write an elementary and short account of representative aspects of the physics of solids. The level of presentation supposes that the reader will have a general familiarity with modern atomic physics to the extent of the undergraduate courses offered under this title in many universities. A course in quantum mechanics is not a prerequisite to reading this book, but the reader should have been exposed to the Planck radiation law, the de Broglie relation, the Bohr theory of the hydrogen atom, the Zeeman effect, and the wave equation for free particles. Advanced topics in solids, in particular those requiring a formal background of quantum mechanics, are developed in appendices.

Solid state physics is a very wide field, and it includes many branches. It is concerned with the physical properties of solids, particularly the special properties exhibited by atoms and molecules because of their association in the solid phase. The existence of powerful theoretical methods and concepts applicable to a wide range of problems has been an important unifying influence in the field. It is quite natural therefore that an introductory textbook should emphasize theoretical models of solids, rather than the details of experimental techniques or the results of measurements on complicated systems which may have great industrial importance. In the selection of material I have frankly favored those areas which may be discussed in terms of simple, concrete, and well-developed models. This selection principle is the explanation of the emphasis on dielectric and magnetic properties and of the absence of emphasis on phosphors and on metallurgical problems, for example.

The major problem in writing this book has been to conform to reasonable limitations on the length, in keeping with the spirit of an introductory textbook. It is not intended to be a general reference book. Several active and important branches of solid state physics have not been mentioned at all. Among the topics omitted are internal friction, photographic theory, thermoelectric effects, phase diagrams, fracture, creep, grain boundaries, melting phenomena, field emission, oxide cathodes, surface physics, radiation damage, crystal counters, piezoelectricity, liquid and solid helium, plastics, and molecular crystals. As nearly every chapter has been or should be the subject of separate monographs by other authors, it is inevitable that the treatment of the subjects which have been included should be incomplete. The discussion of the general subject of x-rays, crystal structure, and crystal symmetry is very much shorter than its importance justifies, but on this subject there exists a number of excellent elementary textbooks with which the reader may better master the subject. In all chapters the references to the literature are intended only to be representative of some of the reviews and the classical papers, along with enough of a selection from recent work to enable the reader to get an impression of the nature of the current activity.

The rapid rise of interest in solid state physics in recent years has suddenly presented universities with the problem of offering adequate instruction in the subject. It seems to me that there should be an introductory or survey course followed by, as a minimum program for graduate students intending to do research in the field, a course in x-ray crystallography and a course in the quantum theory of solids. These two subjects are large, important, and well-developed; it is not possible to deal with them adequately in an introductory course.

It might be useful to teachers to make two remarks drawn from the experience Professor A. F. Kip and I have had in teaching at Berkeley a course along the lines of this book. First, the material is excellently suited to the liberal use of models, demonstrations, exhibits, motion pictures, and other visual aids. Second, a one-semester course for seniors goes well if the qualitative, pictorial, and simpler quantitative topics are emphasized, with the longer quantitative discussions left to the students' reading; this suggestion applies with particular force to the first chapter.

Problem sets are included at the end of every chapter, with problems of considerable length or difficulty marked by an asterisk. A very brief summary of relevant parts of thermodynamics and statistical mechanics is given in Appendix T. Gaussian cgs units are used except where otherwise noted. The value of e, the charge on the electron, is taken as negative in sign: $e = -4.80 \times 10^{-10}$ esu for the electron.

I am greatly indebted to my students who have checked over parts of the volume: E. Abrahams, M. Cohen, H. Kaplan, F. Keffer, J. Tessman, and Y. Yafet. I wish to thank J. Bardeen for reviewing the chapters on superconductivity and semiconductors, and F. Seitz for reviewing the chapters dealing with imperfections in solids; K. K.

Darrow has kindly reviewed several chapters. It is a pleasure to thank R. T. Birge for assistance in connection with the values of fundamental physical constants; N. Bloembergen for the suggestion of a number of problems; Sir Lawrence Bragg and W. M. Lomer for a photograph of a dislocation model; A. von Hippel and P. W. Forsbergh, Jr., for a photograph of ferroelectric domains; H. F. Kay and B. J. Appelbe for a photograph of a crystal growth pattern; A. F. Kip and M. Tinkham for a hyperfine structure photograph; E. R. Parker for a photograph of a low angle grain boundary; H. J. Williams for a ferromagnetic domain photograph; and W. H. Zachariasen for tables of ionic radii. I wish also to acknowledge help and suggestions from W. Brattain, E. Fermi, C. Herring, A. N. Holden, Miss U. Martius, J. Weymouth, and Mrs. E. A. Wood. Mrs. C. E. Thornhill has very kindly assisted in the preparation of the indexes.

CHARLES KITTEL

Berkeley, California
April, 1953

Contents

salts. J. Semiclassical discussion of ferromagnetic spin waves.
K. The Bloch theorem. L. Perturbation of nearly free electrons by
a periodic potential. M. Tight binding approximation for metallic
electrons. N. Brillouin zones of general crystal structures. O.
Electrical conductivity at low temperatures. P. Mobility in
intrinsic semiconductors. Q. Derivation of the Conwell-Weisskopf
formula. R. Fermi level and the chemical potential. S. Stresses
around a dislocation. T. Summary of results of thermodynamics
and statistical mechanics. U. Values of general physical constants.

General References

Atomic physics background

Max Born, *Atomic physics*, Hafner, New York, 5th ed., 1951.

Elementary texts

W. Kleber, *Angewandte Gitterphysik*, W. de Gruyter & Co., Berlin, 2nd ed., 1949.

F. O. Rice and E. Teller, *Structure of matter*, John Wiley & Sons, New York, 1949.

J. C. Slater, *Introduction to chemical physics*, McGraw-Hill Book Co., New York, 1939.

J. C. Slater, *Quantum theory of matter*, McGraw-Hill Book Co., New York, 1951.

Advanced texts

N. F. Mott and H. Jones, *Theory of the properties of metals and alloys*, Clarendon Press, Oxford, 1936.

F. Seitz, *Modern theory of solids*, McGraw-Hill Book Co., New York, 1940.

Data collections and bibliographical aids

Chemical Abstracts (especially the decennial indices).

Gmelins *Handbuch der anorganischen Chemie.*

Landolt-Börnstein *Physikalisch-chemische Tabellen*, J. Springer, Berlin, 5th ed., 1935; 6th ed., 1952.

C. J. Smithells, *Metals reference book*, Butterworths Scientific Publications, London, 1949.

1

Classification of Solids
and Crystal Structures

We discuss first the approximate classification of crystals in terms of the dominant type of chemical binding force keeping the atoms together. The classification of the symmetry properties of crystals is considered next, in relation to both macroscopic physical properties and the arrangement of atoms in the crystal. The application of x-ray diffraction to the determination of the crystal structure is discussed briefly.

EMPIRICAL CLASSIFICATION OF CRYSTAL BINDING

It is useful to make an approximate classification of crystals in terms of the dominant type of chemical binding displayed. It may not be possible or sensible to classify some solids, whereas with others it may be possible[1] to make an approximate quantitative assessment of the contribution of the various types of binding to the total binding energy. The principal types of binding are given in Table 1.1.

The static forces binding atoms and molecules in solids are almost entirely electrostatic in nature, with only insignificant contributions from magnetic interactions. There are also important kinetic effects on the binding energy arising from the quantum motion of the atomic electrons. By and large, the important differences among the several types of crystal bonds may be attributed to qualitative differences in the distribution of electrons around the atoms and molecules. If it were easier to prepare maps showing the distribution of electrons in the interior of crystals, we should be able to define the character of the binding by more quantitative criteria than at present available.

---

[1] See, for example, L. Pauling, *Nature of the chemical bond*, Cornell University Press, Ithaca, 2nd ed., 1945. For the application of molecular beam and microwave spectroscopy to this problem, see C. H. Townes and B. P. Dailey, J. Chem. Phys. **17**, 782 (1949).

IONIC CRYSTALS

In ionic crystals electrons are transferred from atoms of one type to atoms of a second type, so that the crystal is made up of positive and negative ions. The ions arrange themselves so that the Coulomb attraction between ions of opposite sign is stronger than the Coulomb repulsion between ions of the same sign. The *ionic bond* is thus

TABLE 1.1. CLASSIFICATION OF CRYSTAL TYPES

The binding energy is the energy necessary to dissociate the solid into separated atoms, molecules, or ions, as appropriate. The binding energy is taken at room temperature, except for the molecular crystals where it is taken at the melting point. Note that 1 ev/molecule = 23.05 kcal/mole.

Crystal Type	Examples	Binding Energy (kcal/mole)	Characteristics of Type
Ionic	NaCl	180	Strong infrared absorption; low electrical conductivity at low temperatures; good conductivity by ions at high temperatures.
	LiF	240	
Covalent	Diamond	~170	Great hardness; low conductivity at low temperatures when specimens are pure.
	SiC	283	
Metallic	Na	26	High electrical conductivity.
	Fe	94	
Molecular	A	1.8	Low melting and boiling points; very compressible.
	CH_4	2.4	
Hydrogen-bonded	H_2O (ice)	12	Tendency to polymerize (that is, to form groups of many molecules); increased binding energy of molecules in comparison with similar molecules without hydrogen bonds.
	HF	7	

essentially the bond resulting from the electrostatic interaction of oppositely charged ions. Two common crystal structures found for ionic crystals, the sodium chloride and the cesium chloride structures, are shown in Fig. 1.1.

The degree of ionization of the constituent atoms of an ionic crystal is often such that the electronic configurations of all ions correspond to closed electronic shells as in the inert gas atoms. In lithium fluoride the configurations of the neutral atoms are, according to Table 1.2,

$$Li: 1s^2 2s,$$

$$F: 1s^2 2s^2 2p^5,$$

TABLE 1.2. PERIODIC TABLE, WITH THE OUTER ELECTRON CONFIGURATIONS OF NEUTRAL ATOMS IN THEIR GROUND STATES

(Configuration assignments for the rare earth and actinide elements are somewhat uncertain.)

1 H $1s$			
2 He $1s^2$			
	3 Li $2s$		
	4 Be $2s^2$		
	5 B $2s^22p$		
	6 C $2s^22p^2$		
	7 N $2s^22p^3$		
	8 O $2s^22p^4$		
	9 F $2s^22p^5$		
	10 Ne $2s^22p^6$		
11 Na $2p^63s$			
12 Mg $2p^63s^2$			
13 Al $3s^23p$			
14 Si $3s^23p^2$			
15 P $3s^23p^3$			
16 S $3s^23p^4$			
17 Cl $3s^23p^5$			
18 A $3s^23p^6$			
19 K $3p^64s$			
20 Ca $3p^64s^2$			
21 Sc $3d4s^2$			
22 Ti $3d^24s^2$			
23 V $3d^34s^2$			
24 Cr $3d^54s$			
25 Mn $3d^54s^2$			
26 Fe $3d^64s^2$			
27 Co $3d^74s^2$			
28 Ni $3d^84s^2$			
29 Cu $3d^{10}4s$			
30 Zn $3d^{10}4s^2$			
31 Ga $4s^24p$			
32 Ge $4s^24p^2$			
33 As $4s^24p^3$			
34 Se $4s^24p^4$			
35 Br $4s^24p^5$			
36 Kr $4s^24p^6$			
37 Rb $4p^65s$			
38 Sr $4p^65s^2$			
39 Y $4d5s^2$			
40 Zr $4d^25s^2$			
41 Nb $4d^45s$			
42 Mo $4d^55s$			
43 Tc $4d^55s^2$			
44 Ru $4d^75s$			
45 Rh $4d^85s$			
46 Pd $4d^{10}$			
47 Ag $4d^{10}5s$			
48 Cd $4d^{10}5s^2$			
49 In $5s^25p$			
50 Sn $5s^25p^2$			
51 Sb $5s^25p^3$			
52 Te $5s^25p^4$			
53 I $5s^25p^5$			
54 Xe $5s^25p^6$			
55 Cs $5p^66s$			
56 Ba $5p^66s^2$			
57 La $5p^65d6s^2$			
58 Ce $4f^26s^2$			
59 Pr $4f^36s^2$			
60 Nd $4f^46s^2$			
61 Pm $4f^56s^2$			
62 Sm $4f^66s^2$			
63 Eu $4f^76s^2$			
64 Gd $4f^75d6s^2$			
65 Tb $4f^85d6s^2$			
66 Dy $4f^{10}6s^2$			
67 Ho $4f^{11}6s^2$			
68 Er $4f^{12}6s^2$			
69 Tm $4f^{13}6s^2$			
70 Yb $4f^{14}6s^2$			
71 Lu $4f^{14}5d6s^2$			
72 Hf $5d^26s^2$			
73 Ta $5d^36s^2$			
74 W $5d^46s^2$			
75 Re $5d^56s^2$			
76 Os $5d^66s^2$			
77 Ir $5d^9$			
78 Pt $5d^96s$			
79 Au $5d^{10}6s$			
80 Hg $5d^{10}6s^2$			
81 Tl $6s^26p$			
82 Pb $6s^26p^2$			
83 Bi $6s^26p^3$			
84 Po $6s^26p^4$			
85 At $6s^26p^5$			
86 Rn $6s^26p^6$			
87 Fr $6p^67s$			
88 Ra $6p^67s^2$			
89 Ac $6d7s^2$			
90 Th $6d^27s^2$			
91 Pa $5f^26d7s^2$			
92 U $5f^36d7s^2$			
93 Np $5f^57s^2$			
94 Pu $5f^67s^2$			
95 Am $5f^77s^2$			
96 Cm $5f^76d7s^2$			
97 Bk $5f^86d7s^2$			
98 Cf $5f^96d7s^2$			

while the singly charged ions have the configurations

$$Li^+: 1s^2,$$

$$F^-: 1s^2 2s^2 2p^6,$$

as for helium and neon, respectively. The inert gas atoms have closed shells, and the charge distributions are spherically symmetric. We may expect accordingly that the charge distributions on each ion in an

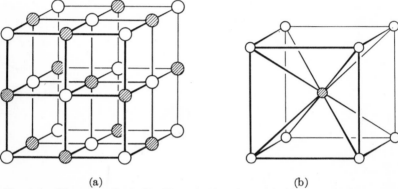

(a)   (b)

Fig. 1.1. The (a) sodium chloride and (b) cesium chloride crystal structures.

ionic crystal may have approximately spherical symmetry, with some distortion near the region of contact with neighboring atoms.

COVALENT CRYSTALS

In an ionic bond it is a good approximation to think of the valence electrons as attached to definite atoms. The Pauli principle applied to ions with filled shells insures a low electron density in the region between the two ions where the charge shells make contact. In a covalent or homopolar bond the charge density between the two atoms may be rather high,[2] and the valence electrons are to an appreciable extent shared between two atoms. The covalent bond is the normal electron-pair bond of chemistry, encountered particularly in organic chemistry. It is characterized by a high density of electrons between the ions and also by marked directional properties. The carbon bond is a good example of the directional properties of the covalent bond: carbon atoms often prefer to join onto each other or to other atoms by

[2] Compare the electron distribution maps obtained by x-ray analysis of diamond and sodium chloride, in Figs. 53 and 66 of Y. K. Syrkin and M. E. Dyatkina, *Structure of molecules and the chemical bond*, Butterworths Scientific Publications, London, 1950.

four bonds making tetrahedral angles with each other. That is, each carbon atom will be at the center of the tetrahedron formed by the nearest neighbor atoms. Diamond (Fig. 14.4) and methane, CH_4, are typical examples of the tetrahedral covalent bond. The diamond structure is loosely packed in a geometrical sense: the tetrahedral bond allows only four nearest neighbors, while a closest-packed structure would require twelve nearest neighbor atoms. The covalent bond is usually formed from two electrons, one from each atom participating in the bond. The spins of the two electrons in the bond are anti-

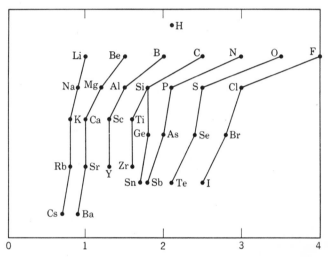

Fig. 1.2. The electronegativity scale of the elements, showing relation to the periodic table. The electronegativities are plotted against the horizontal scale, and different columns of the periodic table are separated vertically. (After L. Pauling, *Nature of the chemical bond*, Cornell University Press.)

parallel. The carbon atom $(2s^2 2p^2)$ tends to fill up the $2p^6$ electronic shell by sharing electrons with four neighbors.

There is apparently a continuous range of crystals between the ionic and the covalent limits. It is often of importance to estimate the extent to which a given bond is ionic or covalent, but this may be difficult to do with any confidence. Pauling[1] has formulated (Fig. 1.2) on a semi-empirical basis an electronegativity scale of some of the elements. Electronegativity is a chemical term meaning the power of an atom in a molecule to attract electrons to itself. The electronegativity is approximately proportional to the sum of the ionization energy and the electron affinity of the atom. A suggested empirical connection between the ionic character of a bond and the difference in electronegativity of the atoms being joined is shown in Fig. 1.3. Atoms with nearly filled shells (Na, Cl) tend to be ionic, whereas atoms not close in the periodic table to the inert gases tend to be covalent (C, Ge, Si, Te).

METAL CRYSTALS

Metals are characterized by high electrical conductivity, so that a portion of the electrons in a metal must be free to move about. The electrons available to participate in the conductivity are called con-duction electrons. In some metals such as the alkali metals the con-duction electrons are largely responsible for the binding energy. We

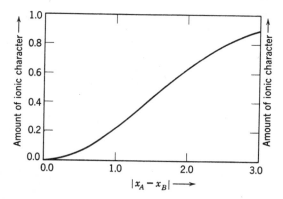

Fig. 1.3. Curve relating amount of ionic character of a bond A—B to the differ-ence in electronegativity $x_A - x_B$ of the atoms. (After L. Pauling, *Nature of the chemical bond*, Cornell University Press.)

may think of an alkali metal crystal as an array of positive ions embedded in a more-or-less uniform sea of negative charge. In some metals such as the transition metals it is thought that there may also be binding effects from covalent-type bonds among the inner electron shells. Transition group elements have incomplete d-electron shells, and are characterized by high binding energy (Table 3.3).

The binding energy of an alkali metal crystal is seen from Table 1.1 to be very considerably less than that of an alkali halide crystal, so that the bond formed by a quasi-free conduction electron is not very strong. Part of the explanation is that the interatomic distances are relatively large in the alkali metals because the kinetic energy of the conduction electrons favors large interatomic distances, leading thus to weak binding. In the transition metals such as iron and tungsten the inner electronic shells make a substantial contribution to the bind-ing. The binding energy of tungsten, for example, is 210 kcal/mole.

MOLECULAR CRYSTALS

Inert gas atoms and saturated molecules are bound together in the solid phase by weak electrostatic forces known as van der Waals forces.[3] These forces arise in the following way: even in an atom or molecule which has on the average an electric dipole moment of zero there will be a fluctuating dipole moment associated with the instantaneous position of the electrons in the atom. The instantaneous electric field associated with the moment will induce a dipole moment in neighboring atoms. The average interaction of the original moment and the induced moment gives rise to an attractive force between the atoms. Forces of this origin are also called dispersion forces. Most organic solids are held together by van der Waals forces.

Molecular crystals are characterized by weak binding, with low melting and boiling points. The crystal structures are often those with dense packing. The inert gas crystals crystallize with cubic close packing, to be discussed below.

HYDROGEN-BONDED CRYSTALS

As neutral hydrogen has only one electron, it should form a covalent bond with only one other atom. It is known, however, that under certain conditions an atom of hydrogen is attracted by rather strong forces to two atoms, thus forming what is called a *hydrogen bond* between them, with a bond energy of about 5 kcal/mole. It is believed that the hydrogen bond[4] is largely ionic in character, being formed only between the most electronegative atoms. The hydrogen atom loses its electron to one of the other atoms in the molecule; the proton forms the hydrogen bond. The small size of the proton permits only two nearest neighbor atoms because they are so close in that more than two of them would get in each other's way; thus the hydrogen bond connects only two atoms.

The hydrogen bond is an important interaction between H_2O molecules and is responsible, together with the electrostatic attraction of the electric dipole moments, for the striking physical properties of water and ice. The hydrogen bond restrains protein molecules to their normal geometrical arrangements. It is also responsible for the polymerization of hydrogen fluoride and formic acid, for example. It is important in certain ferroelectric crystals.

[3] An elementary discussion of the theory of van der Waals forces is given in M. Born, *Atomic physics*, Hafner, New York, 5th ed., 1951.
[4] For a discussion of the hydrogen bond, see L. Pauling, ref. 1.

CLASSIFICATION OF MACROSCOPIC SYMMETRY PROPERTIES

Crystals are found experimentally to possess symmetry in the values of their macroscopic physical properties in different directions, such as elastic and optical constants and thermal expansion. If the external crystal faces are fully developed, their arrangement will have a definite symmetry. It is convenient to dissect the total symmetry of a crystal into simple fundamental symmetry elements applied at a single point. Crystals may be classified into thirty-two symmetry classes on the basis of the number and type of symmetry elements.

SYMMETRY ELEMENTS

A symmetry element is an operation which will bring the crystal into a position indistinguishable from its original position. To

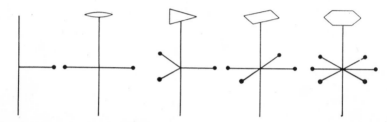

Fig. 1.4. Rotation axes of symmetry, one-, two-, three-, four-, and six-fold. (By permission from *Structure of metals*, by C. S. Barrett. Copyright, 1943. McGraw-Hill Book Co.)

describe the symmetry elements it is most convenient to think in terms of an ideal crystal in which all equivalent faces are developed equally. We now enumerate the fundamental macroscopic symmetry elements: rotation axes, reflection planes, inversion centers, and rotation-reflection axes.

Rotation axis. If a crystal possesses a rotation axis of symmetry, the crystal can be brought into self-coincidence (that is, into a physically equivalent position) by rotation about that axis. The axis may be one-fold, two-fold, three-fold, four-fold, or six-fold, according to whether the crystal is brought into self-coincidence by the operations, respectively, of a turn through 360°, 180°, 120°, 90°, or 60° about the rotation axis (Fig. 1.4). It can be shown that other angles of rotation cannot be symmetry elements of a periodic lattice. The existence of only five rotation elements is originally derived as a consequence of the empirical *law of rational indices*. This law states that, if a suitable set of axes is used, all planes which occur as boundary surfaces of the crystal have intercepts on the three axes whose ratios are rational.

Reflection plane. If one half of the crystal is the reflection of the other half in a plane drawn through the center of the crystal, the crystal possesses a reflection plane as a symmetry element.

Center of inversion. A crystal possesses a center of inversion if the crystal would be brought into self-coincidence by the operation $r \rightarrow -r$, where r is the vector position of a point in the crystal referred to the center of inversion.

Rotation-reflection axis. A crystal has a rotation-reflection axis if it is brought into self-coincidence by combined rotation and reflection in a plane perpendicular to the axis of rotation. Crystals can possess one-, two-, three-, four-, or six-fold rotation-reflection axes.

TABLE 1.3. THE THIRTY-TWO CRYSTAL CLASSES

System	Crystal Class	System	Crystal Class
Triclinic	C_1	Cubic	T
	$C_i = S_2$		T_h
Monoclinic	C_s		T_d
	C_2		O
	C_{2h}		O_h
Orthorhombic	C_{2v}	Rhombohedral	C_3
	$V = D_2$		$C_{3i} = S_6$
	$V_h = D_{2h}$		C_{3v}
Tetragonal	S_4		D_3
	$V_d = D_{2d}$		D_{3d}
	C_4	Hexagonal	C_{3h}
	C_{4h}		D_{3h}
	C_{4v}		C_6
	D_4		C_{6h}
	D_{4h}		C_{6v}
			D_6
			D_{6h}

ENUMERATION OF THE CRYSTAL CLASSES

The most widely used notation for the thirty-two crystal classes or point groups is that of Schoenflies:

C_n describes a group having a single n-fold axis of symmetry.
D_n describes a group having an n-fold axis and n two-fold axes at right angles to it.
S_n describes a group having an n-fold axis of rotary-reflection.
V describes a group with three mutually perpendicular two-fold axes.
T describes a group with four three-fold axes, placed to correspond to the symmetry of a regular tetrahedron (tetrahedral group).
O describes a group with three mutually perpendicular four-fold axes (cubic group).
Subscript v (vertical) signifies the presence of a reflection plane containing the symmetry axis.

Subscript h (horizontal) signifies the presence of a reflection plane perpendicular to a symmetry axis.

Subscript d (dihedral) signifies the presence of a reflection plane bisecting the angle between two two-fold axes.

Subscript i (inversion) means that the group contains the inversion.

Subscript s means that the group contains a reflection plane.

The thirty-two crystal classes are listed in Table 1.3 with the usual classification into seven crystal systems. The systems are explained below.

CRYSTAL SYSTEMS

The classification of crystals into seven crystal systems was developed by classical crystallographers[5] from measurements on the angles

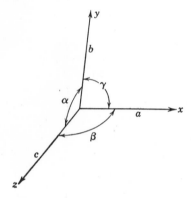

Fig. 1.5. Crystal axes.

of crystal faces, without reference to the internal structure of the crystal. The basis of the classification into systems is the set of *crystal axes* a, b, c shown in Fig. 1.5. The axes are determined as the intersections of three important faces of a crystal, the faces being parallel to planes of symmetry if the crystal possesses such. The axial ratios a/b and c/b are determined by taking a fourth face chosen so that it cuts all three axes at lengths not far removed from equality. The intercepts of the crystal axes by the plane are the lengths of the axes a, b, c. It is usual in macroscopic crystallography to set $b = 1$. The definition of the crystal systems is given in Table 1.4. The division of the thirty-two crystal classes among the seven crystal systems was shown in Table 1.3. A given crystal class is compatible with only one crystal system.

TABLE 1.4. THE CRYSTAL SYSTEMS

Triclinic	$\alpha \neq 90°$; $\beta \neq 90°$; $\gamma \neq 90°$; $c \leq a \leq b$
Monoclinic	$\alpha = \gamma = 90°$; $\beta \neq 90°$; $c \leq a$; b arbitrary
Orthorhombic (rhombic)	$\alpha = \beta = \gamma = 90°$; $c < a < b$
Tetragonal	$\alpha = \beta = \gamma = 90°$; $a = b \neq c$
Hexagonal	$\alpha = \beta = 90°$; $\gamma = 120°$; $a = b$; c arbitrary
Cubic	$\alpha = \beta = \gamma = 90°$; $a = b = c$
Rhombohedral (trigonal)	$\alpha = \beta = \gamma \neq 90°$; $a = b = c$

[5] See, for example, A. E. H. Tutton, *Crystallography and practical crystal measurement*, Macmillan and Co., Ltd., London, 2nd ed., 1922.

SPACE LATTICES AND MICROSCOPIC SYMMETRY PROPERTIES

We have thus far in the discussion of crystal symmetry made no reference to the periodic structure of the crystals. In preparation for the description of crystal structures we consider space lattices, often called Bravais lattices. A parallel three-dimensional net-like arrangement of points is by definition a space lattice, provided that the environment about any particular point is the same as about any other. With each lattice point there may be associated a group of atoms.

Bravais proved that there are only fourteen different space lattices. They are divided among the seven crystal systems as indicated in Fig. 1.6. The meaning of the term unit cell used in the legend is discussed below.

TRANSLATION GROUP AND UNIT CELL

We define an ideal crystal as a body composed of atoms arranged in a lattice such that there exist three fundamental translation vectors **a, b, c,** with the properties:

(a) The atomic arrangement looks the same when viewed from any point **r** as when viewed from the point

$$\mathbf{r}' = \mathbf{r} + n_1\mathbf{a} + n_2\mathbf{b} + n_3\mathbf{c},$$

where n_1, n_2, n_3 are arbitrary integers.

(b) Any two points **r, r'** from which the atomic arrangement looks the same always satisfy (a) with a suitable choice of the integers n_1, n_2, n_3.

We shall consider the fundamental translation vectors as defining the crystal axes **a, .b, c.** This definition supplants the previous macroscopic definition of the axes.

The operation of displacing a crystal parallel to itself by $n_1\mathbf{a} + n_2\mathbf{b} + n_3\mathbf{c}$ is called a translation operation. The totality of such operations, for all values of the integers n_1, n_2, n_3, is known as the translation group of the crystal.

A *unit cell* of a crystal is defined as any polyhedron with the.properties:

(a) When any translation operation is applied to it (other than the identity operation with $n_1 = n_2 = n_3 = 0$), the translated polyhedron never overlaps the original one.

(b) The set of all polyhedra obtained from it by application of all operations of the translation group covers all points of space.

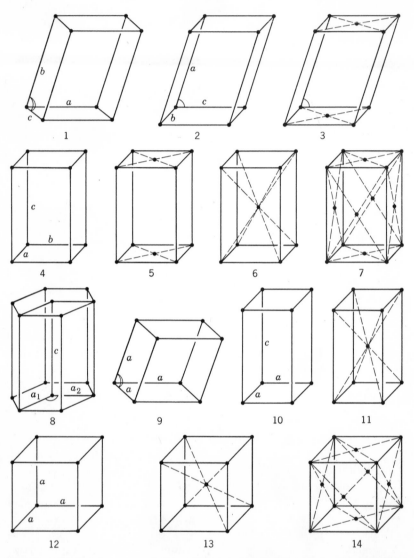

Fig. 1.6.   The fourteen space lattices illustrated by a unit cell of each: (1) triclinic, simple; (2) monoclinic, simple; (3) monoclinic, base centered; (4) orthorhombic, simple; (5) orthorhombic, base centered; (6) orthorhombic, body centered; (7) orthohombic, face centered; (8) hexagonal; (9) rhombohedral; (10) tetragonal, simple; (11) tetragonal, body centered; (12) cubic, simple; (13) cubic, body centered; (14) cubic, face centered.   (By permission from *Structure of metals*, by C. S. Barrett.   Copyright 1943.   McGraw-Hill Book Co.)

There are many shapes which a unit cell can have for a given crystal. A convenient way of choosing the unit cell is to choose an origin O and from it draw the various vectors $n_1\mathbf{a} + n_2\mathbf{b} + n_3\mathbf{c}$ and then bisect each vector with a plane perpendicular to it. The region of space which can be reached from O without crossing any of the planes then satisfies the requirements for a unit cell. The cells are usually drawn, however, with lattice points at all corners. In some space lattices the unit cells are so drawn as to have lattice points at the center of certain faces or at the center of volume in addition to the points at the corners. This is done for convenience so that the symmetry of the unit cell will be more closely that of the crystal. Unit cells with lattice points only at corners are called *primitive cells*.

MILLER INDICES

The position and orientation of a crystal plane is determined by giving the coordinates of three atoms lying in the plane. If each of the atoms lies on a crystal axis, the plane may be specified by giving the positions of the atoms along the axes in terms of the lattice constants. If, for example, the atoms determining the plane have coordinates $(4, 0, 0)$; $(0, 1, 0)$; $(0, 0, 2)$ relative to the axis vectors from some origin, the plane may be specified by the three numbers 4, 1, 2.

It turns out to be more useful to specify the orientation of a plane by *Miller indices*, which are determined as follows:

(1) Find the intercepts on the three basis axes in terms of the lattice constants.
(2) Take the reciprocals of these numbers and reduce to the smallest three integers having the same ratio. The result is enclosed in parentheses: (hkl).

For the plane whose intercepts are 4, 1, 2 the reciprocals are $\frac{1}{4}$, 1, $\frac{1}{2}$, and the Miller indices are (142). If an intercept is at infinity, the corresponding index is zero. The Miller indices of some important planes in a cubic crystal are illustrated by Fig. 1.7.

The indices (hkl) denote a single plane or a set of parallel planes. If a plane cuts an axis on the negative side of the origin, the corresponding index is negative and is indicated by placing a minus sign above the index: $(h\bar{k}l)$. The cube faces of a cubic crystal are (100); (010); (001); $(\bar{1}00)$; $(0\bar{1}0)$; and $(00\bar{1})$. Planes equivalent by symmetry are denoted by curly brackets (braces) around Miller indices; the cube faces are $\{100\}$.

The indices of a direction in a crystal are expressed as the set of the smallest integers which have the same ratios as the components of a vector in the desired direction referred to the axis vectors. The integers are written between square brackets, $[uvw]$. The x axis is the [100] direction; the $-y$ axis is the $[0\bar{1}0]$ direction. A full set of equivalent directions is denoted this way: $\langle uvw \rangle$. In cubic crystals a direction $[uvw]$ is perpendicular to a plane (uvw) having the same indices, but this is not generally true in other crystal systems.

The positions of points in a unit cell are specified in terms of lattice coordinates, in which each coordinate is a fraction of the axial length, a, b, or c, in the direction of the coordinate, with the origin taken at the corner of a unit cell. Thus the coordinates of the central point of a cell are $\frac{1}{2}\frac{1}{2}\frac{1}{2}$, and the face-center positions are $\frac{1}{2}\frac{1}{2}0; 0\frac{1}{2}\frac{1}{2}; \frac{1}{2}0\frac{1}{2}$.

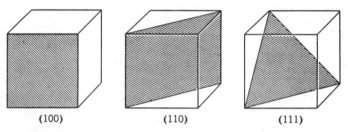

(100)   (110)   (111)

Fig. 1.7.   Miller indices of some important planes in a cubic crystal.

In terms of the Miller indices the law of rational indices states that the indices of crystal faces are three small whole numbers. The law of rational indices is a natural consequence of the atomic nature of crystals.

CUBIC SPACE LATTICES

The cubic space lattices (Fig. 1.6) are the simple cubic (sc), body-centered cubic (bcc), and face-centered cubic (fcc) lattices; their principal properties are summarized in Table 1.5. In the sc lattice

TABLE 1.5.   CHARACTERISTICS OF CUBIC LATTICES

	Simple	Body-Centered	Face-Centered
Unit cell volume	a^3	a^3	a^3
Lattice points per cell	1	2	4
Lattice points per unit volume	$1/a^3$	$2/a^3$	$4/a^3$
Nearest neighbor distance	a	$3^{1/2}a/2$	$a/2^{1/2}$
Number of nearest neighbors	6	8	12
Second neighbor distance	$2^{1/2}a$	a	a
Number of second neighbors	12	6	6

the unit cell is a primitive cell. The primitive cell of the bcc lattice has a volume one-half that of the unit cube. The primitive cell of the fcc lattice is shown in Fig. 1.8 and is a rhombohedron of volume one-quarter that of the unit cube. We may think of a bcc lattice as made up of two interpenetrating sc lattices, and of a fcc lattice as made up of four interpenetrating sc lattices.

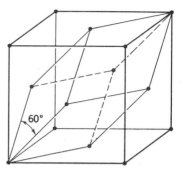

Fig. 1.8. The rhombohedral primitive cell of the face-centered cubic Bravais lattice.

HEXAGONAL SPACE LATTICE

The hexagonal primitive cell is a parallelepiped with $a = b$ and angles $\alpha = \beta = 90°$; $\gamma = 120°$. The relationship of the cell with a prism with hexagonal symmetry is shown by Fig. 1.9. If four cells are packed together as shown, it is possible to carve out of them a hexagonal prism. Hexagonal indices using the four axes a_1, a_2, a_3, c are often used. The c axis, for example, is the [0001] direction in this notation.

HEXAGONAL CLOSE-PACKED STRUCTURE (HCP)

There are two ways of arranging equivalent spheres to minimize the interstitial volume. One way leads to a structure with cubic symmetry and is the face-centered cubic (cubic close-packed) structure; the other has hexagonal symmetry and is called the *hexagonal close-packed structure* (Fig. 1.10). Spheres may be arranged in a single closest-packed layer by placing each sphere in contact with six others. A second similar layer may be packed on top of this by placing each sphere in contact with three spheres of the bottom layer. A third layer can be added in two ways: in the cubic structure the spheres in the third layer are placed over the holes in the first layer not occupied by the second layer; in the hexagonal structure the spheres in the third layer are placed directly over the spheres of the first layer. The two possibilities are illustrated in Fig. 1.11. The c/a ratio for hex-

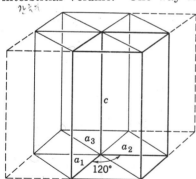

Fig. 1.9. Relation of the primitive cell in the hexagonal system (heavy lines) to a prism of hexagonal symmetry. (By permission from *Structure of metals*, by C. S. Barrett. Copyright 1943. McGraw-Hill Book Co.)

agonal closest-packing of spheres is $(\frac{8}{3})^{\frac{1}{2}} = 1.633$. By convention we refer to crystals as hcp even if the actual c/a ratio may depart somewhat from the theoretical value. The unit cell of the hcp structure is the hexagonal primitive cell but with an extra atom added within the prism, so that the hcp unit cell contains two atoms.

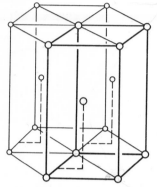

DIAMOND STRUCTURE

The space lattice of diamond is fcc with two atoms 000; $\frac{1}{4}\frac{1}{4}\frac{1}{4}$ associated with each lattice point. The structure is shown in Fig. 14.4. The tetrahedral bonding is to be noted. Each atom has four nearest neighbors.

SPACE GROUPS

Fig. 1.10. The hexagonal close-packed structure. The atom positions in this structure do not constitute a space lattice. The space lattice is *simple hexagonal* with two atoms $(000; \frac{2}{3}\,\frac{1}{3}\,\frac{1}{2})$ associated with each lattice point. (By permission from *Structure of metals*, by C. S. Barrett. Copyright 1943. McGraw-Hill Book Co.)

Taking each one of the fourteen space lattices, we can associate with every lattice point a figure (a molecule or a group of atoms or molecules) possessing all the symmetry operations of the lattice. We obtain in this way a pattern or *space group* possessing the full symmetry of the lattice. The point groups possessing all the symmetry operations of the lattice are, for each crystal system, the last entry under the appropriate system in Table 1.3. Even if a figure of higher symmetry is located at each one of the lattice points, the pattern as a whole will not acquire that higher symmetry. If the figure is of lower symmetry than the lattice, the space group will have lower symmetry.

A space group is an array of symmetry elements on a space lattice. Each symmetry element has a definite location and orientation in a unit cell, and every unit cell contains an identical array. The elements must be arranged so that each operation brings all elements into self-coincidence. We also require that the arrangement of symmetry elements at and around every lattice point be identical throughout the crystal.

Many space groups consist simply of point groups located at the points of the fourteen space lattices. We must also take account of the space groups possessing the translational symmetry elements, which are glide planes and screw axes. A *glide plane* is a reflection

followed by a translation along a direction lying in the reflection plane. A *screw axis* is a rotation followed by translation along the axis of rotation.

There are 230 possible space groups. A full discussion of space groups is not possible in the space available here. We shall not require knowledge of the theory of space groups in order to understand the crystal structures explicitly discussed in this book. Among the books cited at the end of the chapter, that by W. L. Bragg contains an introductory discussion of space groups, and that by A. Schoenflies con-

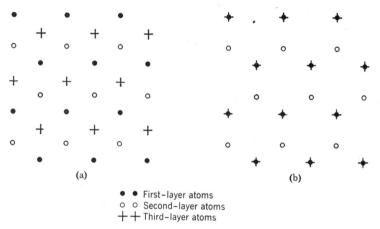

(a)   (b)

● ● First-layer atoms
○ ○ Second-layer atoms
+ + Third-layer atoms

Fig. 1.11. Modes of superposition of close-packed layers of spheres in (a) cubic close-packing and (b) hexagonal close-packing.

tains a complete mathematical treatment; the papers by F. Seitz place the mathematical development in a form convenient for quantum-mechanical applications. The book by Bhagavantam and Venkatarayudu contains a clear discussion of space groups in one- and two-dimensional lattices and may serve as a simple introduction to the principles of space groups.

X-RAY DIFFRACTION BY CRYSTALS

In order to explore the structure of crystals we require waves which interact with atoms and which have a wavelength comparable with the interatomic spacing in crystals; that is, we require a wavelength of the order of $1 \text{ A}(= 10^{-8} \text{ cm})$. The interaction should be weak enough so that the wave can penetrate in a coherent fashion into the crystal for a distance of the order of perhaps 1000 lattice constants. The most convenient waves suitable for our purpose are those associated with x-rays, while the waves associated with neutrons and electrons have found important special applications. A wavelength of 1 A requires energies of the order of 10^4, 10^2, and 10^{-1} ev for x-rays, electrons, and neutrons, respectively, as the reader may verify from the relations $\lambda = hc/W$ for x-rays and $\lambda = h/(2MW)^{\frac{1}{2}}$ for neutrons and electrons, where W is the energy and M is the particle mass. The discussion below is formulated explicitly for x-ray diffraction, although many of the results are applicable also to neutron and electron diffraction.

When an atom is exposed to electromagnetic radiation, the atomic electrons are accelerated, and they radiate at the frequency of the incident radiation. The superposition of the waves scattered by

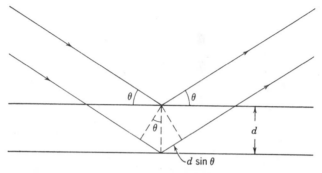

Fig. 1.12.   Derivation of the Bragg equation $2d \sin \theta = n\lambda$; here d is the spacing of parallel atomic planes and $2n\pi$ is the difference in phase between reflections from successive planes.

individual atoms in a crystal results in the ordinary optical refraction. If the wavelength of the radiation is comparable with or smaller than the lattice constant, we will also under certain conditions have diffraction of the incident beam. At optical frequencies ($\sim 10^{15}$ cps) only refraction occurs; at x-ray frequencies ($\sim 10^{18}$ cps) diffraction is important.

BRAGG'S LAW

W. L. Bragg (1913) found that one could account for the position of the diffracted beams produced by a crystal in an x-ray beam by a very simple model according to which x-rays are reflected from various planes of atoms in the crystal. The diffracted beams are found for situations in which the reflections from parallel planes of atoms interfere constructively. The derivation of the Bragg law is indicated in Fig. 1.12.

We consider in the crystal a series of atomic planes which are partly reflecting for radiation of wavelength λ and which are spaced equal

distances d apart.   The radiation is incident in the plane of the paper.
The path difference for rays reflected from adjacent planes is $2d \sin \theta$.
Reinforcement of the radiation reflected from successive planes will
occur when the path difference is an integral number n of wavelengths.
The condition for constructive reflection is that

(1.1) $2d \sin \theta = n\lambda$.

This is the Bragg law.   We shall derive this relation below in a more
sophisticated manner.   It should be emphasized that the Bragg

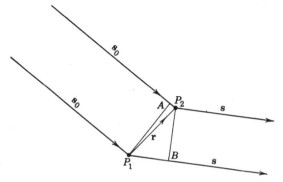

Fig. 1.13.   Calculation of the phase difference of the waves scattered from two
lattice points.

equation results from the periodicity of the structure, without reference to the composition of the repetition unit.

LAUE DIFFRACTION EQUATIONS

We consider the nature of the x-ray diffraction pattern produced by
identical atoms located at the corners (lattice points) of the primitive
cells of a space lattice.   We first look at the scattering from any two
lattice points, P_1 and P_2 in Fig. 1.13, separated by the vector $\mathbf{r}$.   The
unit incident wave normal is $\mathbf{s}_0$, and the unit scattered wave normal is
$\mathbf{s}$.   We examine at a point a long distance away the difference in
phase of the radiation scattered by P_1 and P_2.

If P_1B and P_2A are the projections of $\mathbf{r}$ on the incident and scattered
wave directions, the path difference between the two scattered waves
is

(1.2) $P_2A - P_1B = \mathbf{r} \cdot \mathbf{s}_0 - \mathbf{r} \cdot \mathbf{s} = \mathbf{r} \cdot (\mathbf{s}_0 - \mathbf{s})$

The vector $\mathbf{s}_0 - \mathbf{s} = \mathbf{S}$ has a simple interpretation (Fig. 1.14) as the
direction of the normal to a plane that would reflect the incident
direction into the scattering direction.   This plane is a useful mathe-

matical construction and may be spoken of as the *reflecting plane*. If 2θ is the angle $\mathbf{s}$ makes with $\mathbf{s}_0$, then θ is the angle of incidence, and from the figure we see that $|S| = 2 \sin \theta$, as $\mathbf{s}$ and $\mathbf{s}_0$ are unit vectors.

The phase difference ϕ is $2\pi/\lambda$ times the path difference. We have

(1.3) $$\phi = (2\pi/\lambda)(\mathbf{r} \cdot \mathbf{S}).$$

The amplitude of the scattered wave is a maximum in a direction such that the contributions from each lattice point differ in phase only by integral multiplies of 2π. This is satisfied if the phase differ-

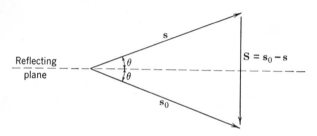

Fig. 1.14.   Construction of the normal to the reflecting plane.

ence between adjacent lattice points is an integral multiple of 2π. If $\mathbf{a}, \mathbf{b}, \mathbf{c}$ are the basis vectors, we must have for the diffraction maxima

$$\phi_a = (2\pi/\lambda)(\mathbf{a} \cdot \mathbf{S}) = 2\pi h;$$

(1.4) $$\phi_b = (2\pi/\lambda)(\mathbf{b} \cdot \mathbf{S}) = 2\pi k;$$

$$\phi_c = (2\pi/\lambda)(\mathbf{c} \cdot \mathbf{S}) = 2\pi l;$$

where h, k, l are integers. If α, β, γ are the direction cosines of $\mathbf{S}$ with respect to a, b, c, we have

$$\mathbf{a} \cdot \mathbf{S} = 2a\alpha \sin \theta = h\lambda;$$

(1.5) $$\mathbf{b} \cdot \mathbf{S} = 2b\beta \sin \theta = k\lambda;$$

$$\mathbf{c} \cdot \mathbf{S} = 2c\gamma \sin \theta = l\lambda.$$

These are the Laue equations. They have solutions only for special values of θ and the wavelength λ.

The Laue equations (1.5) have a simple geometrical interpretation. We recall that α, β, γ are the direction cosines of $\mathbf{S}$, the normal to the reflecting plane, referred to the basis vectors $\mathbf{a}, \mathbf{b}, \mathbf{c}$. The Laue equations state that in a diffraction direction the direction cosines are proportional to h/a, k/b, l/c, respectively. Now the adjacent lattice planes (hkl) intersect the axes at intervals a/h, b/k, c/l, so that by elementary plane geometry the direction cosines of the normal to (hkl) are proportional to h/a, k/b, l/c. Therefore the lattice planes (hkl) must be parallel to the reflecting plane, and the diffraction maxima occur when the scattering direction may be derived from the incident direction by reflection in a lattice plane.

If $d(hkl)$ is the spacing between two adjacent planes of a set (hkl), we have by projection

$$(1.6) \qquad d(hkl) = a\alpha/h = b\beta/k = c\gamma/l.$$

Then, from (1.5), we have

$$(1.7) \qquad 2d(hkl) \sin \theta = \lambda.$$

Now the integers h, k, l of the Laue equations are not necessarily identical with the Miller indices of an actual crystal plane, as the h, k, l may contain a common integral factor n, while in the Miller indices the common factor n has been eliminated. We may then write

$$(1.8) \qquad 2d \sin \theta = n\lambda,$$

where d is the spacing between adjacent planes with Miller indices $(h/n, k/n, l/n)$. This is the *Bragg equation* (1.1), and we have derived it here from the Laue equations. The integer n is called the order of reflection.

We may interpret (1.7) by giving an extended meaning to the spacing $d(hkl)$ when h, k, l have a common factor n: the diffracted wave actually arises from the nth order reflection from the true lattice planes, but we may as a mathematical device think of the diffracted wave as a first order reflection from a set of planes parallel to the true lattice planes but with a spacing $d(hkl)$ equal to $1/n$ of the true spacing.

It is useful to discuss the interference conditions in terms of a mathematical transformation known as the reciprocal lattice, and this method is developed in Appendix A.

ROTATING CRYSTAL METHOD

The Bragg equation suggests the rotating crystal method for structure analysis, and this method is very widely used. A monochromatic x-ray beam is incident on the crystal which is mounted to rotate about a crystal axis (Fig. 1.15). Diffraction occurs whenever a crystal plane makes an angle $\theta = \sin^{-1}(n\lambda/2d)$ with the incident beam. Instead of rotating the crystal we may replace the crystal by a finely powdered sample in which all crystal orientations are present; this is the powder method devised by Debye and Scherrer and by Hull.

We may get an idea of the magnitude of the diffraction angle θ by considering $CuK\alpha_1$ radiation incident on a simple cubic crystal with a lattice constant of 4.00 A. The wavelength[6] of the $CuK\alpha_1$ line is 1.540 A. In the first order $(n = 1)$ reflection from (100) planes $\theta = \sin^{-1}(1.54/8.00) = 11.1°$. As the wavelength is decreased, the angle is decreased: for gamma-rays glancing angles must be used.

ATOMIC SCATTERING FACTOR

The intensity of a given diffracted wave depends on a number of factors. One of these is the atomic scattering factor, which describes

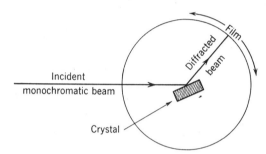

Fig. 1.15.   Schematic diagram of a rotating crystal x-ray camera.

for scattering at a given wavelength λ and angle θ the result of interference effects within the scattering atoms arising from the finite extent of the atoms in relation to the wavelength.

We arrange the coordinate system in Fig. 1.16 so that the incident and reflected wave normals make equal angles with the vertical axis, corresponding to Bragg reflection from the horizontal plane at angle θ. The difference in phase between the radiation scattered by an element of charge at (r, ϕ) and the radiation which would be scattered by the same amount of charge located at the center of the atom is $\phi = (2\pi/\lambda)(\mathbf{r} \cdot \mathbf{S})$, according to (1.3). Then the amplitude scattered by one electron in the actual atom referred to the amplitude which would be scattered by an electron at the center of the atom is, by superposition,

$$(1.9) \qquad f = \int \rho(\mathbf{r}) e^{i(2\pi/\lambda)(\mathbf{r} \cdot \mathbf{S})} \, d\tau,$$

where $\rho(\mathbf{r}) \, d\tau$ is the probability of finding the electron in the element of volume $d\tau$ at $\mathbf{r}$.

[6] The reader should note that x-ray wavelengths in the older literature are often given in X units (XU) defined so that $1000 \, XU = 1.00202 \, A$.

If **r** makes an angle ϕ with **S**, then

(1.10) $\qquad (2\pi/\lambda)(\mathbf{S} \cdot \mathbf{r}) = (4\pi/\lambda) \sin \theta r \cos \phi = \mu r \cos \phi,$

where $\mu = 4\pi(\sin \theta)/\lambda$. If the charge density is spherically symmetrical,

$$f = \int \rho(r) e^{i\mu r \cos \phi} 2\pi r^2 \sin \phi \, dr \, d\phi$$

$$= \int_0^\infty 4\pi r^2 \rho(r) \frac{\sin \mu r}{\mu r} \, dr.$$

Writing $U(r) \, dr = 4\pi r^2 \rho(r) \, dr$ as the probability that an electron lies

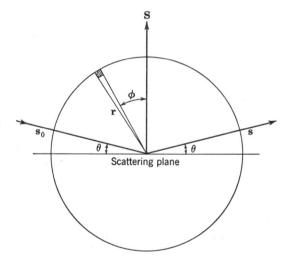

Fig. 1.16. Calculation of the atomic scattering factor f. The normal to the scattering plane is **S**.

between radii r and $r + dr$, we have

(1.11) $\qquad\qquad f = \int_0^\infty U(r) \frac{\sin \mu r}{\mu r} \, dr$

for the *atomic scattering factor*. It is the ratio of the radiation amplitude scattered by the charge distribution in an atom to that scattered by a point electron. Tables of atomic scattering factors calculated by the Hartree and Thomas-Fermi methods have been published.[7] The results for sodium are plotted in Fig. 1.17. At $\theta = 0$ our calculation gives $f = Z$, the number of atomic electrons.

[7] *International tables for the determination of crystal structure;* Borntraeger, Berlin, 1935.

GEOMETRICAL STRUCTURE FACTOR

The Laue and Bragg equations determine the reflections (hkl) which are possible for a given crystal lattice, but the relative intensities of the various reflections depend on the contents of the unit cell, that is, on the number, type, and distribution of atoms in the cell. We must now determine the amplitude of the wave scattered in a given direction by all the atoms in the unit cell. The *structure amplitude* $|F(hkl)|$

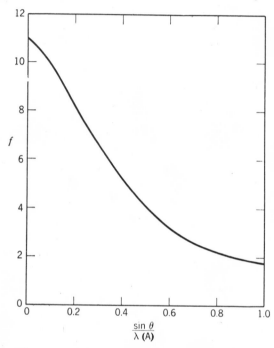

Fig. 1.17.   Atomic scattering factor for sodium.

for a given hkl reflection is the reflection amplitude divided by the amplitude of the wave scattered by a single point electron for the same wavelength.

The value of $F(hkl)$ will be given by

$$(1.12) \qquad F(hkl) \; = \; \sum_i f_i e^{i\phi_i} \; = \; \sum_i f_i e^{i(2\pi/\lambda)\,(\mathbf{r}_i \cdot \mathbf{S})},$$

where the sum is extended over all atoms in a unit cell; ϕ_i is the phase of the wave scattered by the ith atom referred to that of the origin, and $\mathbf{r}_i$ is the vector from the origin to the ith atom.

Now, if u_i, v_i, w_i are the lattice coordinates of the ith atom, we have

$$(1.13) \qquad \mathbf{r}_i \; = \; u_i\mathbf{a} + v_i\mathbf{b} + w_i\mathbf{c}.$$

By the Laue equations

(1.14) $$(\mathbf{r}_i \cdot \mathbf{S}) = \lambda(hu_i + kv_i + lw_i),$$

so that

(1.15) $$F(hkl) = \sum_i f_i e^{i2\pi(hu_i+kv_i+lw_i)},$$

and

(1.16) $$|F|^2 = [\sum f_i \cos 2\pi(hu_i + kv_i + lw_i)]^2 + [\sum f_i \sin 2\pi(hu_i + kv_i + lw_i)]^2.$$

When all the atoms are identical we have, from (1.15), $F(hkl) = f\mathcal{S}$, where $\mathcal{S}$ is called the geometrical structure factor and is given by

(1.17) $$\mathcal{S} = \sum e^{i2\pi(hu_i+kv_i+lw_i)}.$$

A body-centered cubic structure of identical atoms has atoms at 000 and $\frac{1}{2}\frac{1}{2}\frac{1}{2}$. We find

(1.18) $$\mathcal{S} = 1 + e^{i\pi(h+k+l)}.$$

When $h + k + l$ is odd, $\mathcal{S} = 0$, and the intensities of all spectra for which (hkl) satisfy this condition are zero. For example, metallic sodium has a bcc structure; its diffraction spectrum does not contain lines such as (100), (300), (111), or (221), but lines such as (200), (110), and (222) will be present; here the planes are referred to a cubic unit cell. For each of the possible space groups there are characteristic absences of reflections, and from these the space group is determined.

This discussion has assumed that the crystal is large and perfect. The effect of thermal motion on the structure factors may be quite important,[8] as well as the effect of the mosaic or block structure of actual crystals, which is discussed further in Chapter 16.

COLLECTIONS OF CRYSTAL STRUCTURE DATA

The reader who wishes to look up the crystal structure of a substance may profitably consult the book by Wyckoff listed at the end of the chapter, as well as the decennial indices to *Chemical Abstracts;* the *Strukturbericht* and *Structure Reports* are also valuable aids. The principal journal in the field was formerly *Zeitschrift für Kristallographie* (discontinued) and is now *Acta Crystallographica.*

In Table 1.6 we list for convenience the common crystal structures of a number of elements, and their lattice constants at room temperature.

[8] A full discussion is given by R. W. James, *Optical principles of the diffraction of x-rays,* G. Bell and Sons, Ltd., London, 1948.

TABLE 1.6.   COMMON CRYSTAL STRUCTURES OF SELECTED ELEMENTS

Element	Structure	Lattice Constants (at Room Temperature) (Angstroms)	
		a	c or Axial Angle
Aluminum	fcc	4.04	
Argon	fcc	5.43 (20°K)	
Barium	bcc	5.01	
Beryllium	hcp	2.27	3.59
Bismuth	rhombohedral	4.74	$\alpha = 57°14'$
Boron	complex		
Cadmium	hcp	2.97	5.61
Calcium	fcc	5.56	
Cerium	fcc	5.14	
Cesium	bcc	6.05 (92°K)	
Chromium	bcc	2.88	
Cobalt	hcp	2.51	4.07
Copper	fcc	3.61	
Diamond	diamond	3.56	
Gadolinium	hcp	3.62	5.75
Germanium	diamond	5.65	
Gold	fcc	4.07	
Helium	hcp	3.57 (2°K)	5.83
Iron (α)	bcc	2.86	
Lanthanum	fcc	5.29	
Lead	fcc	4.94	
Lithium	bcc	3.50	
Magnesium	hcp	3.20	5.20
Manganese	complex		
Molybdenum	bcc	3.14	
Neon	fcc	4.52 (20°K)	
Nickel	fcc	3.52	
Niobium	bcc	3.29	
Palladium	fcc	3.88	
Platinum	fcc	3.92	
Polonium	sc (?)	3.34	
Potassium	bcc	5.33	
Rubidium	bcc	5.62 (92°K)	
Silicon	diamond	5.42	
Silver	fcc	4.08	
Sodium	bcc	4.28	
Strontium	fcc	6.05	
Tantalum	bcc	3.30	
Thallium	hcp	3.45	5.51
Tin (gray)	diamond	6.46	
Titanium	hcp	2.95	4.73
Tungsten	bcc	3.16	
Uranium	complex		
Vanadium	bcc	3.03	
Xenon	fcc	6.24 (92°K)	
Zinc	hcp	2.66	4.94
Zirconium	bcc	3.61 (850°C)	

Several of the elements listed occur in more than one modification; for these elements the table lists the usual form at room temperature.

PROBLEMS

1.1. Show that the maximum proportion of the available volume which may be filled by hard spheres arranged in various structures is

Simple cubic	$\pi/6$ ($= 0.52$)
Body-centered cubic	$\pi 3^{1/2}/8$ ($= 0.68$)
Face-centered cubic	$\pi 2^{1/2}/6$ ($= 0.74$)
Hexagonal close-packed	$\pi 2^{1/2}/6$ ($= 0.74$)
Diamond	$\pi 3^{1/2}/16$ ($= 0.34$)

We may note that by experiment [O. K. Rice, J. Chem. Phys. **12**, 1 (1944)] it is found that the volume of an arrangement of spheres packed at random into a container exceeds that of the cubic and hexagonal close-packed arrangements by 15 to 20 percent. For further details on the packing of spheres, see A. H. Boerdijk, Philips Research Repts. **7**, 303 (1952), and references cited therein.

1.2. Show that the Laue equations for the incident beam parallel to the z cube edge of a simple cubic crystal give diffracted rays in the yz plane when

$$\lambda/a = 2l/(l^2 + k^2),$$

and
$$\beta_z = (l^2 - k^2)/(l^2 + k^2),$$

where l and k are integers, and β_z is the direction cosine of the diffracted ray relative to the z axis.

1.3. Show that the perpendicular distance between two adjacent planes of a set (hkl) in a cubic lattice of lattice constant a is

$$d(hkl) = a/(h^2 + k^2 + l^2)^{1/2}.$$

Hint: If one plane of the set passes through the origin, the equation of the nearest plane parallel to this plane is $xh + yk + zl = a$.

1.4. Show that the geometrical structure factor for a face-centered cubic lattice referred to a cubic unit cell is

$$S = 1 + e^{i\pi(h+k)} + e^{i\pi(h+l)} + e^{i\pi(l+k)}.$$

Show that no reflections can occur for which the indices are partly even and partly odd.

1.5. Show that the c/a ratio for an ideal hexagonal close-packed structure is $(\frac{8}{3})^{1/2} = 1.633$. Compare this with the experimental values of the ratios for twelve metals possessing hcp structures.

1.6. Hard spheres of radius b are arranged in contact in simple cubic, body-centered cubic, and face-centered cubic structures. Find the radius a of the largest sphere which can fit into the largest interstice in the several structures.

1.7. Describe and discuss the crystal structures of ZnS, MnO, CaF_2, and NiAs.

1.8. What point group describes the symmetry of the interatomic force acting on (a) a carbon atom in a diamond lattice; (b) a zinc atom in a wurtzite lattice; (c) a boron atom in BN?

1.9. Discuss the major experimental differences between x-ray, electron, and neutron diffraction from the standpoint of the observed diffraction patterns [see, for example, C. G. Shull and E. O. Wollan, Science **108**, 69 (1948)].

1.10. Discuss several of the principal methods of growing inorganic and metal single crystals in the laboratory. [Ref.: H. E. Buckley, *Crystal Growth*, John Wiley & Sons, New York, 1951.]

REFERENCES

G. E. Bacon and K. Lonsdale, "Neutron diffraction," Rept. Prog. Phys. **16**, 1 (1953).

S. Bhagavantam and T. Venkatarayudu, *Theory of groups and its application to physical problems*, Andhara University, Waltair, 2nd ed., 1951.

W. L. Bragg, *The crystalline state*, Vol. I., G. Bell and Sons, Ltd., London, 1933.

M. J. Buerger, *X-ray crystallography*, John Wiley & Sons, New York, 1942.

C. W. Bunn, *Chemical crystallography*, Clarendon Press, Oxford, 1945.

A. H. Compton and S. K. Allison, *X-rays in theory and experiment*, Van Nostrand, New York, 1935.

P. H. Groth, *Chemische crystallographie*, 5 volumes, W. Engelmann, Leipzig, 1906.

W. Hume-Rothery, *The structure of metals and alloys*, Institute of Metals, London, 1947.

International tables for x-ray crystallography, Kynoch Press, Birmingham, 1952.

Internationale Tabellen zur Bestimmung von Kristallstrukturen, Borntraeger, Berlin, 1935.

R. W. James, *Optical principles of the diffraction of x-rays*, G. Bell and Sons, Ltd., London, 1948.

K. Lonsdale, *Crystals and x-rays*, G. Bell and Sons, Ltd., London, 1948.

L. Pauling, *Nature of the chemical bond*, Cornell University Press, Ithaca, 1945.

A. Schoenflies, *Theorie der Kristallstruktur*, Borntraeger, Berlin, 1923.

F. Seitz, "A matrix-algebraic development of the crystallographic groups," Z. Krist. **88**, 433 (1934); **90**, 289 (1935); **91**, 336 (1935); **94**, 100 (1936).

Strukturbericht, 7 vols.; Akademische Verlagsgesellschaft, Leipzig, 1913–1939; continued as *Structure Reports*, published by the International Union of Crystallography.

Y. K. Syrkin and M. E. Dyatkina, *Structure of molecules and the chemical bond*, Butterworths Scientific Publications, London, 1950.

W. Voigt, *Lehrbuch der Kristallphysik*, Teubner, Leipzig and Berlin, 1910.

W. A. Wooster, *A textbook on crystal physics*, Cambridge University Press, Cambridge, 1938.

R. W. G. Wyckoff, *Crystal structures*, Interscience Publishers, New York, 1948.

W. H. Zachariasen, *Theory of x-ray diffraction in crystals*, John Wiley & Sons, New York, 1944.

2

Lattice Energy of Ionic Crystals

When we speak of ionic crystals we mean substances such as lithium fluoride and sodium chloride. These are perhaps as simple as any chemical compound existing in nature, and for this reason they have been the subject of a great deal of theoretical calculation, and many of their physical properties have been investigated experimentally over a wide range of temperature. The idealized model of an ionic crystal supposes that the constituents are positive and negative ions bearing charges which are multiples of the electronic charge, with the charge distributed with spherical symmetry on each ion as in the rare gas atoms. The interactions between ions are assumed to be primarily the electrostatic interactions between spherical charge distributions.

It is reasonable to ask how well our assumptions are satisfied in actual crystals. This question is not easy to answer, as in the absence of complete x-ray maps of the electron distribution in the crystal there is no physical method available at present which can determine the quantitative deviation from the ideal ionic state. Pauling's estimates were discussed in Chapter 1. It appears that the binding in many of the alkali halides may be largely ionic, while the binding may be less completely ionic, for example, in substances containing oxygen or sulfur ions.

A short estimate suggests that we are not misguided in looking to electrostatic or Coulomb interactions for a large part of the binding energy of an ionic crystal. The distance between a positive ion and the nearest negative ion in sodium chloride is known to be 2.81×10^{-8} cm, so that the attractive part of the potential energy of the two ions by themselves is

$$e^2/r_0 = (4.8 \times 10^{-10})^2/(2.8 \times 10^{-8}) = 8 \times 10^{-12} \text{ ergs},$$

which is about 5 ev. This value may be compared with the known value 183 kcal/mole, or about 8 ev/molecule, of the heat of formation of the crystal starting with ions at infinite separation. The order of magnitude agreement between the values of 5 and 8 ev/molecule is quite suggestive and leads us to calculate more closely the lattice energy of sodium chloride.

LATTICE ENERGY OF SODIUM CHLORIDE

Sodium chloride crystallizes in the structure shown in Fig. 1.1a. The space lattice is fcc with one Na^+ and one Cl^- ion with each lattice point. We construct the sodium chloride crystal structure by arranging alternately Na^+ and Cl^- ions at the lattice points of a simple cubic lattice. In the crystal each ion is surrounded by six nearest neighbors of the opposite charge and twelve next nearest neighbors of the same charge as the reference ion. We suppose that the Na^+ ion carries a single positive charge, so that the electronic configuration is identical with neon, and that the Cl^- ion carries a single negative charge (argon configuration).

If ϕ_{ij} is the interaction energy between ions i and j, the total energy of any one ion is

$$\phi = \sum_j{}' \phi_{ij},$$

where the prime indicates that the summation is to include all ions except $j = i$. We suppose that ϕ_{ij} may be written as the sum of a central field repulsive potential varying as r_{ij}^{-n} and a Coulomb potential:

(2.1) $$\phi_{ij} = \frac{\lambda}{r_{ij}^n} \pm \frac{e^2}{r_{ij}},$$

where the $+$ sign is to be taken for like charges and the $-$ sign for unlike charges. The repulsive term describes the fact that the ion cores act as if they are fairly hard, and each resists overlapping with the electron distributions of neighboring ion cores. We shall regard λ and n as constants to be determined from observed values of the lattice constant and compressibility. It is actually possible to do somewhat better than this and to compute the repulsive interaction from approximate solutions of the quantum-mechanical problem, but the classical ionic crystal theory we give here is a quite good approximation to the facts.

The value of ϕ does not depend on whether the reference ion i is a positive or a negative ion, and as the sum can be made to converge rapidly its value will not depend on the particular location of the reference ion in the crystal as long as it is not near the surface. Neglecting surface effects, we may write the total lattice energy U_0 of a crystal composed of $2N$ ions as

$$U_0 = N\phi,$$

where N, rather than $2N$, occurs because in taking the total lattice energy we must count each *pair* of interactions only once. The total lattice energy is the energy required to separate the crystal into individual ions at an infinite distance apart.

It is convenient to introduce quantities p_{ij} such that

$$r_{ij} = p_{ij}R,$$

where R is the nearest neighbor separation in the crystal; then

$R = a_0$

$p = \sqrt{n_i^2 + n_j^2 + n_k^2}$

$$\phi_{ij} = \frac{1}{p_{ij}^n}\frac{\lambda}{R^n} \pm \frac{1}{p_{ij}}\frac{e^2}{R}$$

and

(2.2)
$$\phi = \frac{\lambda A_n}{R^n} - \frac{\alpha e^2}{R}.$$

Here

(2.3)
$$A_n = \sum_j{}' p_{ij}^{-n};$$

$$\alpha = \sum_j{}' (\mp)p_{ij}^{-1}.$$

The quantity α is known as the *Madelung constant* and is a property of the crystal lattice. α The Madelung constant is of central importance in the theory of ionic crystals, and methods for the calculation of the constants will be discussed. The sum A_n converges rapidly, as n is usually large, often of the order of 10. We need not, however, attempt to calculate the product λA_n, which involves through λ the quantum-mechanical solution of the repulsive potential problem, if we are content to substitute in our theory the observed value of the lattice constant. The variation of ϕ with R is illustrated in Fig. 2.1.

At the equilibrium separation $\partial\phi/\partial R = 0$, so that

(2.4)
$$-\frac{nA_n\lambda}{R_0^{n+1}} + \frac{\alpha e^2}{R_0^2} = 0.$$

We use this relation to eliminate λA_n from Eq. (2.2), obtaining

$$\phi = -\frac{\alpha e^2}{R_0}\left(1 - \frac{1}{n}\right).$$

The total lattice energy of the crystal of $2N$ ions is then

(2.5)
$$U_0 = -\frac{N\alpha e^2}{R_0}\left(1 - \frac{1}{n}\right).$$

The total binding energy may be attributed almost entirely to the Coulomb energy, as we shall find that n is of the order of 10.

EVALUATION OF THE MADELUNG CONSTANT

The first calculation of the Coulomb energy constant α was made by Madelung.[1] A powerful general method for lattice sum calculations was developed by Ewald,[2] and Evjen[3] has given a rather simple

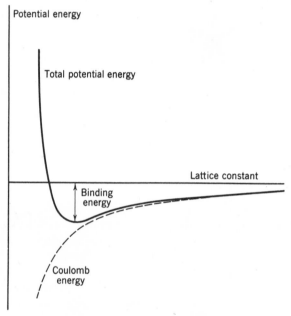

Fig. 2.1.   Dependence of potential energy of an ionic crystal on the value of the lattice constant.

method which arranges the counting in a rapidly convergent way. The definition of the Madelung constant α is, from Eq. (2.3),

$$\alpha = \sum_{j}' (\pm) p_{ij}^{-1},$$

where now, if we take the reference ion as a negative charge, the plus sign will be used for positive ions and the minus sign for negative ions.

[1] E. Madelung, Physik. Z. **19**, 524 (1918).

[2] P. P. Ewald, Ann. Physik **64**, 253 (1921).

[3] H. M. Evjen, Phys. Rev. **39**, 675 (1932); see also K. Højendahl, Kgl. Danske Videnskab. Selskab, Mat.-fys. Medd. **16** (2), 138 (1938); E. J. W. Verwey, Rec. trav. chim. **65**, 521 (1946); F. C. Frank, Phil. Mag. **41**, 1289 (1950).

An equivalent definition is

$$(2.6) \qquad \frac{\alpha}{R_0} = \sum_j \frac{(\pm)}{r_j},$$

where r_j is the distance of the jth ion from the reference ion and is always to be taken as positive.

We shall first compute the value of the Madelung constant for an infinite line of ions of alternating sign, as shown in Fig. 2.2. We pick a

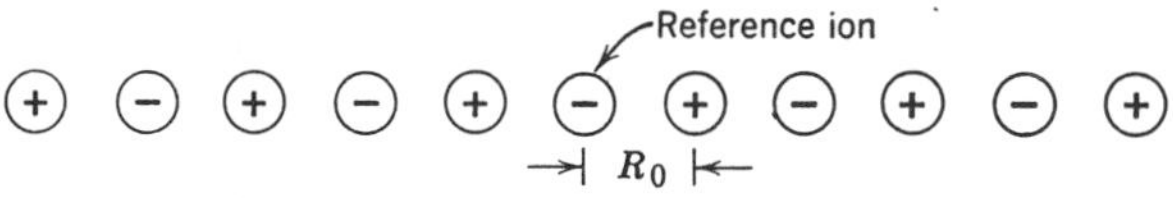

Reference ion

$\oplus \quad \ominus \quad \oplus \quad \ominus \quad \oplus \quad \ominus \quad \oplus \quad \ominus \quad \oplus \quad \ominus \quad \oplus$

$\rightarrow| \; R_0 \; |\leftarrow$

Fig. 2.2. Line of ions of alternating signs with distance R_θ between ions.

negative ion as reference ion, and let R_0 denote the distance between adjacent ions. We have

$$\frac{\alpha}{R_0} = 2 \left[\frac{1}{R_0} - \frac{1}{2R_0} + \frac{1}{3R_0} - \frac{1}{4R_0} + \cdots \right],$$

or

$$\alpha = 2 \left[1 - \frac{1}{2} + \frac{1}{3} - \frac{1}{4} + \cdots \right];$$

the factor 2 occurs because there are two ions, one to the right and one to the left, at each distance r_j. We may conveniently sum this expression by recalling the series expansion

$$\ln(1 + x) = x - \frac{x^2}{2} + \frac{x^3}{3} - \frac{x^4}{4} + \cdots,$$

so that for the one-dimensional chain

$$\alpha = 2 \ln 2.$$

There was no special difficulty about carrying out this calculation for the one-dimensional lattice. However, in three dimensions the series does present greater difficulty. It is not possible to write down the successive terms by a casual inspection, nor is it possible to sum the series conveniently. It is important so to arrange the terms in the series that the contributions from the positive and negative terms nearly cancel, or else the series will not converge.

In the sodium chloride structure there are six positive ions (the nearest neighbors to the negative reference ion) at $p = 1$, giving a positive contribution to α of $\frac{6}{1}$; there are twelve negative ions at

$p = 2^{\frac{1}{2}}$, giving $-12/2^{\frac{1}{2}}$; eight positive ions at $p = 3^{\frac{1}{2}}$, giving $8/3^{\frac{1}{2}}$; six negative ions at $p = 2$, giving $-\frac{6}{2}$; etc., so that

$$\alpha = \frac{6}{1} - \frac{12}{2^{\frac{1}{2}}} + \frac{8}{3^{\frac{1}{2}}} - \frac{6}{2} + \cdots$$
$$= 6.000 - 8.485 + 4.620 - 3.000 + \cdots .$$

The convergence is obviously poor.

We may improve the convergence by arranging the counting according to the schemes of Evjen and others. We work with groups of

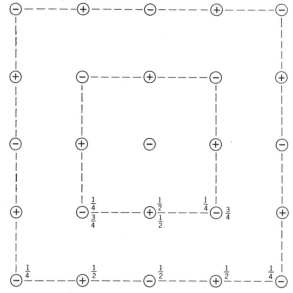

Fig. 2.3. Illustration of the Evjen method applied to a two-dimensional lattice. The weight attached to several charges is indicated. The boundary of the inner square has a net charge $4(\frac{1}{2}) - 4(\frac{1}{4}) = 1$; the outer strip has $4(\frac{1}{2}) - 4(\frac{3}{4}) - 4(\frac{1}{2})$
$$+ 8(\frac{1}{2}) - 4(\frac{1}{4}) = 0.$$

ions which are more or less neutral, if necessary taking fractional charges. The physical motivation for working with neutral groups is that the potential of a neutral assembly of ions falls off faster at a distance from the assembly than if the assembly has an excess of charge. We obtain in the sodium chloride structure nearly neutral groups by considering the charges on cubes, with the understanding that charges on cube faces are to be treated as shared between two cells, on edges between four cells, and on corners between eight.

A simple method of counting is illustrated for a two-dimensional lattice by Fig. 2.3. In the actual sodium chloride structure the first cube surrounding a negative reference ion intercepts six positive charges on cube faces, twelve negative charges on cube edges, and eight positive charges at cube corners—a resultant of one positive charge according to the present scheme of counting fractional charges. The contribution to α from the first cube is

$$\frac{6/2}{1} - \frac{12/4}{2^{1/2}} + \frac{8/8}{3^{1/2}} = 1.45. \quad \text{: } \alpha = M. \; const.$$

On taking into account in similar fashion the ions in the next larger cube enclosing the original cube, we get in this approximation $\alpha = 1.75$, which is close to the accurate value $\alpha = 1.747558$ which has been worked out for the sodium chloride structure by the Ewald method.

The Ewald method is derived and discussed in Appendix B.   Values of Madelung constants for many different crystal structures are tabulated by Sherman[4] in a review article.   Typical values of α are listed below, based on unit charges and referred to the nearest neighbor distance.

Structure	α
Sodium chloride, NaCl	1.747558
Cesium chloride, CsCl	1.762670
Zinc blende, ZnS	1.6381
Wurtzite, ZnS	1.641

The cesium chloride lattice is body-centered cubic and may be easily visualized.   We consider (Fig. 1.1b) cesium ions placed at the lattice points of a simple cubic lattice.   At the center of each cube we place a chlorine ion; this is the desired structure.   It will be seen that the chlorine ions when arranged in the prescribed way also form a simple cubic lattice by themselves.   Each ion is at the center of a cube formed by eight ions of the opposite charge.   As the number of nearest neighbors is eight, we say that the *coordination number* is eight; the coordination number of the sodium chloride lattice is six.

For the same nearest neighbor distance the cesium chloride structure has a slightly ($\sim 1\%$) higher Coulomb energy than the sodium chloride structure, as the value of the Madelung constant α is higher for cesium chloride; however, each ion has eight nearest neighbors contributing to the repulsive energy, while there are only six in sodium chloride.   As the repulsive energy is about 10% of the total energy, we might expect the 2% or 3% difference in repulsive energy to outweigh the Coulomb energy difference and thus to favor the sodium chloride structure by a small amount.   It is indeed the case that many more ionic crystals

[4] J. Sherman, Chem. Revs. 11, 93 (1932).

are known with the sodium chloride structure than with the cesium chloride structure, but as the differences in binding energy are small we can often only decide at a given temperature which will be stable for a particular salt by a consideration of second order contributions to the energy. A detailed discussion of the stability of the two lattices is given by May.[5]

CALCULATION OF THE REPULSIVE POTENTIAL EXPONENT n

We may make a very rough estimate of the value of the exponent n in the repulsive term in the potential energy. We compare the calculated Coulomb energy with the observed total binding energy, and then estimate n on the basis of Eq. (2.5). *31*

Substance	U (Coulomb) (kcal/mole)	U_0 (observed) (kcal/mole)
NaCl	206	183
NaBr	195	173
NaI	180	166
KCl	185	164

We see that the Coulomb energy is of the order of 10% higher than the observed total energy, so that if the repulsive energy were the only additional contribution to be considered we should have to suppose that the value of n was of the order of 10. We must remark that the Coulomb interaction by itself accounts remarkably well for the binding energy, suggesting that our basic assumption about the ionic nature of the compounds has considerable merit.

It is possible to calculate n from independent data. It is convenient to work with the observed values of the compressibility K, defined as

$$(2.7) \qquad K = -\frac{1}{V}\frac{dV}{dp}.$$

At very low temperatures we may neglect thermal effects and write, from the first law of thermodynamics,

$$dU = -p\,dV$$

so that $dp/dV = -d^2U/dV^2$, and (at 0°K),

$$(2.8) \qquad \frac{1}{K} = V\frac{d^2U}{dV^2}.$$

[5] A. May, Phys. Rev. **52**, 339 (1937). For a discussion of transformations observed under high pressure, see P. W. Bridgman, *Physics of high pressure*, Macmillan Co., New York, 2nd ed., 1950.

For the sodium chloride structure, $V = 2NR^3$, where N is the total number of molecules and R is the nearest neighbor distance. We have

$$dU/dV = (dU/dR)(dR/dV);$$

$$d^2U/dV^2 = (dU/dR)(d^2R/dV^2) + (d^2U/dR^2)(dR/dV)^2.$$

At the equilibrium separation, $R = R_0$ and dU/dR is zero, so that

(2.9)
$$\frac{1}{K} = \frac{1}{18NR_0}\left(\frac{d^2U}{dR^2}\right)_{R_0},$$

$\dfrac{dV}{dR} : 6NR^2$

using

(2.10)
$$(dR/dV)^2 = 1/36N^2R^4.$$

$\leftarrow \left(\dfrac{dR}{dV}\right)^2 = \dfrac{1}{36N^2R^4}$

From Eq. (2.2) we have

$$U = N\left[\frac{\lambda A_n}{R^n} - \frac{\alpha e^2}{R}\right],$$

so that

$$\frac{d^2U}{dR^2} = N\left[\frac{n(n+1)A_n\lambda}{R^{n+2}} - \frac{2\alpha e^2}{R^3}\right]$$

At equilibrium, using Eq. (2.4) to eliminate $A_n\lambda$, we have $p31$

$$\left(\frac{d^2U}{dR^2}\right)_{R_0} = \frac{N(n-1)\alpha e^2}{R_0^3}$$

so that

(2.11)
$$\frac{1}{K} = \frac{(n-1)e^2\alpha}{18R_0^4}.$$

We may use this relation to calculate n, as we may measure K, e, and R_0, and we have calculated the Madelung constant α. The compressibility of sodium chloride has been measured by Slater,[6] and he has estimated the extrapolation to absolute zero temperature as $K = 3.3 \times 10^{-12}$ cm^2/dyne. We have then

(2.12)
$$n = 1 + \frac{18R_0^4}{Ke^2\alpha} = 9.4,$$

which is of the magnitude we expected.

Table 2.1 gives a comparison of the observed binding energies of a number of ionic crystals with the calculated values of Slater obtained

[6] J. C. Slater, Phys. Rev. **23**, 488 (1924).

Crystal	Lattice Constant (A)	Lattice Energy (kcal/mole)		
		Theoretical (Mayer *et al.*)	Theoretical (Slater) (0°K)	Experimental
LiF	4.02	240.1	231	
LiCl	5.13	199.2	189	198.1
LiBr	5.49	188.3	180	189.3
LiI	6.00	174.1		181.1
NaF	4.62	213.4		
NaCl	5.63	183.1	178	182.8
NaBr	5.96	174.6	169	173.3
NaI	6.46	163.9		166.4
KF	5.34	189.7	182	
KCl	6.28	165.4	164	164.4
KBr	5.59	159.3	157	156.2
KI	7.05	150.8	148	151.5
RbF	5.64	181.6		
RbCl	6.54	160.7		160.5
RbBr	6.85	153.5	152	153.3
RbI	7.33	145.3	147	149.0
CsF	6.01	173.7		
CsCl†	4.11	152.2		155.1
CsBr†	4.29	146.3		148.6
CsI†	4.56	139.1		145.3
AgF	4.92	219		217.7
AgCl	5.55	203		205.7
AgBr	5.77	197		201.8
AgI‡	6.47	190		199.2
TlCl†	3.83	167		170.1
TlBr†	3.97	164		165.6
TlI†	4.20	159		160.8
MgO	4.20	939		
CaO	4.80	831		
SrO	5.14	766		
BaO	5.52	727		
MgS	5.19	800		
CaS	5.68	737		
SrS	5.87	686		
BaS	6.35	647		
CuCl‡	5.41	216		221.9
CuBr‡	5.68	208		216.0
CuI‡	6.04	199		213.4

Structures are similar to NaCl except when marked as follows:

† CsCl structure
‡ Zinc blende structure

The theoretical lattice energies are from the calculations of Mayer and collaborators as summarized in the Landolt-Börnstein tables; most of the experimental values are taken from Table XXIV in F. Seitz, *Modern theory of solids*, McGraw-Hill Book Co., New York, 1940.

by using values of n derived from compressibility data. The results of rather more refined calculations by Mayer and collaborators are also given. For a discussion of the methods by which the experimental values are obtained from thermochemical data, and the use of the Born-Haber cycle in this connection, the reader is referred to the review article by Sherman.[7]

RECENT WORK

The classical theory of ionic crystals is discussed quite fully in a book by Born,[8] and references to much of the work since that time are given by Seitz,[9] who considers the Born-Mayer theory and the work of Mayer and his collaborators in detail. The latter work is motivated by quantum mechanics, but does not represent a complete quantum-mechanical calculation. A number of correction terms are discussed in detail. The most basic quantum-mechanical discussion of ionic crystals has been made by Löwdin,[10] who starts with radial wave functions of the free ions in the approximation of self-consistent fields with exchange; he computes from these wave functions alone the lattice energy, lattice constant, and various elastic properties. No empirical data are introduced except values of the fundamental physical constants e, m, h, etc. Some of the results at 0°K for sodium chloride and potassium chloride are given in Table 2.2, as taken from Löwdin's thesis.

TABLE 2.2.   COMPARISON OF LÖWDIN'S CALCULATIONS WITH EXPERIMENTAL RESULTS EXTRAPOLATED TO 0°K

	NaCl		KCl	
	Theoretical	Experimental	Theoretical	Experimental
Lattice constant (A)	5.50	5.58	6.17	6.23
Lattice energy (kcal/mole)	183.2	182.8	166.9	164.4
Compressibility (10^{-12} cm^2/dyne)	4.6	3.3	6.0	4.8

IONIC RADII

It is found that the interatomic distances in the alkali halides are approximately additive, so that to a certain extent the ions may be regarded as rigid spheres. The distance at which the ions come into contact is the equilibrium interionic distance. The approximate

[7] J. Sherman, Chem. Revs. **11**, 93 (1932).

[8] M. Born, *Atomtheorie des festen Zustandes*, Teubner, Leipzig, 1923.

[9] F. Seitz, *Modern theory of solids*, McGraw-Hill Book Co., New York, 1940.

[10] Per-Olov Löwdin, Thesis, Uppsala, 1948; Ark. Mat. Astron. Fysik **35A**, Nos. 9, 30 (1947).

validity of the ionic radius concept is a consequence of the very strong dependence of the repulsive forces on interionic distance.

The tailing-off of the radial wave functions according to quantum mechanics tells us that no absolute significance may be attached to a table of ionic radii, but for many purposes a set of radii, such as those in Tables 2.3 and 2.4, may be of value. It is necessary to assign one

TABLE 2.3. IONIC CRYSTAL RADII ACCORDING TO ZACHARIASEN
(Unpublished)

The interionic distance D is represented by $D_N = R_C + R_A + \Delta_N$, for ionic crystals, where N is the coordination number of the cation, R_C and R_A are the standard radii of the cation and anion, and Δ_N is a correction for coordination number. Room temperature.

(a)

N	Δ_N (A)	N	Δ_N (A)	N	Δ_N (A)
1	-0.50	5	-0.05	9	$+0.11$
2	-0.31	6	0	10	$+0.14$
3	-0.19	7	$+0.04$	11	$+0.17$
4	-0.11	8	$+0.08$	12	$+0.19$

(b)   *Standard Radii (in A) for Ions with Inert Gas Configurations*

-2			O 1.46	S 1.90	Se 2.02	Te 2.22	Po 2.30
-1			F 1.33	Cl 1.81	Br 1.96	I 2.19	At 2.27
$+1$	Li 0.68	Na 0.98	K 1.33	Rb 1.48	Cs 1.67	Fr 1.75
$+2$	Be 0.30	Mg 0.65	Ca 0.94	Sr 1.10	Ba 1.29	Ra 1.37
$+3$	B 0.16	Al 0.45	Sc 0.68	Y 0.88	La 1.04	Ac 1.11
$+4$		Si 0.38	Ti 0.60	Zr 0.77	Ce 0.92	Th 0.99
$+5$				Nb 0.67		Pa 0.90
$+6$						U 0.83

(c)   *Actinide Ions*

	Ac	Th	Pa	U	Np	Pu	Am
$+3$	1.11	1.08	1.05	1.03	1.01	1.00	0.99
$+4$		0.99	0.96	0.93	0.92	0.90	0.89
$+5$			0.90	0.89	0.88	0.87	0.86
$+6$				0.83	0.82	0.81	0.80

radius somewhat arbitrarily in constructing a table, as a constant distance may be added to the cations and subtracted from the anions without changing the observed lattice constants in diatomic structures. It is usual in empirical treatments to take the radius of F^- as 1.33 A, when the coordination number (number of nearest neighbors) is 6. The radii in Table 2.4 were calculated theoretically by Pauling with the help of certain empirical data. Empirical radii values for other ions, based on $O^{2-} = 1.40$ A, are given in Table 2.5.

As an example of the use of the tables, we consider $BaTiO_3$ (Fig. 7.1), with a measured average lattice constant of 4.004 A at room temperature. If we suppose that the structure is determined by the Ba-O contacts, we have, from Table 2.3, $D_{12} = 1.29 + 1.46 + 0.19 = 2.94$ A, or $a = 4.15$ A; if the Ti-O contact determines the structure, we have $D_6 = 0.60 + 1.46 = 2.06$, or $a = 4.12$ A. The fact that the actual lattice constant is appreciably smaller than the estimates may perhaps suggest that the bonding is not purely ionic, but is partly covalent. For sodium chloride, which is probably principally ionic, we have $D_6 = 0.98 + 1.81 = 2.79$, or $a = 5.58$ A, while 5.63 A is observed at room temperature.

TABLE 2.4. IONIC CRYSTAL RADII ACCORDING TO PAULING, IN ANGSTROMS

(L. Pauling, *Nature of the chemical bond,* Cornell University Press, Ithaca, 1945, p. 346.)

				H^-	Li^+	Be^{2+}	B^{3+}	C^{4+}	N^{5+}	O^{6+}	F^{7+}
				2.08	0.60	0.31	0.20	0.15	0.11	0.09	0.07
C^{4-}	N^{3-}	O^{2-}	F^-	Na^+	Mg^{2+}	Al^{3+}	Si^{4+}	P^{5+}	S^{6+}	Cl^{7+}	
2.60	1.71	1.40	1.36	0.95	0.65	0.50	0.41	0.34	0.29	0.26	
Si^{4-}	P^{3-}	S^{2-}	Cl^-	K^+	Ca^{2+}	Sc^{3+}	Ti^{4+}	V^{5+}	Cr^{6+}	Mn^{7+}	
2.71	2.12	1.84	1.81	1.33	0.99	0.81	0.68	0.59	0.52	0.46	
				Cu^+	Zn^{2+}	Ga^{3+}	Ge^{4+}	As^{5+}	Se^{6+}	Br^{7+}	
				0.96	0.74	0.62	0.53	0.47	0.42	0.39	
Ge^{4-}	As^{3-}	Se^{2-}	Br^-	Rb^+	Sr^{2+}	Y^{3+}	Zr^{4+}	Nb^{5+}	Mo^{6+}		
2.72	2.22	1.98	1.95	1.48	1.13	0.93	0.80	0.70	0.62		
				Ag^+	Cd^{2+}	In^{3+}	Sn^{4+}	Sb^{5+}	Te^{6+}	I^{7+}	
				1.26	0.97	0.81	0.71	0.62	0.56	0.50	
Sn^{4-}	Sb^{3-}	Te^{2-}	I^-	Cs^+	Ba^{2+}	La^{3+}	Ce^{4+}				
2.94	2.45	2.21	2.16	1.69	1.35	1.15	1.01				
				Au^+	Hg^{2+}	Tl^{3+}	Pb^{4+}	Bi^{5+}			
				1.37	1.10	0.95	0.84	0.74			

TABLE 2.5. EMPIRICAL IONIC RADII
(After Pauling)

NH_4^+	1.48 A	Mn^{2+}	0.80 A	Ti^{3+}	0.69 A
Tl^+	1.44 A	Fe^{2+}	0.75 A	V^{3+}	0.66 A
		Co^{2+}	0.72 A	Cr^{3+}	0.64 A
		Ni^{2+}	0.70 A	Mn^{3+}	0.62 A
				Fe^{3+}	0.60 A

Trivalent rare earth ions, 0.90 ± 0.05 A

PROBLEMS

2.1. Show that the constant A_n in Eq. (2.2) has the value 6.42(6) for the sodium chloride lattice for $n = 10$. Values of A_n are tabulated by J. E. Lennard-Jones and A. E. Ingham, Proc. Roy. Soc. **107A**, 636 (1925).

2.2. Calculate the value of λ in Eq. (2.1) for sodium chloride, taking $n = 10$; $A_{10} = 6.43$; and $R_0 = 2.81 \times 10^{-8}$ cm. *Ans.* $\lambda = 0.7 \times 10^{-88}$ ergs/cm^{10}.

2.3. Show that the constant A_n in Eq. (2.2) has the value 9.56(4) for the cesium chloride lattice for $n = 10$.

2.4. Discuss the probable effect of doubling the ionic charges on the lattice constant, compressibility, and binding energy of sodium chloride; the repulsive potential is to be taken as unchanged.

2.5.* Calculate by the Ewald method given in Appendix B the value of the Madelung constant for the cesium chloride lattice.

2.6.* Using the theory developed in this chapter, calculate for sodium chloride the value of the pressure coefficient of compressibility $(dK/dp)/K$ at zero pressure and at 0°K, using appropriate numerical data. *Ans.* -1.8×10^{-11} cm^2/dyne.

2.7. Suppose that it were possible to permeate the space between ions in an ionic crystal with a homogeneous fluid of dielectric constant ϵ without affecting the repulsive interactions between ions, but reducing the Coulomb interaction by a factor $1/\epsilon$. Calculate the lattice constant and binding energy of sodium chloride in this situation, taking $\epsilon = 81$ as for water. This is to a certain extent the explanation of the solvent properties of water and other dipolar liquids. Compare the binding energy per atom with the approximate thermal energy kT per atom at room temperature.

2.8. Check the Zachariasen radii (Table 2.3) against observed lattice constants for ten crystals chosen from various sections of Wyckoff's compilation or elsewhere.

2.9. Replacing the repulsive potential λr_{ij}^{-n} over all ions by the potential $Ae^{-r/\rho}$ over only nearest neighbor ions, find values of A and ρ for sodium chloride. The exponential potential is suggested by quantum theory and is used in most recent work in the field.

REFERENCES

M. Born, *Atomtheorie des festen Zustandes*, Teubner, Leipzig, 1923.

M. Born and M. Göppert-Mayer, *Handbuch der Physik* **24/2**, 623–794, Springer, Berlin, 1933.

W. Kleber, *Angewandte Gitterphysik*, W. de Gruyter and Co., Berlin, 2nd ed., 1949.

F. Seitz, *Modern theory of solids*, McGraw-Hill Book Co., New York, 1940.

* Problems of considerable length or difficulty are marked with an asterisk.

3

Elastic Constants of Crystals

This chapter is concerned with the elastic constants of single crystals. The elastic constants are of interest because of the insight they give into the nature of the binding forces in solids, and they are also of importance for the thermal properties of solids. We give first a review of the formal phenomenology of elastic constants of single crystals, for small deformations. Polycrystalline specimens may have isotropic elastic properties and may be described approximately by fewer elastic constants than a single crystal, but the values of the constants for single crystals are of fundamental significance.

ANALYSIS OF ELASTIC STRAINS AND STRESSES

The local elastic strain of a body may be specified by six numbers. If α, β, γ are the angles between the unit cell axes $\mathbf{a}$, $\mathbf{b}$, $\mathbf{c}$, the strain may be specified by the changes $\Delta\alpha$, $\Delta\beta$, $\Delta\gamma$; Δa, Δb, Δc resulting from the deformation. This is a good physical specification of strain, but for non-orthogonal axes it leads to mathematical complications. It is usual instead to specify the strain in terms of the six components e_{xx}, e_{yy}, e_{zz}, e_{xy}, e_{yz}, e_{zx} which are defined below.

We imagine that three *orthogonal* axes $\mathbf{f}$, $\mathbf{g}$, $\mathbf{h}$ of *unit length* are embedded securely in the unstrained solid, as shown in Fig. 3.1. We suppose that after a small uniform deformation has taken place the axes, which we now label $\mathbf{f}'$, $\mathbf{g}'$, $\mathbf{h}'$, are distorted in orientation and in length, so that with the same atom as origin we may write.

$$\mathbf{f}' = (1 + \varepsilon_{xx})\mathbf{f} + \varepsilon_{xy}\mathbf{g} + \varepsilon_{xz}\mathbf{h};$$

(3.1)
$$\mathbf{g}' = \varepsilon_{yx}\mathbf{f} + (1 + \varepsilon_{yy})\mathbf{g} + \varepsilon_{yz}\mathbf{h};$$

$$\mathbf{h}' = \varepsilon_{zx}\mathbf{f} + \varepsilon_{zy}\mathbf{g} + (1 + \varepsilon_{zz})\mathbf{h}.$$

The fractional changes of length of the $\mathbf{f}$, $\mathbf{g}$, and $\mathbf{h}$ axes are ε_{xx}, ε_{yy}, ε_{zz}, respectively, to the first order. We define the strain components e_{xx}, e_{yy}, e_{zz} by the relations

(3.2)
$$e_{xx} = \varepsilon_{xx}; \quad e_{yy} = \varepsilon_{yy}; \quad e_{zz} = \varepsilon_{zz}.$$

The strain components e_{xy}, e_{yz}, e_{zx} may be defined as the changes in angle between the axes, so that to the first order

$$e_{xy} = \mathbf{f}' \cdot \mathbf{g}' = \varepsilon_{yx} + \varepsilon_{xy};$$

(3.3)
$$e_{yz} = \mathbf{g}' \cdot \mathbf{h}' = \varepsilon_{zy} + \varepsilon_{yz};$$

$$e_{zx} = \mathbf{h}' \cdot \mathbf{f}' = \varepsilon_{xz} + \varepsilon_{xz}.$$

This completes the definition of the six strain components. A deformation is *uniform* if the values of the strain components are independent of the choice of origin.

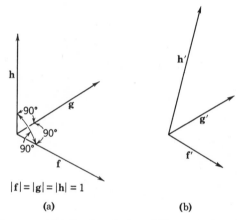

$$|\mathbf{f}| = |\mathbf{g}| = |\mathbf{h}| = 1$$

(a)   (b)

Fig. 3.1. Coordinate axes for the description of the state of strain; the orthogona unit axes in the unstrained state (a) are deformed in the strained state (b).

We note that merely rotating the axes does not change the angle between them, so that for a pure rotation $\varepsilon_{yx} = -\varepsilon_{xy}$; $\varepsilon_{zy} = -\varepsilon_{yz}$; $\varepsilon_{zx} = -\varepsilon_{xz}$. If we exclude pure rotations as not being of interest here, we may without further loss of generality take $\varepsilon_{yx} = \varepsilon_{xy}$; $\varepsilon_{zy} = \varepsilon_{yz}$; $\varepsilon_{zx} = \varepsilon_{xz}$, so that in terms of the strain components we have

$$\mathbf{f}' - \mathbf{f} = e_{xx}\mathbf{f} + \tfrac{1}{2}e_{xy}\mathbf{g} + \tfrac{1}{2}e_{zx}\mathbf{h};$$

(3.4)
$$\mathbf{g}' - \mathbf{g} = \tfrac{1}{2}e_{xy}\mathbf{f} + e_{yy}\mathbf{g} + \tfrac{1}{2}e_{yz}\mathbf{h};$$

$$\mathbf{h}' - \mathbf{h} = \tfrac{1}{2}e_{zx}\mathbf{f} + \tfrac{1}{2}e_{yz}\mathbf{g} + e_{zz}\mathbf{h}.$$

We consider under a deformation which is substantially uniform near the origin a particle originally at the position

(3.5)
$$\mathbf{r} = x\mathbf{f} + y\mathbf{g} + z\mathbf{h}.$$

After deformation the particle is at

(3.6) $\mathbf{r}' = x\mathbf{f}' + y\mathbf{g}' + z\mathbf{h}',$

so that the displacement is given by

(3.7) $\varrho = \mathbf{r}' - \mathbf{r} = x(\mathbf{f}' - \mathbf{f}) + y(\mathbf{g}' - \mathbf{g}) + z(\mathbf{h}' - \mathbf{h}).$

If we write the displacement as

(3.8) $\varrho = u\mathbf{f} + v\mathbf{g} + w\mathbf{h},$

we have from (3.4) and (3.7) the following expressions for the strain components:

$$e_{xx} = \frac{\partial u}{\partial x}; \qquad e_{yy} = \frac{\partial v}{\partial y}; \qquad e_{zz} = \frac{\partial w}{\partial z};$$

(3.9)

$$e_{xy} = \frac{\partial v}{\partial x} + \frac{\partial u}{\partial y}; \qquad e_{yz} = \frac{\partial w}{\partial y} + \frac{\partial v}{\partial z}; \qquad e_{zx} = \frac{\partial u}{\partial z} + \frac{\partial w}{\partial x}.$$

We have written derivatives for application to non-uniform strain. The expressions (3.9) are frequently used in the literature to define the strain components. Occasionally definitions of e_{xy}, e_{yz}, and e_{zx} are given which differ by a factor $\frac{1}{2}$ from those given here. For a uniform deformation the displacement ϱ has the components

$$u = e_{xx}x + \tfrac{1}{2}e_{xy}y + \tfrac{1}{2}e_{zx}z;$$

(3.10) $v = \tfrac{1}{2}e_{xy}x + e_{yy}y + \tfrac{1}{2}e_{yz}z;$

$$w = \tfrac{1}{2}e_{zx}x + \tfrac{1}{2}e_{yz}y + e_{zz}z.$$

DILATION

The fractional increment of volume caused by a deformation is called the *dilation*. The unit cube of edges $\mathbf{f}, \mathbf{g}, \mathbf{h}$ after deformation has a volume

(3.11) $V' = \mathbf{f}' \cdot \mathbf{g}' \times \mathbf{h}' \cong 1 + e_{xx} + e_{yy} + e_{zz},$

where squares and products of strain components are neglected. Thus the dilation is

(3.12) $\delta = \Delta V / V' = e_{xx} + e_{yy} + e_{zz}.$

SHEARING STRAIN

We may interpret the strain components of the type

$$e_{xy} = \frac{\partial v}{\partial x} + \frac{\partial u}{\partial y}$$

as made up of two simple shears. In one of the shears, planes of the material normal to the x axis slide in the y direction; in the other shear, planes normal to y slide in the x direction.

STRESS COMPONENTS

The force acting on a unit area in the solid is defined as the stress. There are nine stress components: X_x, X_y, X_z, Y_x, Y_y, Y_z, Z_x, Z_y, Z_z.

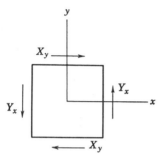

The capital letter indicates the direction of the force, and the subscript indicates the normal to the plane to which the force is applied. Thus the stress component X_x represents a force applied in the x direction to a unit area of a plane whose normal lies in the x direction; the stress component X_y represents a force applied in the x direction to a unit area of a plane whose normal lies in the y direction. The number of independent stress components is reduced to six by applying to an elementary cube as in Fig. 3.2 the condition that the angular acceleration vanish, and hence that the total torque must be zero. It follows that

Fig. 3.2. Demonstration that $Y_x = X_y$ in order that the body may be in equilibrium.

$$Y_z = Z_y; \qquad Z_x = X_z; \qquad X_y = Y_x,$$

and the independent stress components may be taken as X_x, Y_y, Z_z, Y_z, Z_x, X_y.

ELASTIC COMPLIANCE AND STIFFNESS CONSTANTS

Hooke's law states that for small deformations the strain is proportional to the stress, so that the strain components are linear functions of the stress components:

$$e_{xx} = s_{11}X_x + s_{12}Y_y + s_{13}Z_z + s_{14}Y_z + s_{15}Z_x + s_{16}X_y;$$

$$e_{yy} = s_{21}X_x + s_{22}Y_y + s_{23}Z_z + s_{24}Y_z + s_{25}Z_x + s_{26}X_y;$$

$$e_{zz} = s_{31}X_x + s_{32}Y_y + s_{33}Z_z + s_{34}Y_z + s_{35}Z_x + s_{36}X_y;$$

(3.13)

$$e_{yz} = s_{41}X_x + s_{42}Y_y + s_{43}Z_z + s_{44}Y_z + s_{45}Z_x + s_{46}X_y;$$

$$e_{zx} = s_{51}X_x + s_{52}Y_y + s_{53}Z_z + s_{54}Y_z + s_{55}Z_x + s_{56}X_y;$$

$$e_{xy} = s_{61}X_x + s_{62}Y_y + s_{63}Z_z + s_{64}Y_z + s_{65}Z_x + s_{66}X_y.$$

Conversely, the stress components are linear functions of the strain components:

$$X_x = c_{11}e_{xx} + c_{12}e_{yy} + c_{13}e_{zz} + c_{14}e_{yz} + c_{15}e_{zx} + c_{16}e_{xy};$$

$$Y_y = c_{21}e_{xx} + c_{22}e_{yy} + c_{23}e_{zz} + c_{24}e_{yz} + c_{25}e_{zx} + c_{26}e_{xy};$$

(3.14)
$$Z_z = c_{31}e_{xx} + c_{32}e_{yy} + c_{33}e_{zz} + c_{34}e_{yz} + c_{35}e_{zx} + c_{36}e_{xy};$$

$$Y_z = c_{41}e_{xx} + c_{42}e_{yy} + c_{43}e_{zz} + c_{44}e_{yz} + c_{45}e_{zx} + c_{46}e_{xy};$$

$$Z_x = c_{51}e_{xx} + c_{52}e_{yy} + c_{53}e_{zz} + c_{54}e_{yz} + c_{55}e_{zx} + c_{56}e_{xy};$$

$$X_y = c_{61}e_{xx} + c_{62}e_{yy} + c_{63}e_{zz} + c_{64}e_{yz} + c_{65}e_{zx} + c_{66}e_{xy}.$$

The quantities s_{11}, s_{12}, $\cdots$ are called the *elastic constants* or *elastic compliance constants;* the quantities c_{11}, c_{12}, $\cdots$ are called the *elastic stiffness constants* or *moduli of elasticity.* Other names are also current.

ENERGY DENSITY

We calculate the increment of work δW done by the stress system in straining a small cube of side L, with the origin at one corner of the cube and the coordinate axes parallel to the cube edges. We have

(3.15)
$$\delta W = \mathbf{F} \cdot \delta\varrho$$

where $\mathbf{F}$ is the applied force and

(3.16)
$$\delta\varrho = \mathbf{f}\delta u + \mathbf{g}\delta v + \mathbf{h}\delta w$$

is the displacement. If X, Y, Z denote the components of $\mathbf{F}$ per unit area, then

(3.17)
$$\delta W = L^2(X\delta u + Y\delta v + Z\delta w).$$

We note that the displacement of the three cube faces containing the origin is zero, so that the forces all act at a distance L from the origin. Now by definition of the strain components

(3.18)
$$\delta u = L(\delta e_{xx} + \tfrac{1}{2}\delta e_{xy} + \tfrac{1}{2}\delta e_{zx}),$$

etc., so that

$$\delta W = L^3(X_x\delta e_{xx} + Y_y\delta e_{yy} + Z_z\delta e_{zz} + Y_z\delta e_{yz} + Z_x\delta e_{zx} + X_y\delta e_{xy}).$$

The increment δU of elastic energy per unit volume is

(3.19) $$\delta U = X_x\delta e_{xx} + Y_y\delta e_{yy} + Z_z\delta e_{zz} + Y_z\delta e_{yz} + Z_x\delta e_{zx} + X_y\delta e_{xy}.$$

We have $\partial U/\partial e_{xx} = X_x$ and $\partial U/\partial e_{yy} = Y_y$, and on further differentiation

$$\partial X_x/\partial e_{yy} = \partial Y_y/\partial e_{xx}.$$

This leads from (3.14) to the relation

$$c_{12} = c_{21};$$

and in general we have

(3.20) $$c_{ij} = c_{ji},$$

giving fifteen relations among the thirty non-diagonal terms of the matrix of the c's. The thirty-six elastic stiffness constants are in this way reduced to twenty-one coefficients. Similar relations hold among the elastic compliances. The matrix of the c's or s's is therefore symmetrical.

CUBIC CRYSTALS

The number of independent elastic stiffness constants is usually reduced if the crystal possesses symmetry elements, and in the important case of cubic crystals there are only three independent stiffness constants, as we now show. We suppose that the coordinate axes are chosen parallel to the cube edges. In (3.14) we must have

$$c_{14} = c_{15} = c_{16} = c_{24} = c_{25} = c_{26} = c_{34} = c_{35} = c_{36} = 0,$$

as the stress must not be altered by reversing the direction of one of the other coordinate axes. As the axes are equivalent, we have further

$$c_{11} = c_{22} = c_{33},$$

and $$c_{12} = c_{13} = c_{21} = c_{23} = c_{31} = c_{32},$$

so that the first three lines of (3.14) are described by the two independent constants c_{11} and c_{12}. The last three lines of (3.14) are described by the independent constant c_{44}, as

$$c_{44} = c_{55} = c_{66}$$

by equivalence of the axes, and the other constants all vanish because of their behavior on reversing the direction of one or another axis.

The array of values of the elastic stiffness constant is therefore reduced for a cubic crystal to the matrix

(3.21) $$\|c_{ij}\| = \begin{vmatrix} c_{11} & c_{12} & c_{12} & 0 & 0 & 0 \\ c_{12} & c_{11} & c_{12} & 0 & 0 & 0 \\ c_{12} & c_{12} & c_{11} & 0 & 0 & 0 \\ 0 & 0 & 0 & c_{44} & 0 & 0 \\ 0 & 0 & 0 & 0 & c_{44} & 0 \\ 0 & 0 & 0 & 0 & 0 & c_{44} \end{vmatrix}$$

It is readily seen that for a cubic crystal

$$(3.22) \quad U = \tfrac{1}{2}c_{11}(e_{xx}{}^2 + e_{yy}{}^2 + e_{zz}{}^2) + c_{12}(e_{yy}e_{zz} + e_{zz}e_{xx} + e_{xx}e_{yy}) + \tfrac{1}{2}c_{44}(e_{yz}{}^2 + e_{zx}{}^2 + e_{xy}{}^2)$$

satisfies the condition (3.19) for the elastic energy density function. For example,

$$\partial U/\partial e_{yy} = c_{11}e_{yy} + c_{12}e_{zz} + c_{12}e_{xx} = Y_y,$$

by (3.21).

For cubic crystals the compliance and stiffness constants are related by

$$c_{11} = (s_{11} + s_{12})/(s_{11} - s_{12})(s_{11} + 2s_{12});$$

$$(3.23) \qquad c_{12} = -s_{12}/(s_{11} - s_{12})(s_{11} + 2s_{12});$$

$$c_{44} = 1/s_{44}.$$

Values of elastic data for various cubic crystals are tabulated in Table 3.1. The values refer to room temperature. A general review

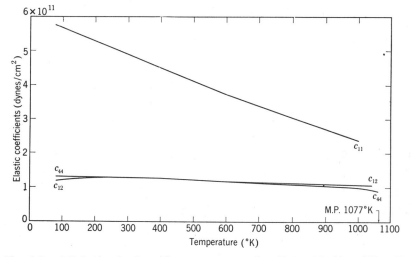

Fig. 3.3. Adiabatic elastic stiffness constants of sodium chloride. [After L. Hunter and S. Siegel, Phys. Rev. **61**, 84 (1942); F. C. Rose, Phys. Rev. **49**, 50 (1936).]

of elastic constant data and of relationships among various coefficients for the crystal classes has been given by Hearmon.[1] In Fig. 3.3 the experimental values of the elastic constants of sodium chloride are plotted over a wide temperature range. The theory of the tem-

[1] R. F. S. Hearmon, Revs. Modern Phys. **18**, 409 (1946).

perature dependence of the elastic constants has been considered by Born[2] and by Fürth.[3]

EXPERIMENTAL DETERMINATION OF ELASTIC CONSTANTS

The classic methods for the measurement of the elastic constants of crystals are described in the review by Hearmon just cited. Since his review the use of the ultrasonic pulse method has become widespread[4] because of its convenience and adaptability to a wide range of experimental conditions. In this method an ultrasonic pulse generated by a

TABLE 3.1. ELASTIC DATA FOR CUBIC CRYSTALS AT ROOM TEMPERATURE

The stiffness and compliance constants given are not necessarily mutually consistent, having been taken in some cases from different sources.

Crystal	Stiffness Constants and Bulk Modulus in 10^{12} dyne/cm^2				Compliance Constants in 10^{-12} cm^2/dyne		
	c_{11}	c_{12}	c_{44}	B	s_{11}	s_{12}	s_{44}
Na (210°K)	0.055	0.042	0.049	0.047	53.5	−23.2	20.4
Fe	2.37	1.41	1.16	1.73	0.76	− 0.28	0.86
K	0.046	0.037	0.026	0.040	82.3	−37.0	38.0
W	5.01	1.98	1.51	3.00	0.26	− 0.073	0.66
Al	1.08	0.62	0.28	0.77	1.59	− 0.58	3.52
Cu	1.70	1.23	0.75	1.39	1.49	− 0.62	1.33
Pb	0.48	0.41	0.14	0.43	9.30	− 4.26	6.94
Diamond	9.2	3.9	4.3	5.7	0.14	− 0.04	0.23
NaCl	0.49	0.124	0.126	0.25	2.4	− 0.50	7.8
KBr	0.35	0.058	0.050	0.16	4.0	− 1.2	7.5
KCl	0.40	0.062	0.062	0.17	2.7	− 0.3	15.6

quartz transducer is transmitted through the test crystal and reflected from the rear surface of the crystal back to the transducer. The elapsed time between initiation and receipt of the pulse is measured by standard electronic methods. The velocity is obtained by dividing the round trip distance by the elapsed time. In a representative arrangement the experimental frequency may be 15 mc, and the pulse length 1 μsec. The wavelength is of the order of 3 × 10^{-4} cm. The crystal specimen may be of the order of 1 cm in length.

The elastic stiffness constants c_{11}, c_{12}, c_{44} of a cubic crystal may be determined from the velocities of three waves. A longitudinal wave propagates along a cube axis with velocity $(c_{11}/\rho)^{1/2}$, where ρ is the

[2] M. Born, J. Chem. Phys. **7**, 591 (1939).
[3] R. Fürth, Proc. Cambridge Phil. Soc. **37**, 34 (1941).
[4] See, for example, H. Huntington, Phys. Rev. **72**, 321 (1947); J. K. Galt, Phys. Rev. **73**, 1460 (1948).

density. A shear wave propagates along a cube axis with velocity $(c_{44}/\rho)^{1/2}$, while a shear wave with particle motion along a $1\bar{1}0$ direction propagates along a 110 direction with velocity $[(c_{11} - c_{12})/2\rho]^{1/2}$. The first two results are derived below, and the latter result is the basis of a problem at the end of the chapter.

ELASTIC WAVES IN CUBIC CRYSTALS

By considering the forces acting on an element of volume in the crystal we find for the equation of motion in the x direction

$$(3.24) \qquad \rho\ddot{u} = \frac{\partial X_x}{\partial x} + \frac{\partial X_y}{\partial y} + \frac{\partial X_z}{\partial z},$$

with similar equations for the y and z directions; ρ is the density. From (3.21) it follows, taking the cube edges as the x, y, z directions, that

$$\rho\ddot{u} = c_{11}\frac{\partial e_{xx}}{\partial x} + c_{12}\left(\frac{\partial e_{yy}}{\partial x} + \frac{\partial e_{zz}}{\partial x}\right) + c_{44}\left(\frac{\partial e_{xy}}{\partial y} + \frac{\partial e_{xz}}{\partial z}\right),$$

which reduces, using (3.9), to

$$(3.25) \quad \rho\ddot{u} = c_{11}\frac{\partial^2 u}{\partial x^2} + c_{44}\left(\frac{\partial^2 u}{\partial y^2} + \frac{\partial^2 u}{\partial z^2}\right) + (c_{12} + c_{44})\left(\frac{\partial^2 v}{\partial x\,\partial y} + \frac{\partial^2 w}{\partial x\,\partial z}\right).$$

One solution is given by a longitudinal wave,

$$u = u_0 e^{i(\omega t - kx)},$$

moving along the x cube edge; from (3.25)

$$-\omega^2\rho = -k^2 c_{11},$$

so that the velocity is

$$(3.26) \qquad v = \omega/k = (c_{11}/\rho)^{1/2}.$$

Another solution is given by a transverse or shear wave moving along the y cube edge, with the particle motion in the x direction:

$$u = u_0 e^{i(\omega t - ky)},$$

which gives, on substitution in (3.25),

$$-\omega^2\rho = -k^2 c_{44},$$

so that

$$(3.27) \qquad v = (c_{44}/\rho)^{1/2}.$$

There is also a solution given by a shear wave moving in the z direction with particle motion in the x direction. In general there are three types of wave motion for a given direction of propagation in the crystal, but only for a few special directions can the waves be classified as pure longitudinal or pure transverse. Further details are given by Mueller,[5] and the general problem has been treated by Schaefer and Bergmann.[6]

ELASTIC ISOTROPY

By minor manipulations we may rewrite (3.25) as

$$(3.28) \quad \rho_0 \ddot{u} = (c_{11} - c_{12} - 2c_{44}) \frac{\partial^2 u}{\partial x^2} + c_{44} \nabla^2 u + (c_{12} + c_{44}) \frac{\partial}{\partial x} \operatorname{div} \varrho,$$

where the displacement $\varrho = u\mathbf{i} + v\mathbf{j} + w\mathbf{k}$ is not to be confused with the density now written as ρ_0. If

$$(3.29) \qquad\qquad c_{11} - c_{12} = 2c_{44},$$

the first term on the right in (3.28) drops out, and we can write on summing with the equations for the y and z motions:

$$(3.30) \quad \rho_0 \ddot{\varrho} = (c_{12} + 2c_{44}) \operatorname{grad} \operatorname{div} \varrho - c_{44} \operatorname{curl} \operatorname{curl} \varrho.$$

This equation has the important property that it is invariant under rotations of the reference axes, as each term in the equation is an invariant. Thus the relation (3.29) is the condition that the crystal should be elastically isotropic; that is, that waves should propagate in all directions with equal velocities. However, the longitudinal wave velocity is not necessarily equal to the transverse wave velocity.

The anisotropy factor A in a cubic crystal is defined as

$$(3.31) \qquad\qquad A = 2c_{44}/(c_{11} - c_{12})$$

and is unity for elastic isotropy. Values of A for representative metals at room temperature follow:

Fe 2.4;   K 6.3;   W 1.0;   Al 1.2;   Cu 3.3;   Pb 3.9.

CAUCHY RELATIONS

There are among the elastic stiffness constants certain relations first obtained by Cauchy. The relations reduce to

$$(3.32) \qquad\qquad c_{12} = c_{44}$$

---

[5] H. Mueller, Z. Krist. **99**, 122 (1938).

[6] C. Schaefer and L. Bergmann, Abhandl. preuss. Akad. Wiss. Math.-naturw. Klasse **14**, 222 (1935).

in a crystal of cubic symmetry. If this is satisfied, the isotropy condition (3.29) becomes $c_{11} = 3c_{44}$. If then a cubic crystal were elastically isotropic *and* the Cauchy relation satisfied, the velocity of the transverse waves would be equal to $\frac{1}{3}^{\frac{1}{2}}$ the velocity of the longitudinal waves.

The conditions[7] for the validity of the Cauchy relations are:

1. All forces must be central, i.e., act along lines joining the centers of the atoms. This is not generally true of covalent binding forces, nor of metallic binding forces.

2. Every atom must be at a center of symmetry; that is, replacing every interatomic vector $\mathbf{r}_{jk}$ by $-\mathbf{r}_{jk}$ should not change the structure.

3. The crystal should be initially under no stress.

In metallic lattices the nature of the binding is not such that we would expect the Cauchy relation to work out well, and this is the case, as shown in Table 3.1. In ionic crystals the electrostatic interaction of the ions is the principal interaction and is central in nature. It is not surprising that the Cauchy relation is moderately well satisfied in the alkali halides, as shown also by the table.

LATTICE THEORY OF ELASTIC COEFFICIENTS

We suppose that two nearby atoms 1, 2 are displaced from equilibrium by ϱ_1, ϱ_2. If $|\varrho_2 - \varrho_1|$ is small in comparison with the lattice constant, the displacement energy may be written

$$\frac{\alpha}{2} (u_2 - u_1)^2 + \frac{\beta}{2} [(v_2 - v_1)^2 + (w_2 - w_1)^2],$$

where the pair of atoms are supposed to have been initially along the x axis. If the forces between the atoms are central, we would have $\beta = 0$.

For a monatomic simple cubic lattice with only nearest neighbor interactions the energy is

$$(3.33) \quad U = \frac{\alpha}{2} \sum_{lmn} [(u_{l+1,m,n} - u_{l,m,n})^2 + (v_{l,m+1,n} - v_{l,m,n})^2$$

$$+ (w_{l,m,n+1} - w_{l,m,n})^2] + \frac{\beta}{2} \sum_{lmn} [(v_{l+1,m,n} - v_{l,m,n})^2$$

$$+ (v_{l,m,n+1} - v_{l,m,n})^2 + \cdots + (u_{l,m,n+1} - u_{l,m,n})^2].$$

[7] C. Zener, Phys. Rev. **71**, 323 (1947); G. Leibfried, Z. Physik **129**, 307 (1951).

If a is the nearest neighbor distance, we may write for a homogeneous pure strain

$$U = \frac{N\alpha a^2}{2}\left(e_{xx}^2 + e_{yy}^2 + e_{zz}^2\right) + \frac{N\beta a^2}{4}\left(e_{yz}^2 + e_{zx}^2 + e_{xy}^2\right).$$

On comparison with (3.22) we see that our model leads to the following expressions for the elastic coefficients:

(3.34) $c_{11} = \alpha/a;$ $c_{12} = 0;$ $c_{44} = \beta/2a.$

We note that with only nearest neighbor forces on the central force assumption $(\beta = 0)$ the simple cubic lattice does not possess any

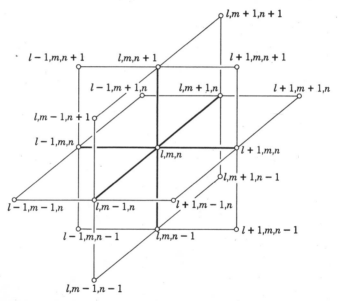

Fig. 3.4.   Location of lattice points for the calculation of elastic constants with interactions out to second nearest neighbor atoms.

resistance to shear. It is apparent, however, that the addition of next nearest neighbor forces will result in resistance to shear by providing force connections along the face diagonals. Following Born and von Kármán,[8] we consider the elastic constants of a monatomic simple cubic lattice counting interactions out to second nearest neighbors, as shown in Fig. 3.4. The force $X(l, m, n)$ in the x direction on the atom at lattice point l, m, n is given by

[8] M. Born and T. von Kármán, Physik. Z. **13,** 297 (1912).

(3.35) $\quad X(l, m, n) = \alpha[u(l + 1, m, n) + u(l - 1, m, n)$
$- 2u(l, m, n)] + \beta[u(l, m + 1, n) + u(l, m - 1, n)$
$+ u(l, m, n + 1) + u(l, m, n - 1) - 4u(l, m, n)]$
$+ \gamma[u(l + 1, m, n + 1) + u(l + 1, m + 1, n) + u(l + 1, m, n - 1)$
$+ u(l + 1, m - 1, n) + u(l - 1, m + 1, n) + u(l - 1, m, n - 1)$
$+ u(l - 1, m - 1, n) - u(l - 1, m, n + 1) - 8u(l, m, n)]$
$+ \delta[u(l, m + 1, n + 1) + u(l, m - 1, n + 1) + u(l, m + 1, n - 1)$
$+ u(l, m - 1, n - 1) - 4u(l, m, n)] + \kappa[v(l + 1, m + 1, n)$
$+ v(l - 1, m - 1, n) - v(l + 1, m - 1, n) - v(l - 1, m + 1, n)$
$+ w(l + 1, m, n + 1) + w(l - 1, m, n - 1)$
$\qquad\qquad - w(l + 1, m, n - 1) - w(l - 1, m, n + 1)].$

The terms in α and β refer to nearest neighbor interactions, those in γ, δ, κ to next nearest neighbor interactions. For central forces $\beta = 0$; $\delta = 0$; $\gamma = \kappa$. On passing from the difference equation (3.35) to a differential equation we find, taking the lattice constant as a,

$$(3.36) \quad a^{-3}X(l,m,n) = \rho\ddot{u} = \frac{\alpha}{a}\frac{\partial^2 u}{\partial x^2} + \frac{\beta}{a}\left(\frac{\partial^2 u}{\partial y^2} + \frac{\partial^2 u}{\partial z^2}\right)$$
$$+ \frac{2\gamma}{a}\left(2\frac{\partial^2 u}{\partial x^2} + \frac{\partial^2 u}{\partial y^2} + \frac{\partial^2 u}{\partial z^2}\right) + \frac{2\delta}{a}\left(\frac{\partial^2 u}{\partial y^2} + \frac{\partial^2 u}{\partial z^2}\right)$$
$$+ \frac{4\kappa}{a}\left(\frac{\partial^2 v}{\partial x\,\partial y} + \frac{\partial^2 w}{\partial x\,\partial z}\right).$$

On comparing (3.36) with (3.25) we find that the two equations are equivalent if we set

$$c_{11} = (\alpha + 4\gamma)/a;$$
$$(3.37) \qquad c_{44} = (\beta + 2\gamma + 2\delta)/a;$$
$$c_{12} + c_{44} = 4\kappa/a.$$

There are not enough independent elastic constants to determine the five atomic force constants. For central forces

$$c_{11} = (\alpha + 4\gamma)/a;$$
$$(3.38) \qquad c_{44} = 2\gamma/a;$$
$$c_{12} = 2\gamma/a.$$

CALCULATIONS FOR METALS

The elastic constants of metals have been calculated by Jones,[9] Fuchs, Zener, and others, with reasonable success. We mention here a

[9] A review of the theory is given by H. Jones, Physica **15**, 13–22 (1949).

TABLE 3.2. COMPRESSIBILITY $K = -(1/V)(dV/dp)$ OF METALS NEAR ROOM TEMPERATURE, IN 10^7 CM^2/KG

1	2	3	4	5	6	7	8	9	10	11	12	13	14	15	16
Li 87	Be 7.8														
Na 156	Mg 29.5											Al 13.4			
K 357	Ca 57	Sc	Ti 8.0	V 6.1	Cr 6.1	Mn 7.9	Fe 5.9	Co 5.4	Ni 5.3	Cu 7.2	Zn 16.9	Ga 20	Ge 13.8	As 44	Se 11.8
Rb 520	Sr 82	Y	Zr 11.0	Nb 5.7	Mo 3.6	Tc	Ru 3.4	Rh 3.6	Pd 5.3	Ag 9.9	Cd 22.5	In 25.0	Sn 18.8	Sb 27.0	Te 50.8
Cs 700	Ba 102	La 35	Hf 9.0	Ta 4.8	W 3.2	Re	Os	Ir 2.7	Pt 3.6	Au 5.8	Hg 37	Tl 34.8	Pb 23.7	Bi 29.2	Po

TABLE 3.3. COHESIVE ENERGY OF METALS, IN KCAL/MOLE AT ROOM TEMPERATURE
(After Seitz)

1	2	3	4	5	6	7	8	9	10	11	12	13	14	15	16
Li 39	Be 75														
Na 26	Mg 36											Al 55			
K 20	Ca 48	Sc 70	Ti 100	V 85	Cr 88	Mn 74	Fe 94	Co 85	Ni 85	Cu 81	Zn 27	Ga 52	Ge 85	As 30	Se
Rb 19	Sr 47	Y 90	Zr 110	Nb (>68)	Mo 160	Tc	Ru 120	Rh 115	Pd 110	Ag 68	Cd 27	In 52	Sn 78	Sb 40	Te
Cs 19	Ba 49	La 90	Hf (>72)	Ta (>97)	W 210	Re	Os 125	Ir 120	Pt 127	Au 92	Hg 15	Tl 40	Pb 48	Bi 48	Po

TABLE 3.4. MELTING POINTS OF METALS (°C)

Li 180	Be 1278														
Na 97.7	Mg 650											Al 660			
K 63.6	Ca 850	Sc	Ti 1800	V 1715	Cr 2000	Mn 1250	Fe 1530	Co 1490	Ni 1452	Cu 1083	Zn 419.5	Ga 30.2	Ge 958.5	As 817	Se 217
Rb 39.0	Sr 800	Y	Zr 1900	Nb 1950	Mo 2600	Tc	Ru 2000	Rh 1970	Pd 1553	Ag 960.5	Cd 320.5	In 155	Sn 231.9	Sb 630.5	Te 453
Cs 28.5	Ba 850	La 826	Hf 2230	Ta 3027	W 3390	Re	Os 2500	Ir 2360	Pt 1771	Au 1063	Hg −38.9	Tl 303.5	Pb 327	Bi 271	Po

TABLE 3.5. REPRESENTATIVE VALUES OF THE VELOCITY OF ELASTIC WAVES IN METALS AT ROOM TEMPERATURE

Metal	Density (g/cm^3)	Longitudinal Wave (infinite medium) (m/sec)	Transverse Wave (m/sec)	Metal	Density (g/cm^3)	Longitudinal Wave (infinite medium) (m/sec)	Transverse Wave (m/sec)
Ag	10.5	3600	1590	Ni	8.8	5630	2960
Al	2.7	6260	3080	Pb	11.4	2160	700
Au	19.3	3240	1200	Pt	21.4	3960	1670
Cd	8.6	2780	1500	Sn	7.3	3320	1670
Cu	8.9	4700	2260	W	19.1	5460	2620
Fe	7.7	5850	3230	Zn	7.1	4170	2410

related theory, due to Zener,[10] of the proclivity of bcc structures to instability at low temperatures. Results obtained by Barrett[11] are in agreement with Zener's predictions; Barrett finds that in lithium, which is bcc at room temperature, a transformation to fcc can be induced if the metal is plastically deformed in the vicinity of 77°K. Zener pointed out that a homogeneous shear of 0.35 in a bcc structure in the (110) plane and the [1$\bar{1}$0] direction will produce an atomic arrangement very nearly fcc. The stiffness constant for this deformation is $\frac{1}{2}(c_{11} - c_{12})$ which is very small (in comparison with c_{44}) for metals and alloys of bcc structure that have filled inner shells of electrons. (See Problem 3.7.) For example, the value of the anisotropy constant A defined by (3.31) is 18.7 for beta-brass (bcc) and only 4.0 for α-brass (fcc). Thermal vibration amplitudes in the [1$\bar{1}$0] direction should accordingly be very large. At high temperatures, because of free energy considerations, a structure permitting large amplitude vibrations will occur, other factors being equal, in preference to a structure permitting only low amplitude vibrations. At low temperatures the vibrations are not important, the internal energy then being the major influence in the free energy $F = U - TS$. We may accordingly expect to find metals which are fcc at low temperatures and which transform to bcc at high temperatures. Lithium is an example of this behavior.

The compressibilities of a number of metals are given in Table 3.2; for comparison and reference, values of the cohesive energy are given in Table 3.3, melting points in Table 3.4, and elastic wave velocities in Table 3.5.

PROBLEMS

3.1. Show that the strain

$$2\omega_z = \frac{\partial v}{\partial x} - \frac{\partial u}{\partial y}$$

represents a rigid rotation about the z-axis by a small angle ω_z. Note that

$$x' = x - \omega_z y;$$

$$y' = y + \omega_z x.$$

3.2. Show that the stresses acting on a plane whose normal makes direction cosines α, β, γ with the coordinate axes may be expressed in terms of the usual stress components by the equations

$$X_n = \alpha X_x + \beta X_y + \gamma X_z;$$

$$Y_n = \alpha Y_x + \beta Y_y + \gamma Y_z;$$

$$Z_n = \alpha Z_x + \beta Z_y + \gamma Z_z.$$

[10] C. Zener, Phys. Rev. **71**, 846 (1947).
[11] C. S. Barrett, Phys. Rev. **72**, 245 (1947).

3.3. Show that the bulk modulus $B = -V\,(dp/dV)$ in cubic crystals is given by

$$B = \frac{c_{11} + 2c_{12}}{3}.$$

3.4. A cubic crystal is subject to tension in the [100] direction. Find expressions for Young's modulus and Poisson's ratio in terms of the elastic compliances or stiffnesses.

3.5. Show that the velocity of propagation of a shear wave moving along a [110] direction with particle motion along a [1$\bar{1}$0] direction in a cubic crystal is

$$v = [(c_{11} - c_{12})/2\rho]^{1/2}.$$

3.6. Show that in a cubic crystal the condition for a longitudinal wave in the [111] direction to have the same velocity as a longitudinal wave in the [110] direction is that $c_{11} - c_{12} = 2c_{44}$.

3.7. Show that in a cubic crystal the effective compliance constant for a shear across the (110) plane in the [$\bar{1}$10] direction is equal to $2(s_{11} - s_{12})$ and the stiffness constant is $\frac{1}{2}(c_{11} - c_{12})$, while in the [001] direction in the same plane the effective compliance constant is s_{44}.

3.8. Make a table comparing the linear compressibility coefficients $(1/l)(dl/dp)$ of hexagonal metal crystals parallel and perpendicular to the axis as a function of the c/a ratio.

REFERENCES

R. F. S. Hearmon, "Elastic constants of anisotropic materials," Revs. Modern Phys. **18**, 409–440 (1946).

K. F. Herzfeld, *Handbuch der Experimentalphysik*. Akademische Verlagsgesellschaft, Leipzig, 1928, vol. 7/2.

A. E. H. Love, *A treatise on the mathematical theory of elasticity*, Dover Publications, New York, 1944.

W. Voigt, *Lehrbuch der Kristallphysik*, Teubner, Berlin, 1910.

W. A. Wooster, *A textbook on crystal physics*, Cambridge University Press, Cambridge, 1938.

C. Zener, *Elasticity and anelasticity of metals*, University of Chicago Press, Chicago, 1948.

4

Lattice Vibrations

In this chapter we discuss the elastic vibrations of crystals. A knowledge of the normal modes of crystal structures leads directly to the theory of the heat capacity of solids, which is treated in Chapter 5. The spectrum of the lattice vibrations is also important in problems which involve the interaction of electrons and photons with the crystal lattice, as in electrical resistivity, infrared absorption, dielectric breakdown, and x-ray diffraction broadening, and the spectrum also affects thermal expansion and thermal conductivity. We use here in a loose sense the term *lattice*, where strictly we should write *structure*, but in the present context the use of lattice is sanctified by convention.

VIBRATIONS OF HOMOGENEOUS LINE IN ONE DIMENSION

We treat a homogeneous elastic line, and suppose that the motion of each element of the line is constrained to be parallel to the line itself; that is, we admit only longitudinal waves. For the present we exclude from consideration transverse waves, which are waves in which the direction of particle motion is perpendicular to the direction of propagation of the wave. Let x denote the positional coordinate of a particular element of the line, and let u denote the displacement of the element from its equilibrium position; then the value of the strain e, defined as the fractional change of length, is

$$(4.1) \qquad e = \partial u / \partial x.$$

If F is the force producing the strain, we define the elastic stiffness c by the equation

$$(4.2) \qquad F/e = c.$$

We study then the propagation of longitudinal waves on a homogeneous line of linear density ρ and elastic stiffness c. We consider the forces acting on an element of length Δx. At one end of the element the strain is $e(x)$, and at the other end it is $e(x + \Delta x) = e(x) + (\partial e/\partial x) \Delta x = e(x) + (\partial^2 u/\partial x^2) \Delta x$, so that the resultant force acting on the element is $c(\partial^2 u/\partial x^2)\,\Delta x$. Setting the force equal to the mass of the element $\rho\,\Delta x$ times the acceleration $\partial^2 u/\partial t^2$, we have the wave equation

$$(4.3) \qquad \frac{\partial^2 u}{\partial x^2} = \left(\frac{\rho}{c}\right)\frac{\partial^2 u}{\partial t^2},$$

with velocity

$$(4.4) \qquad v_0 = (c/\rho)^{\frac{1}{2}},$$

independent of frequency. It is plausible that the velocity should increase with the stiffness and decrease with the density. The solutions are of the form $e^{i(\omega t \pm kx)}$, where $\omega = kv_0$. The quantity k is equal to $2\pi/\lambda$ if λ is the wavelength; k is usually called the _wave vector_.

WAVE MOTION OF A LINE OF SIMILAR ATOMS

We consider a line of similar atoms of mass M spaced with lattice constant a as shown in Fig. 4.1, and let u_n denote the displacement of

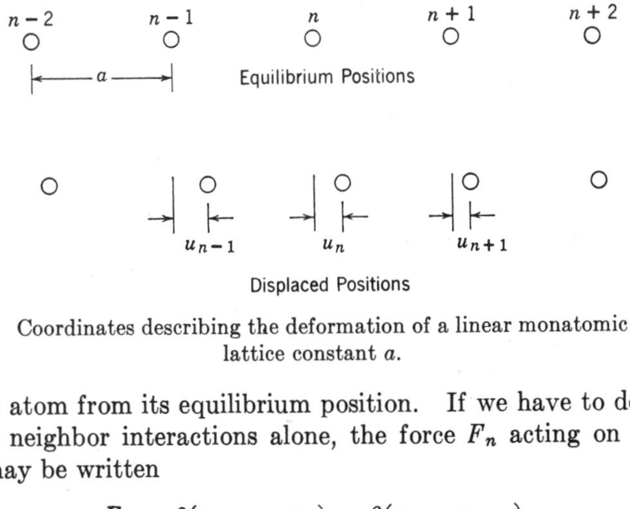

Fig. 4.1.   Coordinates describing the deformation of a linear monatomic lattice of lattice constant a.

the nth atom from its equilibrium position. If we have to deal with nearest neighbor interactions alone, the force F_n acting on the nth atom may be written

$$(4.5) \qquad F_n = \beta(u_{n+1} - u_n) - \beta(u_n - u_{n-1}),$$

the first term in parentheses on the right being the increase in length of the bond between atoms n and $n + 1$, the second term being the increase in length of the bond between atoms n and $n - 1$. If both bonds increase in length, the two forces on atom n will be oppositely directed. Here β is the force constant. Looked at on a macroscopic scale, the line has a linear density $\rho = M/a$, as there are $1/a$ atoms per unit length, and an elastic stiffness $c = \beta a$. The latter result follows as the force required to stretch a single bond is

$$F = \beta(u_n - u_{n-1}) = \beta ae,$$

and by the definition of the elastic stiffness must be equal to ce, so that $c = \beta a$.

We now examine the propagation of waves along the line of particles; we expect to find that as long as the wavelength is much longer than the particle spacing, the waves propagate in the manner prescribed by the macroscopic wave equation (4.3), but for very short wavelengths new features may enter the problem.

The equation of motion of the nth atom is, using (4.5),

$$(4.6) \qquad M\ddot{u}_n = \beta(u_{n+1} + u_{n-1} - 2u_n),$$

where β is the force constant and M the atomic mass. We look for solutions of the form

$$(4.7) \qquad u_n = \xi e^{i(\omega t + kna)},$$

as na is the quantity most similar to the line variable x in the continuum, a being the nearest neighbor distance and n the running index. On substituting this trial function in the equation of motion we find that it is a solution if

$$-\omega^2 M = \beta(e^{ika} + e^{-ika} - 2).$$

Now

$$e^{ika} + e^{-ika} - 2 = (e^{ika/2} - e^{-ika/2})^2 = -4 \sin^2 (ka/2),$$

so that we have a solution if

$$(4.8) \qquad \omega = \pm (4\beta/M)^{1/2} \sin (ka/2).$$

The dependence of ω on k for the positive branch of the curve is shown in Fig. 4.2.

It is seen that the maximum frequency which can be propagated in the lattice is $\omega_m = (4\beta/M)^{1/2}$, corresponding to the values $k_m = \pm \pi/a$. Values of k outside these limits do not give us anything new: for example, the motions of two successive particles in the chain are described by the ratio $u_n/u_{n+1} = e^{-ika}$, which reduces to -1 for $k = k_m$, so that here the particles move 180° out of phase with each other. Larger values of k merely reproduce motions already described by values of k within the limits $\pm k_m$.

For low k or long wavelengths, (4.8) reduces, on setting $\sin ka/2 \cong ka/2$, to

(4.9) $$\omega \cong (\beta/M)^{\frac{1}{2}}ka = (c/\rho)^{\frac{1}{2}}k = v_0k,$$

where $v_0 = (c/\rho)^{\frac{1}{2}}$ is, according to (4.4), the wave velocity on the equivalent homogeneous line. The actual atomic nature of the line affects the propagation when k becomes comparable with k_m.

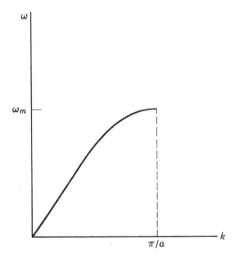

Fig. 4.2.   Plot of frequency ω vs. wave number k for a monatomic linear lattice.

The phase velocity is a function of the wave number and is

(4.10) $$v = \frac{\omega}{k} = v_0\left[\frac{\sin (ka/2)}{ka/2}\right].$$

In actual substances the order of magnitude of the limit on k is

$$|k_m| = \frac{\pi}{a} \approx 10^8 \text{ cm}^{-1},$$

and because sound velocities in solids are of the order of magnitude of 3×10^5 cm/sec the cut-off frequency is

$$\omega_m = v_mk_m = 2v_0k_m/\pi \approx 2 \times 10^{13} \text{ rad/sec.}$$

The cut-off frequency lies in the infrared region. The highest ultrasonic frequency yet generated in the laboratory is 10^9 in quartz, and this is very considerably below the limiting frequency. Estimates of elastic constants at frequencies of 10^{11} to 10^{12} cps may be made by the study of non-Bragg diffuse x-ray reflections.[1]   The lattice waves modulate the crystal to make possible reflections in directions not coinciding with those occurring in the unperturbed lattice.

ENUMERATION OF NORMAL MODES FOR FINITE LINE

One is often concerned, as in calculating the heat capacity, with the distribution of normal modes in a crystal.   As a simple illustration of the method of analysis used in determining the distribution, we consider the case of a one-dimensional line of length L carrying $N + 1$ particles at separation a.   We suppose that the particles $n = 0$ and $n = N$ at the ends of the line are held fixed; the allowed modes, which are constructed by taking linear combinations of the running wave solutions $u_n = \xi e^{i(\omega t + kna)}$ of the previous section, are then of the form

$$(4.11) \qquad u_{k,n} = C_k e^{i\omega_k t} \sin kna;$$

here k is restricted by the boundary conditions to the values

$$(4.12) \qquad k = \pi/L, 2\pi/L, 3\pi/L, \cdots, N\pi/L,$$

and C_k is an arbitrary complex number determining the amplitude and phase of the motion.

The solution for $k = \pi/L$ has $u \propto \sin n\pi a/L$ and vanishes for $n = 0$ and $n = N$ as required, with a maximum for $n = N/2$.   The solution for $k = N\pi/L = \pi/a = k_m$ has $u \propto \sin n\pi$, permitting no motion at all, because $\sin n\pi$ vanishes at each particle.   There are $N - 1$ allowed values (eigenvalues) of k, which is equal to the number of particles allowed to move.   Each allowed value of k is associated with a solution (eigenfunction) of the form (4.11).   These features of the one-dimensional problem are characteristic also of the lattice vibration problems in two and three dimensions.

We sometimes wish to know the number of modes per unit range of k. We shall denote this quantity by $w(k)$; it is sometimes called the density of states in k-space.   For our one-dimensional line there is one mode for each interval $\Delta k = \pi/L$, so that

$$(4.13) \qquad w(k) = L/\pi.$$

Another method of enumerating states which is often used is to consider the medium unbounded, but to impose the physically reasonable requirement that the solutions should be periodic over some sufficiently large distance L, so that $u(na) = u(na + L)$.   This may be

[1] See, for example, G. N. Ramachandran and W. A. Wooster, Acta Cryst. **4**, 335, 431 (1951).

required without changing the physical nature of the problem in any essential respect. This is the method of *periodic boundary conditions*. Then, in (4.7),

$$k = \pm 2\pi/L, \ \pm 4\pi/L, \ \pm 6\pi/L, \ \cdots, \ \pm N\pi/L.$$

This method of enumeration gives essentially the same number of states as given by (4.12), but we have now both plus and minus values of k, while doubling the interval between successive states. The smoothed density of states interpreted in terms of absolute values of k is unchanged.

ONE-DIMENSIONAL CRYSTAL WITH TWO KINDS OF ATOMS

With two kinds of atoms, as in an ionic crystal, the results show new features. We consider a one-dimensional crystal with two kinds of atoms, spaced a apart. Atoms of mass M are located at the odd-numbered lattice points $2n - 1, \ 2n + 1, \ \cdots$; atoms of mass m are located at the even-numbered lattice points $2n, \ 2n + 2, \ \cdots$. The equations of motion under the assumption of nearest neighbor interactions are

(4.14)
$$m\ddot{u}_{2n} = \beta(u_{2n+1} + u_{2n-1} - 2u_{2n});$$
$$M\ddot{u}_{2n+1} = \beta(u_{2n+2} + u_{2n} - 2u_{2n+1}).$$

We look for solutions of the form

(4.15)
$$u_{2n} = \xi e^{i(\omega t + 2nka)},$$
$$u_{2n+1} = \eta e^{i(\omega t + [2n+1]ka)},$$

which lead, on substitution in the equations of motion, to

(4.16)
$$-\omega^2 m\xi = \beta\eta(e^{ika} + e^{-ika}) - 2\beta\xi;$$
$$-\omega^2 M\eta = \beta\xi(e^{ika} + e^{-ika}) - 2\beta\eta.$$

This set of homogeneous equations has a non-trivial solution only if the determinant of the coefficients of the unknowns ξ, η vanishes:

(4.17)
$$\begin{vmatrix} 2\beta - m\omega^2 & -2\beta \cos ka \\ -2\beta \cos ka & 2\beta - M\omega^2 \end{vmatrix} = 0$$

or

(4.18)
$$\omega^2 = \beta\left(\frac{1}{m} + \frac{1}{M}\right) \pm \beta\left[\left(\frac{1}{m} + \frac{1}{M}\right)^2 - \frac{4\sin^2 ka}{Mm}\right]^{1/2}$$

For small k the two roots are

(4.19)
$$\omega^2 = 2\beta\left(\frac{1}{m} + \frac{1}{M}\right),$$

and

(4.20) $$\omega^2 = \frac{2\beta}{M + m} k^2 a^2.$$

For $k = \pi/2a$, the roots are

(4.21) $$\omega^2 = 2\beta/m,$$

and

(4.22) $$\omega^2 = 2\beta/M.$$

The variation of ω with k as given by (4.18) is shown in Fig. 4.3 for the case $m > M$. It is seen that the dispersion relation has two branches, one called the *acoustical branch* and the other the *optical branch*.

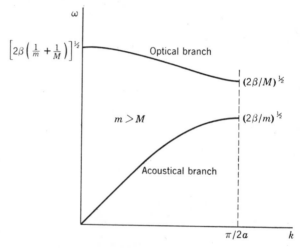

Fig. 4.3. ª Optical and acoustical branches of the frequency vs. wave number relation for a diatomic linear lattice, showing the limiting frequencies.

We may understand the nature of the two branches by considering the motions of the two types of atoms, as shown for transverse waves in Fig. 4.4. The ratio of the amplitudes is ξ/η, and for small k in the optical branch we find, from (4.16) and (4.19),

(4.23) $$\xi/\eta = -M/m,$$

which shows that the atoms vibrate against each other in such a way that the center of mass of the cell is fixed. If the ions are oppositely charged, we may excite a motion of this type with electric fields, as, for example, by a light wave; for this reason the branch is called the optical branch.

The other solution for small k is

(4.24) $$\xi = \eta;$$

the atoms (and their center of mass) move together, as in acoustical) vibrations, hence the term acoustical branch.

VIBRATIONS OF TWO- AND THREE-DIMENSIONAL LATTICES

There is usually no particular problem in setting up the equations of motion, analogous to (4.6), for two- and three-dimensional lattices. The equation of motions in three dimensions were first written down and the solutions indicated by Born and von Kármán.[2] The solutions

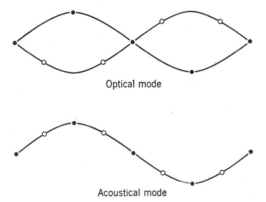

Optical mode

Acoustical mode

Fig. 4.4. Nature of the optical and acoustical modes illustrated by the particle amplitudes for the two modes at the same wavelength. The drawing is for transverse waves.

are readily found in terms of plane waves of the form $\exp i(\omega t - \mathbf{k} \cdot \mathbf{r}_j)$. The enumeration of the states of the system offers greater difficulties than in one dimension; for references to the considerable literature on this problem the paper by Bowers and Rosenstock[3] may be consulted. Some of the results will be discussed in the next chapter.

INFRARED ABSORPTION

We consider now the response of the diatomic linear crystal to electromagnetic radiation in the infrared part of the spectrum, for example at a wavelength of 100 μ (10^{-2} cm) and a frequency of 3×10^{12} cps. The wave vector of the radiation field is $k = 2\pi/\lambda \approx 600$ cm^{-1}, and this is very much smaller than the cut-off of the lattice vibrations,

[2] M. Born and T. von Kármán, Physik. Z. **13**, 297 (1912).

[3] W. A. Bowers and H. B. Rosenstock, J. Chem. Phys. **18**, 1056 (1950); see also W. A. Nierenberg, J. Chem. Phys. **19**, 659 (1951).

which is $k_m = \pi/2a \approx 10^8$ cm^{-1}. We may therefore, in dealing with electromagnetic excitation of the optical branch, suppose that the wave vector of the excited mode is essentially zero.

In this limit the equations of motion (4.16) of the two types of ions in a field $E = E_0 e^{i\omega t}$ reduce to

$$-\omega^2 m\xi = 2\beta(\eta - \xi) - eE_0;$$

$$-\omega^2 M\eta = -2\beta(\eta - \xi) + eE_0;$$

where E_0 is the amplitude of the electric intensity of the radiation field and $\pm e$ is the ionic charge. We solve these equations for ξ and η, obtaining

(4.25)
$$\eta = \frac{(e/M)E_0}{\omega_0{}^2 - \omega^2};$$

(4.26)
$$\xi = \frac{-(e/m)E_0}{\omega_0{}^2 - \omega^2};$$

where

(4.27)
$$\omega_0{}^2 = 2\beta\left(\frac{1}{m} + \frac{1}{M}\right),$$

corresponding to the $k = 0$ limit of the optical branch. We may, according to (4.25) and (4.26), expect the infrared absorption to go through a maximum near the frequency ω_0.

We have seen earlier in this chapter that the force constant β is related to the elastic stiffness c of the line by the relation $c = \beta a$, where a is the interatomic separation. As in a three-dimensional crystal there will be of the order of $1/a^2$ lines per unit area, the force constant will be of the order of $\beta \approx ac_{11}$, where c_{11} is one of the usual elastic stiffness constants and is approximately 5×10^{11} dynes/cm^2, for sodium chloride. Therefore $\beta \approx (3 \times 10^{-8})(5 \times 10^{11}) = 1.5 \times 10^4$ dynes/cm, which leads to the rough estimate for sodium chloride:

$$\omega_0{}^2 \approx 2(1.5 \times 10^4)\left(\frac{1}{35.5} + \frac{1}{23.0}\right)\frac{1}{1.67 \times 10^{-24}},$$

or $\omega_0 \approx 3.6 \times 10^{13}$ rad/sec and $\lambda_0 \approx 50$ μ, in satisfactory order-of-magnitude agreement with the observed absorption maximum at $\lambda_0 = 61\mu$.

It is characteristic of ionic crystals that they have an absorption maximum in the infrared associated with the motion of charges of opposite sign toward each other. There is also a maximum in the intensity reflected from the surface of a crystal, and the position of this maximum is close[4] to the wavelength for which the absorption is a maximum. The wavelength at maximum reflection is known as the residual ray or *Reststrahl* wavelength, and the selective reflection has been employed experimentally to obtain narrow bands of radiation in the far infrared. Positions of the absorption and reflection maxima are given in Table 4.1, and the transmission through a thin film of

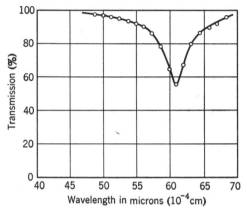

Fig. 4.5. Transmission of infrared radiation through a thin (0.17 μ) sodium chloride film. (After R. B. Barnes.)

sodium chloride is shown in Fig. 4.5. We shall return to the theory of the *Reststrahl* absorption in Chapter 6.

TABLE 4.1. WAVELENGTHS OF MAXIMUM ABSORPTION AND REFLECTION FOR ALKALI HALIDES

[From R. B. Barnes, Z. Physik **75**, 723 (1932).]

Crystal	Absorption (μ)	Reflection (μ)
NaCl	61.1	52.0
KCl	70.7	63.4
RbCl	84.8	73.8
CsCl	102.0	. . . . .
TlCl	117.0	91.9
KI	102.0	94.0
RbI	129.5	. . . . .
TlI	. . . . .	151.8

PROBLEMS

4.1. From (4.8) show that the group velocity is $v_g = v_0 \cos (ka/2)$, where $v_0 = (\beta a^2/M)^{1/2}$.

[4] T. H. Havelock, Proc. Roy. Soc. (London) **A86**, 1 (1912). The separation of the two maxima occurs because the reflection and absorption coefficients involve the real and imaginary parts of the refractive index in different ways.

4.2. Show that the differential equation governing transverse waves on a monatomic linear lattice is similar to that for longitudinal waves. Find an expression
for the transverse phase velocity in terms of the force constant β for the change of
length of a bond and the wave number k.

4.3.* We consider transverse vibrations of a square lattice of N rows and N
columns of identical atoms, and let $u_{l,m}$ denote the displacement, normal to the
plane of the lattice, of the atom in the lth row and mth column. The mass of each
atom is M, and α is the force constant for nearest neighbors. Show that the equation of motion is

$$M(d^2u_{ij}/dt^2) = \alpha[(u_{i+1,j} - 2u_{i,j} + u_{i-1,j}) + u_{i,j+1} - 2u_{i,j} + u_{i,j-1})],$$

for $1 \leq i, j \leq N$. Assume solutions of the form

$$u_{ij} = e^{i\omega t} \sin \frac{ip\pi}{N+1} \sin \frac{jq\pi}{N+1}; \qquad p, q = 1, 2, \cdots, N,$$

corresponding to standing waves in the lattice, with dummy rows of atoms at i,
$j = 0, N + 1$ which are held fixed. Show that the N^2 vibration frequencies are

$$M\omega_{pq}^2 = 2\alpha \left(2 - \cos \frac{p\pi}{N+1} - \cos \frac{q\pi}{N+1} \right),$$

which may be written as

$$M\omega^2 = 2\alpha(2 - \cos k_x a - \cos k_y a),$$

where a is the lattice constant, and

$$k_x = p\pi/[a(N+1)]; \qquad k_y = q\pi/[a(N+1)].$$

We note that the region of k-space for which solutions are defined is a square of
side approximately π/a; this region is called the first Brillouin zone. Show that
the k values marking the boundary are associated with the maximum wavelength
for which Bragg reflection can occur in the structure.

4.4. Discuss the principal experimental· methods used in the spectroscopy of
the far infrared region, with particular reference to the spectra of solids.

REFERENCES

L. Brillouin, *Wave propagation in periodic structures*, McGraw-Hill Book Co.,
    New York, 1946.
C. Schaefer and F. Matossi, *Das ultrarote Spektrum*, J. Springer, Berlin, 1930.

5

Thermal Properties of Solids

We first discuss the exact theory of the heat capacity of monatomic and diatomic lattices in one dimension and compare the result with an approximate method of treatment due to Debye. The Debye theory is then carried out for a three-dimensional lattice with particular reference to the low temperature region. Anharmonic effects are treated in connection with the heat capacity at high temperatures, thermal expansion, and thermal conductivity.

HEAT CAPACITY OF A ONE-DIMENSIONAL LATTICE

CLASSICAL THEORY

The usual statement of classical statistical mechanics applied to a system of N particles moving in one dimension under harmonic (linear) forces is that there are $2N$ effective degrees of freedom; N from the kinetic energy and N from the potential energy, each contributing $\frac{1}{2}kT$ to the internal energy; here k is the Boltzmann constant. The derivation of this result is sketched in Problem 5.1. The total internal energy is

(5.1) $$U = NkT,$$

and the heat capacity is

(5.2) $$C_v = (\partial U/\partial T)_v = Nk,$$

which is independent of temperature. In three dimensions we obtain by the same reasoning

(5.3) $$C_v = 3Nk. \; = 3P = 6$$

This result of classical theory is in reasonably good agreement with experiment at sufficiently high temperatures, but at low temperatures the observed heat capacities fall to very low values. The introduction of quantum theory corrects the situation. We treat the normal modes of vibration as harmonic oscillators as suggested above; therefore we must calculate the energy of a harmonic oscillator on quantum theory.

71

ENERGY OF A HARMONIC OSCILLATOR—QUANTUM THEORY

It is an elementary result of quantum theory that the energy levels of a harmonic oscillator of angular frequency ω may be written

(5.4) $$W_n = n\hbar\omega,$$

where n is the quantum number or occupation number. The levels are uniformly spaced, with separation $\hbar\omega$. In thermal equilibrium the probability that a given oscillator will be in the quantum state n is proportional to the Boltzmann factor $e^{-W_n/kT}$. The average energy of an oscillator is then

$$\bar{W} = \sum_n W_n e^{-W_n/kT} \Big/ \sum_n e^{-W_n/kT}$$

$$= \hbar\omega \sum_n n e^{-nx} \Big/ \sum_n e^{-nx},$$

where $x = \hbar\omega/kT$. Now

$$\frac{\sum n e^{-nx}}{\sum e^{-nx}} = -\frac{d}{dx} \log \sum e^{-nx} = -\frac{d}{dx} \log \frac{1}{1 - e^{-x}} = \frac{1}{e^x - 1},$$

so that

(5.5) $$\bar{W} = \frac{\hbar\omega}{e^{\hbar\omega/kT} - 1}.$$

For $\hbar\omega \ll kT$, this reduces to $\bar{W} = kT$, the classical limit; while, for $\hbar\omega \gg kT$, $\bar{W}$ approaches zero.

HEAT CAPACITY OF ONE-DIMENSIONAL CRYSTAL—QUANTUM THEORY

The internal energy of the one-dimensional crystal on quantum theory is then

(5.6) $$U = \sum_k \frac{\hbar\omega_k}{e^{\hbar\omega_k/kT} - 1},$$

where the sum is over all the normal modes of the crystal. It is customary to refer to a quantized lattice vibration as a *phonon*, by analogy with photon for the electromagnetic field. We may, when the number of particles is large, approximate the sum by an integral:

(5.7) $$U = \int_0^{k_m} \frac{\hbar\omega}{e^{\hbar\omega/kT} - 1} w(k) \, dk,$$

where $w(k) \, dk$ is the number of modes between k and $k + dk$. Using (4.13), we have

$$U = \frac{L}{\pi} \int_0^{k_m} \frac{\hbar\omega}{e^{\hbar\omega/kT} - 1} \, dk = \frac{L}{\pi} \int_0^{\omega_m} \frac{\hbar\omega}{e^{\hbar\omega/kT} - 1} \frac{dk}{d\omega} \, d\omega.$$

Now from (4.8)

a = nearest neighbor distance.

(5.8) $$k = \frac{2}{a} \sin^{-1} (\omega/\omega_m),$$

$V_o =$

so that

(5.9) $$\frac{dk}{d\omega} = \frac{2}{a(\omega_m{}^2 - \omega^2)^{\frac{1}{2}}},$$

and

(5.10) $$U = \frac{2\hbar L}{\pi a} \int_0^{\omega_m} \frac{\omega \, d\omega}{(e^{\hbar\omega/kT} - 1)(\omega_m{}^2 - \omega^2)^{\frac{1}{2}}},$$

where ω_m is equal to $2v_0/a$. The heat capacity is obtained on differentiating this expression with respect to temperature.

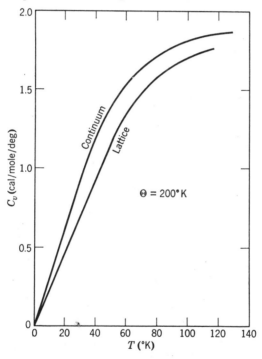

Fig. 5.1. Calculated heat capacity of a one-dimensional monatomic lattice, in the continuum approximation, and on the exact theory. The curves are adjusted so that $\hbar\omega_{max} = k\Theta$, with $\Theta = 200°K$, on both calculations. [After M. Blackman, Proc. Roy. Soc. (London) **A148**, 365 (1935).]

The equations are difficult to integrate, and one very often works in specific heat theory with an approximation due to Debye in which the exact dispersion relation (5.8) is replaced by the continuum approximation $\omega = v_0 k$ (cf. 4.9) valid for the equivalent homogeneous line. In this approximation $dk/d\omega$ is simply $1/v_0$, and we have

$$(5.11) \qquad U = \frac{L}{\pi v_0} \int_0^{\omega_m} \frac{\hbar\omega}{e^{\hbar\omega/kT} - 1} \, d\omega.$$

The upper limit to the integral, ω_m, is here to be determined by the condition that the number of states considered should come out equal to $N = L/a$. Now $k_m = \pi/a$ as before, so that $\omega_m = v_0 k_m = \pi v_0/a$.

In Fig. 5.1 we compare the results given by Blackman[1] for the heat capacities as calculated from the exact expression (5.10) for the internal energy of a one-dimensional crystal, and as calculated from the "Debye approximation" (5.11).

DEBYE APPROXIMATION IN THREE DIMENSIONS

Our first task is to determine $w(k)$, the number of modes between k and $k + dk$. We apply the method of periodic boundary conditions, requiring that the vibrational wave $e^{i\mathbf{k}\cdot\mathbf{r}}$ be periodic at the boundaries of a cube of side L. Then $k_x L$, $k_y L$, $k_z L$ must be multiples of 2π, so that the allowed values of k may be represented by the points of a simple cubic lattice in k-space, with lattice constant $2\pi/L$. The number of states with wave number less than $|k|$ is then given closely by the volume, measured in units $2\pi/L$, of the sphere of radius $|k|$, which is

$$(4\pi/3)k^3/(2\pi/L)^3,$$

whence, per unit volume of specimen,

$$(5.12) \qquad w(k) = 3k^2/2\pi^2,$$

where the factor 3 arises because elastic waves of given k occur with three different polarizations which in an isotropic medium reduce to two shear waves and one longitudinal wave. The internal energy per unit volume is then, from (5.7),

$$(5.13) \qquad U = \int_0^{k_m} \frac{\hbar\omega}{(e^{\hbar\omega/kT} - 1)} \frac{3k^2}{2\pi^2} \, dk,$$

or, using the Debye or continuum approximation $\omega = v_0 k$,

$$(5.14) \qquad U = \frac{3\hbar}{2\pi^2 v_0^3} \int_0^{\omega_m} \frac{\omega^3 \, d\omega}{e^{\hbar\omega/kT} - 1}.$$

The upper limits k_m and ω_m are determined by the condition that the total number of modes be equal to $3N$, where N is the number of atoms

[1] M. Blackman, Proc. Roy. Soc. (London) **A148**, 365 (1935).

per unit volume.   Therefore

(5.15) $k_m{}^3/2\pi^2 = 3N$.

If we set
$$x = \hbar\omega/kT, \qquad \omega^3 \doteq \frac{k^3 T^3}{\hbar^3}\, x$$
we have

(5.16) $U = \dfrac{3k^4T^4}{2\pi^2\hbar^3 v_0{}^3} \displaystyle\int_0^{x_m} \dfrac{x^3\,dx}{e^x - 1}$,

where

(5.17) $x_m = \hbar\omega_m/kT = \hbar k_m v_0/kT = (\hbar v_0/kT)(6\pi^2 N)^{\frac{1}{3}} = \Theta/T$,

this being the definition of the Debye characteristic temperature Θ. The heat capacity is given by differentiating (5.14) or (5.16) with respect to temperature:

(5.18) $C_v = 9Nk(T/\Theta)^3 \displaystyle\int_0^{x_m} \dfrac{e^x x^4\,dx}{(e^x - 1)^2}.$

Tables have been calculated for U, C_v, and other quantities on the Debye theory and are given in the Landolt-Börnstein tables, Eg. I, p. 702.   The heat capacity is plotted in Fig. 5.2.   At $T \gg \Theta$ the heat capacity (5.18) approaches the classical Dulong and Petit value of $3R$ per mole, which is found to hold quite well.

At very low temperatures we may approximate (5.16) by letting the upper limit go to infinity.   We have[2]
$$\int_0^\infty \frac{x^3\,dx}{e^x - 1} = 6\zeta(4) = 6\sum_1^\infty \frac{1}{n^4} = \frac{\pi^4}{15}$$

where $\zeta(4)$ is the Riemann zeta function.   Thus, for $T \ll \Theta$,
$$U = 3\pi^4 NkT^4/5\Theta^3,$$
and, from $C_v = dU/dT$,

(5.19) $C_v = (12\pi^4 Nk/5)(T/\Theta)^3 = 234Nk(T/\Theta)^3$,

exhibiting the Debye T^3 approximation.

A discussion of methods for the determination of a suitable average sound velocity v_0 to be used in calculating Θ has been published by Blackman,[3] who also emphasizes that the temperatures at which the T^3 approximation holds for actual lattices are considerably lower than one might have thought necessary on the Debye theory; it may be

[2] E. T. Whittaker and G. N. Watson, *Modern analysis*, Cambridge University Press, Cambridge, 4th ed., 1935, pp. 265–266.

[3] M. Blackman, Repts. Prog. Phys. **8**, 11 (1941).

necessary to go below $T = \Theta/50$ to get reasonably pure T^3 behavior. It is customary to test the applicability of the Debye approximation by calculating Θ as a function of temperature by fitting a Debye curve to the experimental heat capacity curve at various temperatures. If

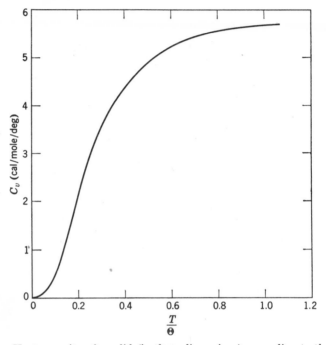

Fig. 5.2. Heat capacity of a solid (in three dimensions), according to the Debye approximation.

the Debye approximation were strictly valid, Θ as determined in this way would be independent of temperature. Results assembled by Blackman[3] are given in Table 5.1.

TABLE 5.1. VARIATION OF DEBYE Θ WITH TEMPERATURE

	Θ as determined at temperature		
	$T \approx \Theta$	$T \approx \Theta/6$	$T \approx \Theta/12$
Substance	(°K)	(°K)	(°K)
Au	180	172	162
Ag	220	210	209
Cu	315	317	319
Pb	88	87	85
Li	430	379	356
Na	150	159	...
K	99	98	...
W	310	305	337
KCl	230	225	218

The values of Θ obtained from thermal data at low temperatures are in quite good agreement with values of Θ calculated from elastic data when a suitable averaging over possible propagation directions is carried out:

	T (°K)	Θ (thermal) (°K)	Θ (elastic) (°K)
NaCl	10	308	320
KCl	3	230	246
Ag	4	237	216
Zn	4	308	305

Representative values of the Debye characteristic temperature for a number of substances are given in Table 5.2. These data are quite useful in solid state problems, as Θ enters into a number of different phenomena, including electrical resistivity, thermal conductivity, and x-ray diffraction line broadening.

TABLE 5.2. REPRESENTATIVE VALUES OF THE DEBYE Θ

Substance	(°K)	Substance	(°K)	Substance	(°K)
A	85	Fe	420	Pb	88
Ag	215	Ge	290	Pt	225
Al	398	Ir	283	Ta	245
Au	180	K	99.5	W	310
Be	1000	Li	328–430	Zn	235
C (diamond)	1860	Mg	290	NaCl	281
Ca	230	Mo	379	KCl	230
Cd	160	Na	159	KBr	177
Cr	485	Ne	63	CaF$_2$	474
Cu	315	Ni	370	FeS$_2$	630

DIATOMIC LATTICE

One can obtain an exact expression for the heat capacity of a diatomic lattice in one dimension, and Blackman has given numerical results for several values of the mass ratio. If the mass ratio m/M is $\gg 1$, however, the total spread in frequency of the optical branch becomes quite small; this fact suggests a simple approximation to the heat capacity. If the total number of atoms is $2N$, we treat the N normal modes of the optical branch as equivalent to N simple harmonic oscillators of frequency (Eq. 4.19):

$$\omega_0 \cong \left[2\beta \left(\frac{1}{m} + \frac{1}{M} \right) \right]^{1/2} \cong [2\beta/M]^{1/2}.$$

We then treat the N degrees of freedom of the acoustical branch in the Debye approximation, (5.11) or (5.16).

EINSTEIN FUNCTION

The heat capacity of a system of simple harmonic oscillators of the same frequency was first considered by Einstein,[4] who proposed to use

[4] A. Einstein, Ann. Physik **22**, 180, 800 (1907); **34**, 170 (1911).

this as an approximation to the *entire* heat capacity of solids. The internal energy

$$(5.20) \qquad U = N \frac{\hbar\omega}{e^{\hbar\omega/kT} - 1}$$

leads, on differentiation with respect to temperature, to the heat capacity

$$(5.21) \qquad C_v = Nk(\hbar\omega/kT)^2 e^{\hbar\omega/kT}/(e^{\hbar\omega/kT} - 1)^2;$$

the expression on the right is called an Einstein function. The Einstein approximation represented a great advance at the time because it explained the tendency of the heat capacity to decrease and approach zero at very low temperatures; the heat capacity on classical theory is independent of temperature. The Einstein approximation does not, however, give correctly the details of the approach of the heat capacity to zero, and Debye first explained the low temperature results. It is, however, reasonably correct to use the Einstein function for the heat capacity of the optical modes when the mass ratio of the ions differs considerably from unity.

THERMAL EXPANSION

We may understand the origin of thermal expansion by considering the effect of anharmonic terms in the potential energy on the separation of a pair of atoms at a temperature T. We take the potential energy of the atoms at a displacement x from their equilibrium separation at 0°K as

$$(5.22) \qquad V(x) = cx^2 - gx^3 - fx^4,$$

where the term in x^3 represents the asymmetry of the mutual repulsion of the atoms and the term in x^4 represents the general "softening" of the vibration at large amplitudes.

We calculate the average displacement by using the Boltzmann distribution function, which weights the possible values of x according to their thermodynamic probability:

$$(5.23) \qquad \bar{x} = \frac{\int_{-\infty}^{\infty} xe^{-V(x)/kT} \, dx}{\int_{-\infty}^{\infty} e^{-V(x)/kT} \, dx}.$$

For small displacements (low anharmonic energy) we expand the integrands:

$$\int x e^{-V/kT} dx \cong \int e^{-cx^2/kT}[x + (gx^4/kT) + (fx^5/kT)] dx$$
$$= (g/kT)(kT/c)^{5/2}(3\pi^{1/2}/4);$$
$$\int e^{-V/kT} dx \cong \int e^{-cx^2/kT} dx = (\pi kT/c)^{1/2};$$

so that

(5.24) $$\bar{x} = 3kTg/4c^2,$$

giving a constant value of the temperature coefficient of thermal expansion. Values of the linear expansion coefficients are given in Table 5.3.

TABLE 5.3. LINEAR COEFFICIENTS OF THERMAL EXPANSION
NEAR ROOM TEMPERATURE
$l_t = l_0(1 + \beta t)$

Substance	$10^6 \times \beta$ (per deg C)	Substance	$10^6 \times \beta$ (per deg C)
Au	14	CsCl	50
Li	56	Jena glass (2954—III)	6
Na	71	AlBr$_3$	400
K	83	Zn (parallel to axis)	64
Ni	13	(perpendicular to axis)	14
Pt	9	Te (parallel to axis)	−1.6
KCl	100	(perpendicular to axis)	27

Now kT is classically just the mean energy $\bar{u}$ of the oscillator in the harmonic approximation, so that we may write (5.24) as

(5.25) $$\bar{x} = 3\bar{u}g/4c^2,$$

which suggests that the approximate quantum-mechanical result would be obtained by substituting for $\bar{u}$ the energy (5.5) of a harmonic oscillator in quantum mechanics. On this argument we should expect the thermal expansion coefficient to decrease rather abruptly as the temperature drops below the characteristic temperature of the oscillator and to go to zero as $T \to 0°K$; this is indeed the observed behavior.[5] The third law of thermodynamics requires that the thermal expansion coefficient vanish as $T \to 0°K$.

EQUATION OF STATE OF SOLIDS

It is possible, by making approximations similar to those made in the Debye theory of specific heats, to derive theoretical expressions[6]

[5] Low temperature measurements on fused quartz and on a Jena glass are reported by W. H. Keesom and D. W. Doborzynski, Physica 1, 1085, 1089 (1934).

[6] E. Grüneisen, Handbuch der Physik 10, 1–59 (1926); P. Debye, in Vorträge über die kinetische Theorie der Materie und Elektrizität, by M. Planck et al., Teubner, Leipzig, 1914; J. C. Slater, Introduction to chemical physics, McGraw-Hill Book Co., New York, 1939, Chap. XIII.

for the equation of state, the thermal expansion coefficient, and the temperature variation of the elastic constants, provided that one or two empirical parameters are introduced in the case of cubic crystals. Further constants are required for crystals of lower symmetry.

By a well-known thermodynamic relation

$$(5.26) \qquad U = F - T(\partial F/\partial T)_V = [\partial (F/T)/\partial (1/T)]_V,$$

where U is the internal energy and F is the Helmholtz free energy; the pressure is given by

$$(5.27) \qquad p = -(\partial F/\partial V)_T.$$

Now we may write approximately

$$(5.28) \qquad F = U_0(V) + F_D(T,V),$$

where $U_0(V)$ is the internal energy at $0°K$ and F_D is the contribution (in the Debye approximation) of the lattice vibrations to the free energy. In the spirit of the Debye approximation we may suppose that the dependence of F_D on the volume V is adequately described by specifying the dependence of the Debye temperature Θ on V. Thus, from (5.27) and (5.28),

$$(5.29) \qquad p = -(\partial U_0/\partial V) - (\partial F_D/\partial \Theta)(\partial \Theta/\partial V).$$

In the Debye approximation the internal energy U_D due to lattice vibrations involves T times a function of Θ/T; therefore by (5.26) F_D must be of the same form:

$$(5.30) \qquad F_D = Tf(\Theta/T),$$

so that

$$(5.31) \qquad \partial F_D/\partial \Theta = f' = \Theta^{-1}[(\partial/\partial(1/T))(F_D/T)] = U_D/\Theta.$$

Thus from (5.29) we have the *Debye equation of state*,

$$(5.32) \qquad p = -(\partial U_0/\partial V) + \gamma U_D/V,$$

where

$$(5.33) \qquad \gamma = -d(\log \Theta)/d(\log V) = -(V/\Theta)(d\Theta/dV)$$

is known as the Grüneisen constant. We note that, if ω_k is an eigenfrequency of the solid, $\gamma = -d(\log \omega_k)/d(\log V)$, where we suppose that γ is independent of k.

GRÜNEISEN RELATION

On differentiating (5.32) we have

$$(5.34) \qquad (\partial p/\partial T)_v = \gamma C_v/V.$$

Now the linear expansion coefficient β is one-third of the volume expansion coefficient, so that

$$(5.35) \quad \beta = (1/3V)(\partial V/\partial T)_p = -(1/3V)(\partial p/\partial T)_v/(\partial p/\partial V)_T$$

$$= (K/3)(\partial p/\partial T)_v = K\gamma C_v/3V,$$

where K is the compressibility. The relation

$$(5.36) \qquad \beta = K\gamma C_v/3V$$

connecting the linear expansion coefficient with the specific heat is satisfied experimentally for cubic crystals, taking γ as independent of temperature.

In Table 5.4 we give a comparison of γ calculated by Grüneisen from (5.36) with γ calculated by Slater[7] from Bridgman's measurements of the change of compressibility with pressure, for a number of metals. The agreement is really quite good.

TABLE 5.4. VALUES OF THE GRÜNEISEN γ

Metal	Grüneisen, Eq. (5.36)	Slater-Bridgman
Fe	1.60	1.68
Co	1.87	2.1
Ni	1.88	2.2
Cu	1.96	1.9
Pd	2.23	2.4
Ag	2.40	2.5
W	1.62	1.7
Pt	2.54	3.3

THERMAL CONDUCTIVITY IN NON-METALS

It is useful in discussing the conduction of thermal energy in dielectric substances to introduce (following Debye) the concept of the mean free path of the lattice waves or *phonons*, as they are often called. The mean free path concept is suggested by analogy with the use of the molecular mean free path in the kinetic theory of transport phenomena in gases. For a qualitative discussion we *define* a quantity Λ, having the character of a mean free path, by the equation

$$(5.37) \qquad K = \tfrac{1}{3}Cv\Lambda,$$

where K is the thermal conductivity, C the heat capacity per unit volume, and v the average sound velocity. The factor $\tfrac{1}{3}$ is somewhat arbitrary. This equation is derived below as (12.88). Typical values of Λ are given in Table 5.5.

[7] J. C. Slater, Phys. Rev. **57**, 744 (1940); J. S. Dugdale and D. K. C. MacDonald, Phys. Rev. **89**, 832 (1953).

The usual heat conduction equation for the flux of thermal energy in a linear specimen is

$$(5.38) \qquad Q = K(T_1 - T_2)/L.$$

Here Q = heat transfer crossing unit area per unit time; $T_1 - T_2$ = temperature drop between ends; L = length of specimen. On substituting for K the expression given by (5.37), we have

$$(5.39) \qquad Q = \tfrac{1}{3}C(T_1 - T_2)(\Lambda v/L).$$

In this form the equation may be interpreted very simply: $C(T_1 - T_2)$ is the excess energy density at one end of the specimen with respect to the other end; this excess is propagated down the specimen with an effective transport velocity which is just the velocity of sound reduced by the ratio of the mean free path to the length of the specimen.[8]

TABLE 5.5. PHONON MEAN FREE PATH VALUES
[Calculated from (5.37), using $v = 5 \times 10^5$ cm/sec
as the average sound velocity]

Crystal	T (°C)	C (cal/cc)	K (cal/cm–deg–sec)	Λ (cm)
Quartz†	0	0.48	0.03	40×10^{-8}
	−190	0.13	0.12	540×10^{-8}
NaCl	0	0.45	0.017	21×10^{-8}
	−190	0.24	0.064	150×10^{-8}

† Parallel optic axis.

PHONON MEAN FREE PATHS

The phonon mean free path Λ is determined principally by two processes, geometrical scattering and scattering by other phonons. If the forces between atoms were purely harmonic, there would be no mechanism for collisions between different phonons, and the mean free path would be limited solely by collisions of a phonon with the crystal boundary, and by lattice imperfections. There are situations to be discussed below where these effects are dominant. With anharmonic lattice interactions there is a coupling between different phonons which limits the value of the mean free path.

The theory of the effect of anharmonic coupling on thermal conductivity is one of the most complicated problems in solid state physics.

[8] This result for the transport velocity is expected from statistical considerations. It may be noted that the effective transport velocity which obtains in the problem of the one-dimensional random walk is proportional to $\Lambda v/L$, where Λ is now the length of a unit step. One verifies this by calculating $\bar{v} = \int_0^\infty (L/t)\, q(L;t)\, dt$, where $q(L;t)$ is the distribution function Eq. (32) in S. Chandrasekhar, Rev. Modern Phys. **15**, 1 (1943).

An approximate calculation has been given by Debye,[9] and Peierls[10] has considered the problem in great detail. They both show that Λ is proportional to $1/T$ at high temperatures, in agreement with experiment. We can understand this dependence in terms of the number of phonons with which a given phonon can interact: at high temperature

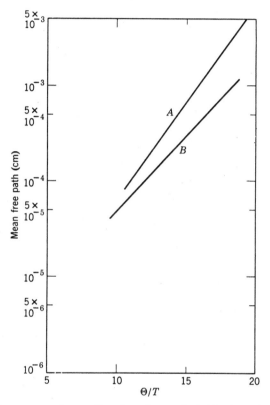

Fig. 5.3.   Phonon mean free paths plotted on a logarithmic scale against Θ/T. *A*, synthetic sapphire $(\Theta \simeq 980°K)$; *B*, diamond $(\Theta \simeq 1840)$. (After Berman, Simon, and Wilks.)

the excitation of phonons is proportional to T. At low temperatures Peierls finds Λ approximately proportional to $e^{-\Theta/2T}$, and this has been approximately verified in an appropriate temperature range by Berman, Simon, and Wilks,[11] as shown in Fig. 5.3. In addition to being

[9] P. Debye, in *Vorträge über die kinetische Theorie der Materie und Elektrizität*, by M. Planck *et al.*, Teubner, Leipzig, 1914.

[10] R. Peierls, Ann. Physik **3**, 1055 (1929).

[11] Berman, Simon, and Wilks, Nature **168**, 277 (1951).

an important mechanism in determining the mean free path, anharmonic interaction is the only mechanism in solids whereby the frequency distribution of phonons may be brought into thermal equilibrium. In thermal conductivity one needs not only a way of limiting the mean free path, but also a way of establishing an equilibrium distribution of phonons at a given temperature.

Geometrical effects may also be important in limiting the mean free path. We must consider scattering by crystal boundaries, lattice imperfections, and amorphous structures. When Λ becomes comparable with the width of the test specimen, the value of Λ is limited by

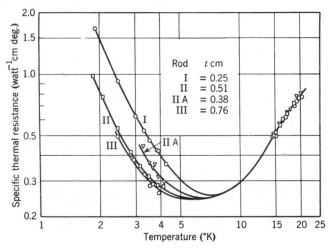

Fig. 5.4. Thermal resistivity of single crystal of potassium chloride as measured by Biermasz and de Haas. Below 5°K the resistivity is a function of the crystal thickness t.

the width, and the thermal conductivity becomes a function of the dimensions of the specimen! This effect was discovered by de Haas and Biermasz,[12] and the explanation was suggested by Peierls and worked out by Casimir;[13] measurements on potassium chloride crystals are given in Fig. 5.4.

Klemens[14] has considered lattice defect scattering in detail, and he suggests that the presence of impurities is the chief factor in determining the conductivity of potassium chloride and potassium bromide between 10° and 90°K.

[12] W. J. de Haas and T. Biermasz, Physica 2, 673 (1935); 4, 752 (1937); 5, 47, 320, 619 (1938); see also R. Berman, Proc. Roy. Soc. (London) A208, 90 (1951).

[13] H. B. G. Casimir, Physica 5, 495 (1938); R. E. B. Makinson, Proc. Cambridge Phil. Soc. 34, 474 (1938).

[14] P. G. Klemens, Proc. Roy. Soc. (London) A208, 108 (1951).

In glasses the thermal conductivity (Fig. 5.5) decreases as the temperature is lowered; this effect is present even at room temperature. Furthermore, the values of the thermal conductivity at room temperature run about an order of magnitude lower for glasses than for

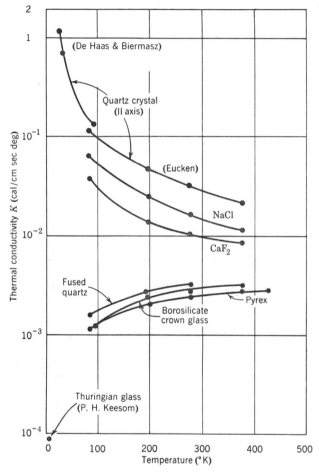

Fig. 5.5.   Temperature dependence of the thermal conductivity of various crystals and glasses.

crystals.   The mean free path in quartz glass at room temperature is 8 A, which is of the order of magnitude of the dimensions of a silicon dioxide tetrahedron (7 A).   The present concept of the nature of the glassy state[15] (Fig. 5.6) pictures a glass such as fused quartz as a ran-

[15] W. H. Zachariasen, J. Am. Chem. Soc. **54**, 3841 (1932); B. E. Warren, J. App. Phys. **8**, 645 (1937); **13**, 602 (1942).

dom, but continuous, network of silicon-oxygen bonds. The effective crystallite size is only of the order of a single tetrahedron of the structure. We expect then that (except at low temperatures where the phonon wavelengths are long) the phonon mean free path will be constant, limited by the crystallite size, and the decline in the conductivity as the temperature is lowered may be attributed to the decline in the heat capacity.[16]

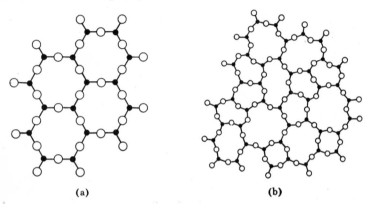

(a)   (b)

Fig. 5.6.   Schematic two-dimensional analogues, after Zachariasen, illustrating the difference between: (a) the regularly repeating structure of a crystal; and (b) the random network of a glass.

TABLE 5.6.   THERMAL CONDUCTIVITY VALUES

	cal/cm-sec-deg C	
	$-190°C$	$0°C$ or $20°C$
Al	0.61	0.54
Cd ($\parallel$ hex. axis)	0.22	0.20
($\perp$ hex. axis)	0.27	0.25
Fe	0.44	0.22
Au	....	0.73
Cu	1.38	0.94
Mg	0.45	0.41
Ni	0.27	0.20
Na	0.37	0.33
Ag	1.02	1.00
KF	0.057	0.017
NaCl	0.064	0.017
KCl	0.050	0.017
CaF_2	0.093	0.025
Chrome alum	0.0026	0.0045
Potassium alum	0.0030	0.0047

[16] C. Kittel, Phys. Rev. **75**, 972 (1949); F. Birch and H. Clark, Am. J. Sci. **238**, 613 (1940); for liquids, see P. W. Bridgman, Proc. Am. Acad. Arts Sci. **59**, 109 (1923).

Synthetic sapphire (Al_2O_3) has one of the highest values of the conductivity[11]—60 watts/cm-deg at 50°K. Glasses have values as low as 5×10^{-4} watt/cm-deg at 2°K, and Berman[17] has suggested that the conductivity of microcrystalline graphite at 1°K may be 10^{-5} watt/cm-deg. It may be noted that the maximum of the thermal conductivity in sapphire is greater than the maximum of 50 watts/cm-deg in copper according to the measurements of Berman and MacDonald,[18] shown for comparison purposes in Fig. 12.6. Selected thermal conductivities are given in Table 5.6. The thermal conductivity of metals is treated in Chapter 12.

PROBLEMS

5.1. Show that the classical average internal energy of a one-dimensional harmonic oscillator in thermal equilibrium at temperature T is kT, where k is the Boltzmann constant. *Note:* The energy $w(p,q) = (p^2/2m) + (m\omega^2 q^2/2)$, where p is the momentum, q the displacement, and ω the frequency. The result of classical statistical mechanics is that in equilibrium the probability of finding the system between p and $p + dp$ and between q and $q + dq$ is proportional to

$$e^{-w(p,q)/kT} \, dp \, dq,$$

so that the average value of w is given by

$$\bar{w} = \int_{-\infty}^{\infty} \int_{-\infty}^{\infty} w e^{-w/kT} \, dp \, dq \Big/ \int_{-\infty}^{\infty} \int_{-\infty}^{\infty} e^{-w/kT} \, dp \, dq.$$

We may observe that the expression for $\bar{w}$ may be written in a more compact form if we introduce the partition function $Z = \iint e^{-w/kT} \, dp \, dq$; then

$$\bar{w} = kT^2 \, d(\log Z)/dT.$$

5.2. Show from (5.11) that the heat capacity of a monatomic linear lattice in the Debye approximation is proportional to T/Θ, for low temperatures such that $T \ll \Theta$, where Θ is the effective Debye temperature in one dimension and is defined as $\Theta = \hbar\omega_m/k = \hbar\pi v_0/ka$, k being the Boltzmann constant.

5.3. Using the anharmonic potential $V(x) = cx^2 - gx^3 - fx^4$, show that the approximate heat capacity of the classical anharmonic oscillator is

$$C \cong k \left[1 + \left(\frac{3f}{2c^2} + \frac{15g^2}{8c^3} \right) kT \right].$$

Note: $\log (1 + x) \cong x - \frac{1}{2}x^2$ for $x \ll 1$; the calculation is shorter if the partition function (Problem 5.1) is employed.

5.4. Show by thermodynamics that

$$C_p - C_v = 9\beta^2 T/K,$$

[17] R. Berman, Phys. Rev. **76**, 315 (1949).

[18] R. Berman and D. K. C. MacDonald, Proc. Roy. Soc. (London) **A211**, 122 (1952).

where C_p is the heat capacity per unit volume at constant pressure, C_v at constant volume, β is the temperature coefficient of linear expansion, and K is the compressibility. Estimate $C_p - C_v$ for copper at 300°K and at 1000°K.

5.5. Derive an expression for the free energy $F = U - TS$ of a collection of quantum harmonic oscillators, and show that the classical limit is

$$F \cong U_0 + kT \sum_k \log (\hbar\omega_k/kT).$$

5.6. Writing $\Theta_E = \hbar\omega/k$, find the limiting form at low temperatures of the Einstein heat capacity (5.21). Give a qualitative physical reason for the difference in the way the heat capacities on the Einstein and Debye theories approach zero.

5.7. By equating the elastic energy per unit cell $\frac{1}{2}ce^2a^3$ with kT, show that the local thermal strain in a crystal at room temperature may be of the order of 0.1; here e is the strain; c is an average elastic constant, and a is the lattice constant.

5.8. A solid contains N particles per cubic centimeter, each of which can occupy a position with energy $+W$, or a position with energy $-W$. The particles are distributed over these energy levels according to a Boltzmann distribution function. Calculate the specific heat as a function of temperature due to this degree of freedom and give a sketch of this dependence. Such a specific heat curve is known as a Schottky anomaly. What is the difference in entropy at absolute zero and at very high temperatures?

REFERENCES

M. Blackman, "The theory of the specific heat of solids," Repts. Prog. Phys. **8**, 11 (1941).

A. Eucken, *Handbuch der Experimentalphysik*, Akademische Verlagsgesellschaft, Leipzig, vol. 8/1, 1929.

R. H. Fowler and E. A. Guggenheim, *Statistical thermodynamics*, Cambridge University Press, Cambridge, 1939.

J. C. Slater, *Introduction to chemical physics*, McGraw-Hill Book Co., New York, 1939; Chaps. XIII–XV.

6

Dielectric Properties

In this chapter we discuss first the relationship between the applied electric field and the local electric field acting on an atom. The interaction of the local field with the atom determines the polarization, yet the local field may itself be a function of the polarization. We then discuss the electric polarization of atoms, molecules, and crystals in static fields and at high frequencies. The polarization is defined as the dipole moment per unit volume, the dipole moment $\mathbf{P}$ of the specimen as a whole being defined as $\mathbf{P} = \Sigma e_i \mathbf{r}_i$. The sum is extended over all charges in the system; on the supposition that the system is neutral the sum is independent of the origin chosen for the position vector $\mathbf{r}_i$.

LOCAL ELECTRIC FIELD

The calculation of the local field at an atom or ion as affected by the polarization of the specimen as a whole is a problem of central importance in dielectric and magnetic theory. We consider first a solid dielectric with a simple cubic crystal structure; we suppose that the specimen is in the form of an ellipsoid with one of the axes parallel to the applied electric field (Fig. 6.1).

The field $\mathbf{E}_{loc}$ at any atom may be written as a sum

(6.1) $$\mathbf{E}_{loc} = \mathbf{E}_0 + \mathbf{E}_1 + \mathbf{E}_2 + \mathbf{E}_3,$$

where $\mathbf{E}_0$ is the electric field applied from external sources; $\mathbf{E}_1$ is the "depolarization field" resulting from polarization charges on the outer surface of the specimen. We imagine as a mathematical fiction a small sphere cut out of the specimen around the reference point; then $\mathbf{E}_2$ is the field of the polarization charges on the inside of the cavity left by the sphere, and $\mathbf{E}_3$ is the field of the atoms within the cavity.

The addition $\mathbf{E}_1 + \mathbf{E}_2 + \mathbf{E}_3$ to the local field is just the total effect at one atom of the dipole moments of all the other atoms in the specimen:

(6.2) $$\mathbf{E}_1 + \mathbf{E}_2 + \mathbf{E}_3 = \sum_i \frac{3(\mathbf{p}_i \cdot \mathbf{r}_i)\mathbf{r}_i - r_i^2 \mathbf{p}_i}{r_i^5}.$$

If we are far enough away from the individual dipoles of a uniformly polarized specimen, we may, according to an elementary transformation occurring in electrostatic theory, calculate the field of the specimen as equal to the field of a surface charge distribution of density P_n on the surfaces of the specimen, P_n being the normal component of the polarization P at the surfaces. The idea in creating the cavity is that we may treat the field E_3 of the dipoles within the cavity on a microscopic basis by such a sum as (6.2), while the rest of the specimen

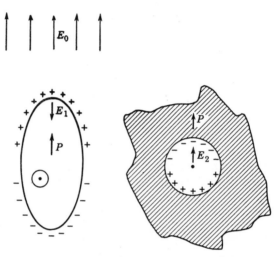

Fig. 6.1. Contributions to the local electric field at the ion at the center of the spherical cavity, showing the applied field E_0, the depolarization field E_1, and the Lorentz field E_2. The local field is the sum of these plus the field of the dipoles within the cavity.

is treated macroscopically by means of integrals over the effective surface charges. One integral is taken over the outer surface, and it gives E_1; the other integral is taken over the surface of the spherical cavity, and it gives E_2. The field E_1 is readily seen from Fig. 6.1 to be opposite in direction to the polarization and hence is called the *depolarization field*.

DEPOLARIZATION FIELD

The calculation of the depolarization field is a well-known problem in classical electricity, and we summarize the results here. It is found that specimens of homogeneous composition will be uniformly polarized when placed in a uniform external field as long as the external shape of the specimen is that of a general ellipsoid or a limiting case of a general ellipsoid. If the ellipsoid is oriented with one of the principal axes parallel to the applied field, the polarization will be parallel to the applied field, as will the depolarization field E_1, which it is found may be calculated from the polarization P by a relation of the form

(6.3) $$E_1 = -NP.$$

The constant N is known as the *depolarization factor* or, more commonly, as the *demagnetization factor*, and its value depends on the axial ratio. It is exceptionally important in the field of magnetism. Values of N are plotted in Fig. 6.2 for ellipsoids of revolution, and additional cases

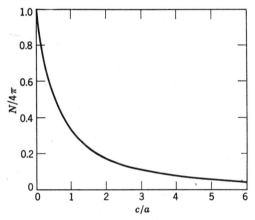

Fig. 6.2. Demagnetization factor N parallel to the figure axis of ellipsoids of revolution, as a function of the axial ratio c/a.

have been calculated by Osborn[1] and by Stoner.[2] In the several limiting cases we have the following values:

Shape	Axis	N
Sphere	any	$4\pi/3$
Thin slab	normal	4π
Thin slab	in plane	0
Long circular cylinder	longitudinal	0
Long circular cylinder	transverse	2π

The demagnetization factor only has a rigorous meaning for homogeneous general ellipsoids in uniform applied fields. An important property of the demagnetization factor is that $N_a + N_b + N_c = 4\pi$,

[1] J. A. Osborn, Phys. Rev. **67**, 351 (1945).

[2] E. C. Stoner, Phil. Mag. **36**, 803 (1945); for approximate values for non-ellipsoidal shapes, see J. Würschmidt, *Theorie des Entmagnetisierungsfaktor*, Vieweg, Braunschweig, 1925; J. L. Snoek, Physica **1**, 649 (1933); R. M. Bozorth and D. M. Chapin, J. Appl. Phys. **13**, 320 (1942).

where N_a, N_b, N_c are the demagnetization factors along the three principal axes of a general ellipsoid.

The field E_2 due to the polarization charges on the surface of the fictitious cavity was calculated first by Lorentz. If θ is the polar angle (Fig. 6.3) referred to the polarization direction as axis, the surface charge density on the surface of the cavity is $-P \cos \theta$. The electric field at the center of the spherical cavity of radius a is

$$(6.4) \quad E_2 = \int_0^\pi (a^{-2})(2\pi a \sin \theta)(a\ d\theta)(P \cos \theta)(\cos \theta) = 4\pi P/3.$$

The cavity field is actually uniform, but for our purpose we need only the field at the center, which is what we have just calculated.

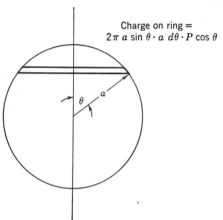

Charge on ring =
$2\pi a \sin \theta \cdot a\ d\theta \cdot P \cos \theta$

Fig. 6.3. Calculation of the field in a spherical cavity in a uniformly polarized medium.

FIELD OF DIPOLES INSIDE CAVITY

The field E_3 caused by the dipoles within the cavity is the only term in the sum which depends on the crystal structure. We shall first consider a simple cubic structure, for which it is readily shown that $E_3 = 0$ if all the atoms may be replaced by point dipoles parallel to each other. Taking the axis of the dipoles as the z axis, the field at the reference point caused by the other dipoles is

$$(6.5) \qquad E_3 = \sum_i \frac{3p_i z_i^2 - p_i r_i^2}{r_i^5}.$$

By the symmetry of the lattice and the cavity, $\Sigma(z_i^2/r_i^5) = \Sigma(y_i^2/r_i^5) = \Sigma(x_i^2/r_i^5)$, so that $\Sigma(r_i^2/r_i^5) = 3\Sigma(z_i^2/r_i^5)$, whence $E_3 = 0$.

The proof we have given for the vanishing of E_3 actually obtains for all cases in which the environment of the reference point is cubic, as long as the dipoles are parallel. Thus $E_3 = 0$ for induced polarization on simple cubic, body-centered cubic, and face-centered cubic lattices, as well as for an isotropic distribution. Later, in considering the ferroelectric properties of barium titanate (Fig. 7.1), we shall see that here $E_3 \neq 0$; although the crystallographic symmetry is cubic, the environment of the oxygen ions is not cubic. Values of E_3 for tetragonal and simple hexagonal lattices have been given by Mueller.[3]

FIELD IN DIELECTRIC BETWEEN CONDENSER PLATES

The classical definition of the macroscopic (average) electric field intensity E inside a dielectric is that E is the average field inside a long needle-shaped cavity, parallel to the polarization (Fig. 6.4), while the

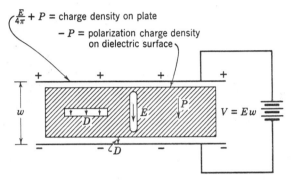

$\frac{E}{4\pi} + P$ = charge density on plate

$-P$ = polarization charge density on dielectric surface

$V = Ew$

Fig. 6.4. Definitions of D and E; the voltage V across the condenser plates is E times the separation w, if we neglect the air gaps between the plates and the dielectric.

displacement D is defined as the average field inside a disk-shaped cavity normal to the polarization. The difference

$$(6.6) \qquad D - E = 4\pi P$$

is caused by the field $4\pi P$ of the polarization charge density P on the flat surfaces of the disk cavity; the polarization charges on the needle cavity may be neglected. Inside a spherical cavity the field is $E + (4\pi/3)P$.

Measurements of the polarization P or of the dielectric constant $\epsilon = D/E$ are usually made by measuring the capacity $C = Q/V$ of a condenser filled with the dielectric. In the absence of the dielectric we suppose that the field between the condenser plates is E', so that the surface charge density on each plate is $\pm E'/4\pi$. When the dielectric is inserted, polarization charge densities $\pm P$ are induced on the surfaces of the dielectric, and these charges are then effectively

[3] H. Mueller, Phys. Rev. **47**, 947 (1935); **50**, 547 (1936); see also L. W. McKeehan Phys. Rev. **43**, 1022, 1025 (1933).

neutralized by a flow of charge around the condenser circuit. The field E inside the needle-shaped cavity is the sum of a field $-4\pi P$ from the polarization charges and $E' + 4\pi P$ from the original and the neutralization charges on the condenser plates. Thus for the condenser arrangement $E = E'$, and, from (6.1), (6.3), and (6.4), $E_{\text{loc}} = E_0 + E_1 + E_2 + E_3 = (E + 4\pi P) + (-4\pi P) + (4\pi P/3) + (0)$ for structures such that $E_3 = 0$. Then

(6.7) $$E_{\text{loc}} = E + \frac{4\pi}{3} P.$$

That is, the value of the macroscopic average field E is the same as the field existing between the condenser plates before the dielectric is inserted; the field acting at the center of an atom is E plus a contribution $4\pi P/3$ from the field produced by the polarization of the other atoms in the specimen. It is seen further that the condenser plates, if put in close contact with the dielectric, have the effect of shorting-out the depolarization charge.

DIELECTRIC CONSTANT AND POLARIZABILITY

The dielectric constant ϵ is defined as

(6.8) $$\epsilon = D/E = 1 + 4\pi(P/E) = 1 + 4\pi\chi,$$

where χ is the susceptibility. The polarizability α is defined as

(6.9) $$\alpha_i = p_i/E_{\text{loc}}{}^i,$$

where the subscript i refers to a particular type of atom. The polarization is then

$$P = \sum_i E_{\text{loc}}{}^i N_i \alpha_i,$$

where N_i is the number per unit volume of atoms of type i.

If the local field is connected with the applied field by the Lorentz relation (6.7), we have

(6.10) $$\frac{P}{E} = \frac{\sum N_i \alpha_i}{1 - \frac{4\pi}{3} \sum N_i \alpha_i} = \frac{\epsilon - 1}{4\pi},$$

which may be solved for $\sum N_i \alpha_i$ to give

(6.11) $$\frac{\epsilon - 1}{\epsilon + 2} = \frac{4\pi}{3} \sum N_i \alpha_i,$$

which is a common form of the relation between the dielectric constant
and the atomic polarizabilities; (6.11) may be rewritten as the Clausius-
Mossotti equation (or, with $\epsilon = n^2$, the Lorenz-Lorentz equation),

(6.12)
$$\frac{M}{\rho}\frac{\epsilon - 1}{\epsilon + 2} = \frac{4\pi}{3} L\alpha,$$

where M is the molecular weight, ρ the density, L Avogadro's number,
n the refractive index, and α the total polarizability per molecule.
The left-hand side of this equation is called the *molar polarizability*.

MEASUREMENT OF DIELECTRIC CONSTANTS

The usual methods of measuring dielectric constants are based on a
comparison of the capacity C'' of a condenser filled with the substance

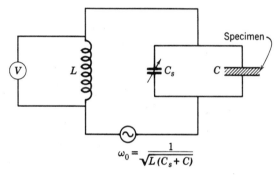

$$\omega_0 = \frac{1}{\sqrt{L(C_s + C)}}$$

Fig. 6.5. Schematic diagram of apparatus for the measurement of dielectric
constants.

and the capacity C' of the empty condenser. The ratio $C''/C' = \epsilon$,
the dielectric constant. The determination of the value of the
capacity may in principle be accomplished by an LC resonant circuit
as shown in Fig. 6.5, where C_s is a calibrated variable condenser and C
is the condenser in which the specimen may be placed. By varying
the calibrated condenser so as to keep the resonance frequency $\omega_0 =$
$[L(C_s + C)]^{-\frac{1}{2}}$ constant when C is inserted and then filled, we may
determine C' and C'', and thus ϵ. The dielectric loss may be obtained
from the sharpness of the tuning near resonance.

Descriptions of the actual circuits employed are abundant in the
literature. At microwave frequencies the technique of measurement
is altered somewhat, and here one often measures essentially the wavelength λ of the microwave radiation in the specimen, obtaining the
dielectric constant from the relation $\lambda(\text{vacuum})/\lambda(\text{specimen}) = (\epsilon\mu)^{\frac{1}{2}}$,
where μ is the permeability.

ELECTRONIC POLARIZABILITIES

The total polarizability of an atom or ion may usually be separated into three parts:[4] electronic, ionic, and orientational. The electronic contribution arises from the displacement of electrons in an atom relative to the nucleus; that is, from the deformation of the electron shell about a nucleus. The ionic or atomic contribution comes from the displacement and deformation of a charged ion with respect to

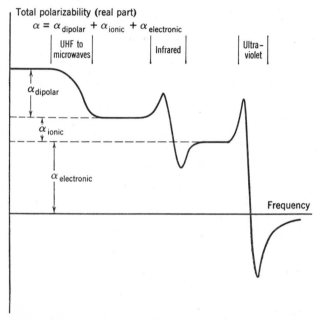

Fig. 6.6.   Frequency dependence of the several contributions to the polarizability (schematic).

other ions.   The orientational or dipolar polarizability arises when the substance is built up of molecules possessing a permanent electric dipole moment which may be more or less free to change orientation in an applied electric field.   It is possible to separate experimentally the different contributions, and one way of doing this is indicated in Fig. 6.6.   The usual situation is that both the ionic and the dipolar contributions are seldom large together in the same substance: in ordinary ionic crystals there is no dipolar contribution.   In dipolar organic

---

[4] In heterogeneous materials there is usually also an *interfacial polarization* arising from the accumulation of charge at structural interfaces.   This is of little fundamental interest, but of considerable practical interest as commercial insulating materials are usually heterogeneous.

molecules Sugden[5] estimates that the average ionic polarizability is about 10% of the electronic polarizability.

In the optical range of frequency the dielectric constant arises almost entirely from the electronic polarizability, so that in the optical range (6.11) reduces to

$$(6.13) \qquad \frac{n^2 - 1}{n^2 + 2} = \frac{4\pi}{3} \Sigma N_i \alpha_i \text{ (electronic)};$$

here we have used the relation $n^2 = \epsilon$, where n is the refractive index. By applying this relation to large numbers of crystals we may determine empirical values of the electronic polarizabilities which are reasonably consistent with the observed values of the refractive index. Values obtained in this way are given in Table 6.1. The scheme is not

TABLE 6.1. ELECTRONIC POLARIZABILITIES OF IONS

Values from L. Pauling, Proc. Roy. Soc. (London) **A114**, 181 (1927) and from unpublished work by Shockley, Tessman, and Kahn (STK). The STK polarizabilities are for the D lines of sodium.

Units cm$^3 \times 10^{-24}$

	He	Li$^+$	Be^{2+}	B^{3+}	C^{4+}
Pauling	0.201	0.029	0.008	0.003	0.0013
STK		0.021			
	O^{2-}	F$^-$	Ne	Na$^+$	Mg^{2+}	Al^{3+}	Si^{4+}
Pauling	3.88	1.04	0.390	0.179	0.094	0.052	0.0165
STK	(2.4)	0.652		0.400			
	S^{2-}	Cl$^-$	A	K$^+$	Ca^{2+}	Sc^{3+}	Ti^{4+}
Pauling	10.2	3.66	1.62	0.83	0.47	0.286	0.185
STK	(5.5)	2.97		1.326	1.1		(0.19)
	Se^{2-}	Br$^-$	Kr	Rb$^+$	Sr^{2+}	Y^{3+}	Zr^{4+}
Pauling	10.5	4.77	2.46	1.40	0.86	0.55	0.37
STK	(7.)	4.17		1.97	1.6		
	Te^{2-}	I$^-$	Xe	Cs$^+$	Ba^{2+}	La^{3+}	Ce^{4+}
Pauling	14.0	7.10	3.99	2.42	1.55	1.04	0.73
STK	(9.)	6.44		3.33	2.5		

entirely self-consistent, as the electronic polarizability of an ion may depend slightly on the environment in which it is placed.

CLASSICAL THEORY OF ELECTRONIC POLARIZABILITY

According to classical mechanics an electron bound harmonically to an atom will show resonance absorption at a frequency $\omega_0 = (\beta/m)^{1/2}$, where β is the force constant. The average displacement of the electron occasioned by the application of a field E_{loc} will be given by

$$eE_{\text{loc}} = \beta \bar{x} = m\omega_0^2 \bar{x},$$

[5] J. A. Sugden, Trans. Faraday Soc. **30**, 734 (1934).

so that the static electronic polarizability is

(6.14) $\alpha(\text{electronic}) = p/E_{\text{loc}} = e\bar{x}/E_{\text{loc}} = e^2/m\omega_0^2.$

The electronic polarizability will depend on frequency, and it is shown in Problem 6.3 that the result is, for frequency ω,

(6.15) $\alpha(\text{electronic}) = \dfrac{e^2/m}{\omega_0^2 - \omega^2},$

but in the visible region the dispersion is not usually very important in the dielectric materials of most interest.   The corresponding expression in quantum theory is

(6.16) $\alpha(\text{electronic}) = \dfrac{e^2}{m}\displaystyle\sum_j \dfrac{f_{ij}}{\omega_{ij}^2 - \omega^2},$

where the oscillator strength f_{ij} is given by

(6.17) $f_{ij} = 2\omega_{ij}m|x_{ij}|^2/\hbar$

in the usual notation.   This result is derived in most books on quantum theory, and it is derived in Appendix C for the limiting case $\omega = 0$.

The electronic polarizability is of the order of magnitude, for hydrogen,

$$\alpha \approx \frac{e'^2}{m\omega_0^2} \approx \frac{e^2}{m}\left(\frac{\hbar^3}{me^4}\right)^2 = \frac{\hbar^6}{m^3 e^6} = a_{\text{H}}^3 \approx 10^{-25}\ \text{cm}^3.$$

IONIC POLARIZABILITIES

In sodium chloride the square of the refractive index is $(1.50)^2 = 2.25$, while the static dielectric constant is 5.62.   The difference $\Delta\epsilon$ between the static and optical dielectric constants may be ascribed in ionic crystals to the ionic polarizability; in sodium chloride we see that $\Delta\epsilon = 3.37$.   The ionic polarization arises from the displacement of ions of opposite sign when an electric field is applied, and also from the deformation of the electronic shells of the ions as a result of the relative motion of the ions.

We consider the situation in a sodium chloride crystal when a uniform external field E_0 is applied.   Each Na^+ ion is displaced in one direction, and each Cl^- ion in the opposite direction.   The total relative displacement x is given in terms of the problem discussed in Chapter 4 by setting $\omega = 0$ in (4.25) and (4.26).   Then

(6.18) $x = \eta - \xi = \dfrac{eE_0}{\omega_0^2}\left(\dfrac{1}{m} + \dfrac{1}{M}\right),$

where in the present fairly crude treatment we associate E_0 with the applied electric field, neglecting local field effects; ω_0 is the infrared absorption frequency.

The ionic polarization is

$$P = \frac{e(\eta - \xi)}{\Omega},$$

where Ω is the volume per molecule and is equal to $2a^3$ for the sodium chloride structure, a being the nearest neighbor distance. Then

$$(6.19) \qquad P = \frac{e^2 E_0}{2\omega_0^2 a^3} \left(\frac{1}{m} + \frac{1}{M}\right),$$

which gives directly the Born equation

$$(6.20) \qquad \Delta\epsilon = \frac{2\pi e^2}{\omega_0^2 a^3} \left(\frac{1}{m} + \frac{1}{M}\right).$$

This exhibits the connection of $\Delta\epsilon$ with the residual ray frequency ω_0. Values of $\Delta\epsilon$ calculated by using this equation are in fairly good agreement with the experimental values. For sodium chloride,

$$\Delta\epsilon = \frac{(6.28)(4.80 \times 10^{-10})^2}{(3.2 \times 10^{13})^2 (2.81 \times 10^{-8})^3 (1.66 \times 10^{-24})} \left(\frac{1}{23} + \frac{1}{35.5}\right) = 2.7,$$

in fair agreement with the observed $\Delta\epsilon = 3.4$.

There are actually some subtle points neglected in the derivation of the Born equation, points which are connected with differences in the local field effective for optical frequencies and for quasi-static frequencies. Szigeti[6] has shown that the Born equation holds on the assumption of non-deformable and non-overlapping ions. An improved approximate expression is given by Szigeti:

$$(6.21) \qquad \Delta\epsilon = \left(\frac{n^2 + 2}{3}\right)^2 \frac{2\pi(e^*)^2}{\omega_t^2 a^3} \left(\frac{1}{m} + \frac{1}{M}\right),$$

where ω_t is the eigenfrequency of the transverse optical branch, and e^* is "effective" charge on an ion. Values of e^* are given in Table 6.2. Szigeti has also found a relation involving the compressibility K and the dielectric constant ϵ_0 for static frequencies:

$$(6.22)] \qquad \frac{1}{K} = \frac{\epsilon_0 + 2}{6(n^2 + 2)} (m\omega_t^2 / a).$$

[6] B. Szigeti, Trans. Faraday Soc. **45**, 155 (1949); Proc. Roy. Soc. (London) **A204**, 51 (1950).

We have written both (6.21) and (6.22) in a somewhat specialized form for sodium chloride structures. A comparison of observed and calculated compressibilities is made in Table 6.2.

TABLE 6.2. DIELECTRIC DATA FOR ALKALI HALIDES HAVING THE SODIUM CHLORIDE STRUCTURES AND TEST OF THE SZIGETI RELATIONS

	ϵ_0	n^2	e^*/e	K_{calc}/K_{obs}
LiF	9.27	1.92	0.87	1.0
NaF	6.0	1.74	0.93	0.83
NaCl	5.62	2.25	0.74	0.99
NaBr	5.99	2.62	0.69	1.13
NaI	6.60	2.91	0.71	1.05
KCl	4.68	2.13	0.80	0.96
KBr	4.78	2.33	0.76	0.95
KI	4.94	2.69	0.69	0.99
RbCl	5	2.19	0.84	0.89
RbBr	5	2.33	0.82	0.83
RbI	5	2.63	0.89	0.66

It is seen from the table that the ratio K_{calc}/K_{obs} is on the whole closer to unity than the ratio e^*/e. Of course it is possible that, owing to an admixture of homopolar bonding, the degree of ionization of the ions in the crystal is somewhat incomplete; however, the generally excellent agreement of the calculated lattice energies with the experimental values, as discussed in Chapter 2, would seem to make it improbable that values of e^*/e differ from unity by more than perhaps 2%. At the present time this disagreement has not been resolved in a satisfactory fashion, although the question is of basic importance in the theory of the dielectric properties of ionic crystals.

ORIENTATIONAL POLARIZABILITIES

The polarizability arising from the orientation in an applied electric field of molecules possessing a permanent electric dipole moment is usually discussed only with reference to gases and liquids, but it is of importance in some solids. This type of polarization was first discussed by Debye (1912), who showed that by assuming that molecules could have permanent dipole moments one could explain the high dielectric constant of water, alcohol, and similar liquids, and the temperature dependence of their dielectric constants. The problem of the dielectric constant of water is that the static dielectric constant is 81 (at room temperature), whereas the dielectric constant at optical frequencies is $(1.33)^2 = 1.76$. It is now known that the difference is caused chiefly by the orientational polarization which is effective at low frequencies, but is damped out for wavelengths shorter than about 1 cm.

In the absence of thermal agitation and of interactions among themselves, molecules with permanent dipole moments would all line up completely on application of an arbitrarily small electric field, so that the dielectric constant would be infinite. Actually, the orienting tendency of the electric field is partly compensated by the thermal agitation, and in solids and some liquids it is hindered by close-range mutual interactions of the molecules.

We consider the effect of the thermal motion on molecules which are free to move. The potential energy of a molecule of permanent moment **p** in a field **E** is, as shown in Appendix G,

(6.23) $$V = -\mathbf{p} \cdot \mathbf{E} = -pE \cos \theta,$$

where θ is the angle between the moment and the field direction. The polarization will be

$$P = Np \,\overline{\cos \theta},$$

where N is the number of molecules per unit volume and $\overline{\cos \theta}$ is the average over a distribution in thermal equilibrium.

According to the Boltzmann distribution law the relative probability of finding a molecule in an element of solid angle $d\Omega$ is proportional to $e^{-V/kT}$, so that

(6.24) $$\overline{\cos \theta} = \int e^{-V/kT} \cos \theta \, d\Omega \Big/ \int e^{-V/kT} \, d\Omega.$$

The integration is to be carried out over all solid angles, so that

$$\overline{\cos \theta} = \int_0^\pi 2\pi \sin \theta \cos \theta \, e^{PE \cos \theta/kT} \, d\theta \Big/ \int_0^\pi 2\pi \sin \theta \, e^{PE \cos \theta/kT} \, d\theta.$$

We let $x = \cos \theta$ and $a = pE/kT$, so that

(6.25) $$\overline{\cos \theta} = \int_{-1}^1 e^{ax} x \, dx \Big/ \int_{-1}^1 e^{ax} \, dx = \frac{d}{da} \ln \int_{-1}^1 e^{ax} \, dx$$

$$= \operatorname{ctnh} a - \frac{1}{a} \equiv L(a).$$

This may be viewed as the definition of the Langevin function $L(a)$, which was first introduced in connection with the magnetic susceptibility of paramagnetic substances. The function is plotted in Fig. 6.7, and the saturation property for $pE \gg kT$ is clearly seen.

The most important situation experimentally is when $pE \ll kT$. Dipole moments are of the order of 10^{-18} esu, so that for $E = 3000$ v/cm = 10 statv/cm, $pE \approx 10^{-17}$ ergs, and at room temperature $kT \approx 4 \times 10^{-14}$ ergs. Thus $pE/kT \approx 1/4000$, and our condition is satisfied. In this limit of $a \ll 1$,

(6.26) $$L(a) \cong \frac{a}{3} = \frac{pE}{3kT},$$

so that the polarization is

(6.27) $$P = \overline{Np \cos \theta} = Np^2 E/3kT,$$

and the polarizability (per molecule) is

(6.28) $$\alpha(\text{dipolar}) = p^2/3kT.$$

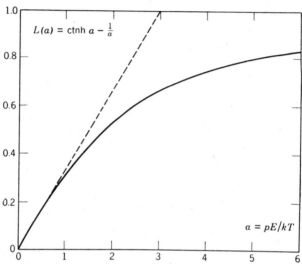

Fig. 6.7. Plot of Langevin function $L(a)$ as function of $a = pE/kT$; the initial slope is shown by the dashed line.

At room temperature this is of the order of $(10^{-18})^2/10^{-13} \approx 10^{-23}$ cm^3, of the same order of magnitude as the electronic polarizability. The total polarizability may then be written, if we let α_0 denote the deformation polarizability (that is, the sum of the electronic and ionic contributions),

(6.29) $$\alpha = \alpha_0 + p^2/3kT,$$

an expression which is known as the Langevin-Debye equation, and which has been of great importance in interpreting molecular structures. The dipole moment p is determined in practice by plotting either α or the molar polarizability (6.12) as a function of $1/T$; the slope is simply related to p. In this way one obtains, for example, the following dipole moments: $p(\text{HCl}) = 1.03 \times 10^{-18}$ esu; $p(\text{HBr})$

$= 0.79 \times 10^{-18}$ esu; $p(\text{HI}) = 0.38 \times 10^{-18}$ esu; $p(\text{H}_2\text{O}) = 1.87$ $\times 10^{-18}$ esu. The moments are often expressed in Debye units, where a Debye unit is 10^{-18} esu, of the order of the electronic charge times an interatomic distance.

THE POLARIZABILITY CATASTROPHE

In early work the dielectric constant was calculated from the polarizability by use of the Clausius-Mossotti equation (6.12), but although this equation holds fairly accurately for non-polar substances it fails completely in pure polar liquids or solids. To see this failure we neglect the deformation polarizability α_0 and substitute (6.28) in (6.10), obtaining

$$(6.30) \qquad \epsilon = 1 + \frac{4\pi N p^2}{3k(T - T_c)},$$

where we have set

$$(6.31) \qquad T_c = 4\pi N p^2 / 9k.$$

We may not conclude, however, from (6.30) that the dielectric constant would really become infinite at $T = T_c$, but rather that saturation effects should enter and the substance should become spontaneously polarized or "ferroelectric." Actually, ferroelectric behavior is at present unknown in dipolar substances, although it is found in crystals which are more or less ionic in binding. The latter cases are discussed in the following chapter, where it is shown that the mechanism leading to ferroelectricity is usually quite different from that contemplated here. Using the known dipole moment of 1.87 Debye units, we may estimate from (6.31) the critical temperature which would be expected for water. We have

$$T_c = \frac{(12.6)(6.03 \times 10^{23}/18)(1.87 \times 10^{-18})^2}{9(1.38 \times 10^{-16})} \cong 1200°\text{K},$$

in striking contradiction of the fact that neither water nor ice is ferroelectric.

Onsager[7] pointed out that the theoretical basis of the Lorentz field (6.7), from which the catastrophe stems, does not include the case of permanent dipole moments, as here the moments are not in general all parallel, as was assumed in the discussion of the terms E_2 and E_3 in

---

[7] L. Onsager, J. Am. Chem. Soc. **58**, 1486 (1936); for a discussion of various attempts to develop a theory valid for polar liquids and solids, see J. H. Van Vleck, Ann. N.Y. Acad. Sci. **40**, 293 (1940).

the general expression (6.1) for the local field. Onsager has developed
an approximate theory for polar substances. If the induced polarization is neglected, the Onsager model gives

(6.32) $\epsilon = \frac{1}{4}[1 + 3x + 3(1 + \frac{2}{3}x + x^2)^{\frac{1}{2}}],$ $x = 4\pi Np^2/3kT.$

It is easily seen that this expression, which is derived in Appendix D,
does not gives a critical point. Further discussion of the problem
would lead us too far afield. An exact solution has not yet been
obtained. Several interesting general theorems relating to the dielectric constant have been discovered by Fröhlich.[8] It may be noted
that internal interactions which favor one direction of mutual orientation of adjacent molecules over the opposite direction may also tend to
eliminate the critical point displayed by (6.30); the effect is known as
"hindered rotation."

DIPOLE ORIENTATION IN SOLIDS

As we expect molecules in gases and liquids to be fairly free to
rotate, the permanent dipole moments may be expected to make their
full orientational contribution to the polarizability, as calculated
above. In molecular solids the ability of a molecule to rotate depends
very much on its shape and on the strength of its interactions with the
environment. The closer the approach to sphericity and the lower the
dipole moment, the easier the molecule will rotate. Thus solid
methane (CH_4), which is a symmetrical non-polar molecule, rotates
quite freely in the solid state,[9] and the molecules in solid hydrogen
rotate so freely that the Raman lines of gaseous H_2 are found at nearly
the same frequencies in the solid phase.[10] In less symmetrical molecules such as HCl and H_2O, at high temperatures there appear to be
several stable orientations for each molecule in the solid, and a molecule will change direction from one stable orientation to another in a
time which is called the relaxation time.

The dielectric constant of solid H_2S as a function of temperature is
shown in Fig. 6.8. The principal feature of the curve is the sharp

[8] H. Fröhlich, Trans. Faraday Soc. 44, 238 (1948).

[9] For an account of the nuclear resonance experiments from which supporting
evidence is derived, see N. L. Alpert, Phys. Rev. 75, 398 (1949).

[10] L. Pauling, Phys. Rev. 36, 430 (1930). It is not possible to determine the
position of hydrogen atoms in a crystal by using x-rays, because of the low scattering power of hydrogen. Neutron diffraction is a possible tool, especially if
deuterium is substituted for hydrogen. The transition in ND_4Cl has been investigated by neutron diffraction by H. A. Levy and S. W. Peterson, Phys. Rev. 86,
766 (1952).

increase in the dielectric constant as the temperature is lowered and the sudden drop below 105°K which is thought to mark the transition to an ordered state in which the directions of the H_2S molecules are "frozen" in a regular array whose nature has not yet been determined. The behavior of the dielectric constant above the transition temperature is suggestive of free rotation, but we can show that a similar variation with temperature arises even when there are only a discrete number of allowed orientations for each dipole.

Suppose, for example, that a dipole of moment p has two allowed directions, (a) parallel and (b)·antiparallel to the applied field E.

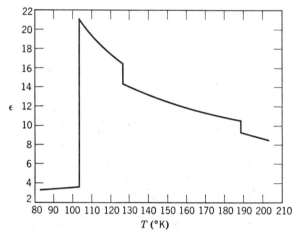

Fig. 6.8.   Dielectric constant temperature curve of solid hydrogen sulfide at 5 kc/sec. [After Smyth and Hitchcock, J. Am. Chem. Soc. **56**, 1084 (1934).]

The ratio of the occupation numbers of the two sites will be, using the Boltzmann distribution function,

$$N_A/N_B = e^{2Ep/kT},$$

so that the fractional excess oriented parallel to the field is, writing $x = Ep/kT$,

$$(6.33) \qquad \frac{N_A - N_B}{N_A + N_B} = \frac{e^x - e^{-x}}{e^x + e^{-x}} = \tanh x \cong x,$$

provided that $Ep/kT \ll 1$. If there are N molecules per unit volume, the polarization will be, in this approximation,

$$(6.34) \qquad P = Npx = Np^2E/kT,$$

which is, apart from a numerical factor, identical with the result (6.27) derived for freely rotating dipoles.

DIPOLE RELAXATION AND DIELECTRIC LOSSES

The principal part of the difference between the low frequency dielectric constant and the high frequency dielectric constant as measured by the square of the optical refractive index may be attributed to the damping out or relaxation of the orientational contribution to the

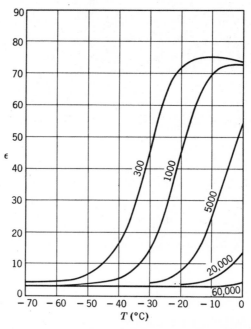

Fig. 6.9. Variation of the dielectric constant of ice with temperature and frequency, in cycles per second. [After Smyth and Hitchcock, J. Am. Chem. Soc. **54**, 4631 (1932).]

dielectric constant. In inhomogeneous dielectrics the Maxwell-Wagner interfacial polarization mechanism discussed in Problem 6.7 leads to another type of relaxation which we shall not go into here. The orientational relaxation frequencies vary over a wide range and may be strongly dependent on the temperature. In water at room temperature, relaxation occurs at about 3×10^{10} cps, corresponding to a wavelength for electromagnetic radiation of 1 cm. In ice at $-20°C$ we see from Fig. 6.9 that the relaxation frequency is of the order of 1 kc/sec.

DEBYE RELAXATION TIME

Debye[11] has given an elegant discussion of dielectric relaxation in polar liquids and in solutions of polar molecules in non-polar solvents; his central result is that the orientational part of the polarizability depends on frequency as

$$(6.35) \qquad \alpha = \frac{\alpha_0}{1 + i\omega\tau},$$

where τ is the relaxation time and α_0 is the static orientational polarizability. Debye has suggested further that in liquids the relaxation time is related to the viscosity η by the approximate relation

$$(6.36) \qquad \tau = 4\pi\eta a^3/kT,$$

where a is the radius of the molecule, which is supposed to be spherical. For water at room temperature we obtain $\tau \approx 10^{-11}$ sec, using $a \approx 10^{-8}$ cm and $\eta = 0.01$ poise, giving a relaxation frequency in approximate agreement with the experimental measurements on water. The form of the expression (6.36) for the relaxation time may be understood by making the plausible supposition that the relaxation frequency $\omega_0 = 1/\tau$ is marked by the approximate equality of the thermal rotational energy kT and the work done against the frictional torque in rotation through 1 radian. According to Stokes the frictional torque is $8\pi\eta a^3\omega$, whence the work done by the frictional torque acting for 1 radian is $(8\pi\eta a^3\omega/a)(a)(1) = 8\pi\eta a^3\omega$. Setting this equal to kT for $\omega = \omega_0$, we have

$$\tau \equiv 1/\omega_0 \cong 8\pi\eta a^3/kT,$$

in approximate agreement with (6.36). The idea underlying this discussion is that the thermal energy is insufficient to rotate the molecule against the viscous resistance when ω exceeds ω_0.

RELAXATION IN SOLIDS

Following Debye, we may make a crude model of dielectric relaxation in dipolar solids by supposing that each molecule of the solid carries a permanent electric moment p which can be oriented in two directions, parallel (1) or antiparallel (2) to the field E. We suppose that there are n_1, n_2 molecules in the two groups at a given time and that the probability that a particle in group 1 makes a transition to

---

[11] P. Debye, *Polar molecules*, Chemical Catalog Co., New York, 1929, Chap. V. For a discussion of the transition from resonance to relaxation-type behavior, see J. H. Van Vleck and V. F. Weisskopf, Revs. Modern Phys. **17**, 227 (1945).

group 2 in time δt is $w_{12}\delta t$, while the probability of the reverse process is $w_{21}\delta t$. Then

$$dn_1/dt = -w_{12}n_1 + w_{21}n_2;$$
(6.37)
$$dn_2/dt = w_{12}n_1 - w_{21}n_2.$$

For equilibrium $dn_1/dt = dn_2/dt = 0$; therefore we must have

(6.38) $n_1/n_2 = w_{21}/w_{12}.$

However, in equilibrium n_1 and n_2 must satisfy the Boltzmann distribution, so that

(6.39) $n_1 = A e^{pE/kT}; \qquad n_2 = A e^{-pE/kT},$

where A is a constant. According to (6.38) we must have

(6.40) $w_{12} = (1/2\tau)e^{-pE/kT}; \qquad w_{21} = (1/2\tau)e^{pE/kT}.$

Taking $pE \ll kT$, we have from (6.37)

$$2\tau(dn_1/dt) = -(n_1 - n_2) + (pE/kT)(n_1 + n_2);$$
(6.41)
$$2\tau(dn_2/dt) = (n_1 - n_2) - (pE/kT)(n_1 + n_2).$$

If E varies with angular frequency ω, the equations (6.41) have the solution

(6.42) $n_1 - n_2 = \dfrac{(n_1 + n_2)}{1 + i\omega\tau}\dfrac{pE}{kT},$

so that τ as introduced in (6.40) plays the part of a relaxation time. If there are N molecules per unit volume, the polarizability is given by

(6.43) $\alpha = \dfrac{P}{E} = \dfrac{p(n_1 - n_2)}{E} = \dfrac{Np^2}{kT} \cdot \dfrac{1}{1 + i\omega\tau},$

of essentially the same form as (6.35).

The relaxation times in solids are usually much longer than in liquids. This is somewhat parallel to the behavior of diffusion rates in liquids and solids. Breckenridge[12] has related the observed dielectric losses in alkali halide crystals to the presence of lattice defects in the crystals, with considerable success.

COMPLEX DIELECTRIC CONSTANTS AND THE LOSS ANGLE

In the presence of relaxation effects the dielectric constant may conveniently be taken as complex. For a polarizability

$$\alpha = \frac{\alpha_0}{1 + i\omega\tau}$$

[12] R. G. Breckenridge, in *Imperfections in nearly perfect crystals*, edited by Shockley, Hollomon, Maurer, and Seitz, John Wiley & Sons, New York, 1952.

the dielectric constant is, taking the local field as equal to the applied field,

$$\epsilon = \epsilon_1 - i\epsilon_2 = 1 + \frac{4\pi\alpha_0}{1 + i\omega\tau}$$

$$= 1 + \frac{4\pi\alpha_0}{1 + \omega^2\tau^2} - i\frac{4\pi\alpha_0\omega\tau}{1 + \omega^2\tau^2},$$

so that

$$(6.44) \quad \epsilon_1 = \mathfrak{R}(\epsilon) = 1 + \frac{4\pi\alpha_0}{1 + \omega^2\tau^2}; \qquad \epsilon_2 = -\mathfrak{g}(\epsilon) = \frac{4\pi\alpha_0\omega\tau}{1 + \omega^2\tau^2};$$

where $\mathfrak{R}$ and $\mathfrak{g}$ denote real and imaginary parts, respectively. The variation of ϵ_1 and ϵ_2 with frequency is shown in Fig. 6.10.

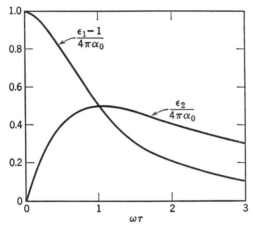

Fig. 6.10. Frequency dependence of real and imaginary parts of the dielectric constant $\epsilon = \epsilon_1 - i\epsilon_2$, for a relaxation mechanism.

The power dissipation per unit volume is given by

$$(6.45) \qquad\qquad \mathcal{P} = j_p E,$$

where j_p is a component of the current density which is in phase with E. We have

$$(6.46) \qquad j = \sigma E + \frac{1}{4\pi}\frac{\partial D}{\partial t} = \left(\sigma + \frac{i\omega\epsilon}{4\pi}\right) E,$$

which, for $\sigma = 0$ and $\epsilon = \epsilon_1 - i\epsilon_2$, becomes

$$j = \left(\frac{\epsilon_2\omega}{4\pi} + \frac{i\epsilon_1\omega}{4\pi}\right) E,$$

so that the power dissipation is

(6.47) $$\mathcal{P} = \frac{E^2}{4\pi}\omega\epsilon_2 = \frac{\epsilon_1 E^2}{4\pi}\omega \tan \delta,$$

where the *loss angle* or *power factor* is defined as

(6.48) $$\tan \delta = \epsilon_2/\epsilon_1.$$

The Q *factor* of a system is defined as

(6.49) $$Q = \frac{\text{maximum stored energy}}{\text{average energy loss per radian}},$$

which in the dielectric case reduces to

(6.50) $$Q = \frac{\epsilon_1 E_0{}^2/8\pi}{(\epsilon_1 \overline{E^2}/4\pi)\tan\delta} = \frac{1}{\tan\delta},$$

where we have used the fact that the average value of E^2 over a cycle is $E_0{}^2/2$, the amplitude being E_0.

Values of ϵ and $\tan\delta$ for several insulating materials at a frequency of 25,000 mc/sec are given in Table 6.3

TABLE 6.3. DIELECTRIC CONSTANT AND POWER FACTOR VALUES
AT 25,000 MC/SEC
[R. P. Penrose, Trans. Faraday Soc. **42A,** 108 (1946)]

Material	ϵ_1	$\tan \delta$
Polystyrene	2.55	0.0008
Perspex	2.65	0.012
Paraffin wax	2.26	0.0001
Lead glass	6.8	0.009
Ebonite	2.73	0.0038

PROBLEMS

6.1. Show that the expression (6.14) applied to the first Bohr orbit of the hydrogen atom gives $\alpha = a_H{}^3$, where a_H is the Bohr radius. Consider a semiclassical model of the ground state of the hydrogen atom in an electric field normal to the plane of the orbit, and show that for this model $\alpha = a_H{}^3$. *Note:* If the applied field is in the x direction, then the x component of the field of the nucleus at displaced position of the electron orbit must be equal to the applied field. The correct quantum-mechanical result is larger than this by the factor $\frac{9}{2}$.

6.2. In the local field problem the' cavity need not be chosen as spherical, but may be of any shape possessing at least cubic symmetry. We may for example take the cavity as a cube with a face normal parallel to the polarization. In this case the polarization charge density on the upper and lower faces of the cube is uniform and equal to $\pm P$, while the other faces do not carry any charge. Show that, for this cavity, $E_2 = 4\pi P/3$, just as for the spherical cavity.

6.3. For light of frequency ω show that the classical expression for the polarizability of a single electron bound to a nucleus is

$$\alpha = \frac{e^2/m}{\omega_0{}^2 - \omega^2},$$

where ω_0 is the resonance frequency of the electron.

6.4. Show that the polarizability of a conducting metallic sphere of radius a is $\alpha = a^3$; this result is most easily obtained·by noting that $E = 0$ inside the sphere and then using the depolarization factor. This result gives values of α of the order of magnitude of the observed polarizabilities of atoms. A lattice of N conducting spheres per unit volume has dielectric constant $\epsilon = 1 + 4\pi N a^3$, for $N a^3 \ll 1$; this result has been used in the construction of artificial dielectrics for use in microwave lenses [W. E. Kock, Bell System Tech. J. **27**, 58 (1948)].

6.5. Show that the dielectric constant at incident frequency ω of a medium containing N free electrons per unit volume is

$$\epsilon = 1 - (4\pi N e^2/m\omega^2).$$

The presence of the mass in the denominator suggests that we may neglect the contribution of the positive ions present. We suppose, following C. G. Darwin [Proc. Roy. Soc. (London) **A146**, 17 (1934); **A151**, 512 (1935)], that the local field in this case is equal to the applied field E_0. The index of refraction for x-rays is commonly slightly less than unity; e.g., for calcite at 1.54 A, $n - 1 = -8.8 \times 10^{-6}$.

6.6. Using the result of Problem 6.5 discuss the effect of negative values of ϵ on the propagation of electromagnetic waves. We define the cut-off frequency as that for which $\epsilon = 0$; calculate the value of N for a cut-off frequency of 30 mc/sec, and show that the cut-off frequency for metallic sodium would be 1.4×10^{15} cps if there is one free electron present for each sodium atom, in close agreement with the experimental value [R. W. Wood, Phys. Rev. **44**, 353 (1933)].

6.7. Show that a parallel-plate condenser made up of two parallel layers of material, one layer with dielectric constant ϵ, zero conductivity, and thickness d, and the other layer with $\epsilon = 0$ for convenience, finite conductivity σ, and thickness qd, behaves as if the space between the condenser plates were filled with a homogeneous dielectric with dielectric constant

$$\epsilon^* = \frac{\epsilon(1 + q)}{1 + (i\epsilon\omega q/4\pi\sigma)},$$

where ω is ·the angular frequency [K. W. Wagner, Arch. Elecktrotech. **2**, 371 (1914)]. Values of ϵ as high as 10^4 or 10^5, caused largely by the Maxwell-Wagner mechanism, are sometimes found, but the high values are always accompanied by large losses. An analysis of the dielectric properties of a nickel zinc ferrite is given by C. G. Koops, Phys. Rev. **83**, 121 (1951).

REFERENCES

R. Becker, *Theorie der Elektrizität*, Teubner, Leipzig and Berlin, 6th ed., Vol. II, 1933.

C. J. F. Böttcher, *Theory of electric polarisation*, Elsevier, Amsterdam, 1952.

P. Debye, *Polar molecules*, Chemical Catalog Co., New York, 1929.

Dielectrics conference, Ann. N.Y. Acad. Sci. **40**, 289–482 (1940).

Dielectrics discussion, Trans. Faraday Soc. **42A** (1946).

H. Fröhlich, *Theory of dielectrics: dielectric constant and dielectric loss*, Clarendon Press, Oxford, 1949.

R. J. W. Le Fèvre, *Dipole moments*, Methuen and Co., London, 2nd ed., 1948.

E. J. Murphy and S. O. Morgan, "Dielectric properties of insulating materials," Bell System Tech. J. **16**, 493 (1937); **17**, 640 (1938); **18**, 502 (1939).

L. Rosenfeld, *Theory of electrons*, Interscience Publishers, New York, 1951.

C. P. Smyth, *Dielectric constant and molecular structure*, Chemical Catalog Co., New York, 1931.

J. H. Van Vleck, *Theory of electric and magnetic susceptibilities*, Clarendon Press, Oxford, 1932.

7

Ferroelectric Crystals

A ferroelectric crystal is defined as a crystal which exhibits a spontaneous electric dipole moment; in other words, a crystal for which even in the absence of an applied electric field the center of positive charge does not coincide with the center of negative charge. It is a necessary, but not sufficient, condition for ferroelectricity that the crystal lack a center of symmetry. All ferroelectrics will be piezoelectric, but not all piezoelectrics will be ferroelectric (e.g., quartz). The occurrence of ferroelectricity is generally interpreted to be the result of a polarization catastrophe as treated in the preceding chapter; we discuss this at greater length below.

After a ferroelectric crystal is polarized in a given direction, the action of the polarization outside the crystal is gradually neutralized by the collection on the crystal surface of free charges from the atmosphere and by conduction within the crystal. In a number of substances the polarization appears to have a very high coercive force— the direction of the spontaneous polarization may not be changed by an electric field of the maximum intensity which it is possible to apply without causing electrical breakdown of the crystal. We are often able to observe the spontaneous moment in these substances only when they are heated, as raising the temperature changes the value of the polarization. Thus crystals, such as tourmaline, which only develop an observable spontaneous electric moment on heating are called *pyroelectric*, while crystals with a lower coercive force, such that the direction of the spontaneous moment can be altered by an electric field, are called *ferroelectric* and often have very high dielectric constants.

ELECTRETS

There is another class of substances known as *electrets*, discovered by Eguchi in 1925, which may display "permanent" electric moments. Electrets are produced by the solidification of mixtures of certain organic waxes in a strong electric field. Some of the wax molecules carry permanent dipole moments; these are oriented by the electric field, and frozen in their orientation by the solidification. The moments produced in this way may persist for several years, yet it is generally believed that the polarized state of an electret is only metastable, and that the stable state would be unpolarized. We shall not consider electrets here; for a review of their properties the reader is referred to a paper by Gutmann.[1]

CLASSIFICATION OF FERROELECTRIC CRYSTALS

We list in Table 7.1 some of the crystals which are commonly considered ferroelectric, along with the transition (Curie) temperature T_c at which the crystal changes from the low temperature polarized state to the high temperature unpolarized state. Rochelle salt has both an upper and a lower Curie point, between which the crystal is ferroelectric. The maximum value of the spontaneous polarization P_s is listed where known.

The crystals considered in the table may be classified into several quite natural groups. First there is Rochelle salt and the associated isomorphous salts. Rochelle salt is a quite complicated crystal, and little progress has been made toward understanding its behavior on a microscopic basis, although Mueller[2] and others have formulated a phenomenological theory which correlates a number of experimental facts. It seems possible that the ferroelectric behavior of Rochelle salt is connected intimately with the action of the molecules of water of hydration in the crystal. This is suggested by the observation that the substitution of D_2O for H_2O changes the range in which the crystal is ferroelectric from 41.7°C for the ordinary Rochelle salt to 58.5°C for the deuterated salt,[3] which is quite a large effect. It may be noted, however, that the observed spontaneous polarization 800 esu is considerably less than the polarization which would result from the parallel orientation of all the water molecules; there are 1.52×10^{22} of these per cubic centimeter, and the moment per molecule is 1.85×10^{-18} esu (in the vapor), corresponding to a polarization of 28,000 esu, while the observed spontaneous polarization is only 800 esu.

The second group of ferroelectric crystals consists of crystals with "hydrogen bonds" in which the motion of the protons is specifically connected with the ferroelectric properties; the group comprises potassium dihydrogen phosphate (KH_2PO_4) and the isomorphous

[1] F. Gutmann, Revs. Modern Phys. 20, 457 (1948).

[2] H. Mueller, Phys. Rev. 57, 829 (1940); 58, 565 (1940).

[3] Holden, Kohman, Mason, and Morgan, Phys. Rev. 56, 378 (1939); J. Hablützel, Helv. Phys. Acta. 12, 489 (1939).

TABLE 7.1. DATA ON CRYSTALS REPORTED TO BE FERROELECTRIC

Crystal	Structure	T_c (°K)	P_s (esu)	Reference
$NaK(C_4H_4O_6)\cdot 4H_2O$ (Rochelle salt)	complex	297 (upper) 255 (lower)	800	a
$NaK(C_4H_2D_2O_6)\cdot 4D_2O$	complex	308 (upper) 249 (lower)		b
$LiNH_4(C_4H_4O_6)\cdot H_2O$	complex	106	630	c
KH_2PO_4	complex	123	16,000	d
RbH_2PO_4	complex	147		e
KH_2AsO_4	complex	96.5		f
$BaTiO_3$	perovskite	391	48,000	g
$KTaO_3$	perovskite			h
$NaTaO_3$	perovskite			h
$KNbO_3$	perovskite	708		h
$NaNbO_3$	perovskite	913		h
$LiTaO_3$	ilmenite		70,000(425°C)	i
$LiNbO_3$	ilmenite			i
WO_3	modified perovskite	220 (?)		j

[a] Discovered by J. Valasek, Phys. Rev. **17**, 475 (1921); for summary of properties see H. Mueller, Ann. N.Y. Acad. Sci. **40**, 321 (1940); the isomorphous Ta-Na and Rb-Na salts are also ferroelectric.

[b] Holden, Kohman, Mason, and Morgan, Phys. Rev. **56**, 378 (1939); A. N. Holden and W. P. Mason, Phys. Rev. **57**, 54 (1940).

[c] W. J. Merz, Phys. Rev. **82**, 562 (1951); B. T. Matthias and J. K. Hulm, Phys. Rev. **82**, 108 (1951).

[d] G. Busch and P. Scherrer, Naturwiss. **23**, 737 (1935); B. Zwicker and P. Scherrer, Helv. Phys. Acta **17**, 346 (1944); W. Bantle, Helv. Phys. Acta **15**, 373 (1942).

[e] Bärtschi, Matthias, Merz, and Scherrer, Helv. Phys. Acta **18**, 240 (1945).

[f] G. Busch and E. Ganz, Helv. Phys. Acta **15**, 501 (1942).

[g] Discovered independently in various countries during World War II; for general discussions of the properties see B. Wul, J. Phys. (U.S.S.R.) **10**, 95 (1946), and A. von Hippel, Revs. Modern Phys. **22**, 221 (1950).

[h] B. T. Matthias, Phys. Rev. **75**, 1771 (1949); E. A. Wood, Acta Cryst. **4**, 353 (1951); P. Vousden, Acta Cryst. **4**, 68 (1951).

[i] B. T Matthias and J. P. Remeika, Phys. Rev. **76**, 1886 (1949).

[j] B. T. Matthias, Phys. Rev. **76**, 430 (1949); B. T. Matthias and E. A. Wood, Phys. Rev. **84**, 1255 (1951).

For further crystals see G. A. Smolenski and N. V. Kozhevnikova, Doklady Akad. Nauk S.S.S.R. **76**, 519 (1951).

salts. The behavior of the deuterated crystal strongly suggests that the hydrogen atoms are of central importance in this case:

	KH_2PO_4	KD_2PO_4
Curie temperature	123°K	213°K
Saturation polarization	16,000 esu	27,000 esu

The substitution of deuterons for protons nearly doubles both T_c and P_s, although the fractional change in the molecular weight of the compound is less than 2%. This is an extraordinarily large isotope effect, which has been discussed by Pirenne[4] in terms of the motion of the protons and deuterons in a square-well potential.

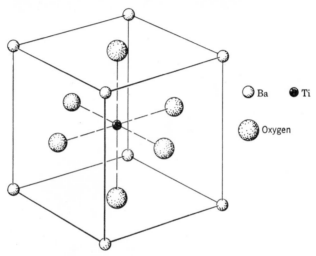

Fig. 7.1. The perovskite crystal structure of barium titanate. The structure is cubic, with Ba^{2+} ions at the cube corners, O^{2-} ions at the face centers, and a Ti^{4+} ion at the body center. Below the Curie temperature the structure is slightly deformed with respect to that described here. The prototype crystal is calcium titanate (perovskite).

The third group of ferroelectrics consists of ionic crystals with crystal structures closely related to the perovskite and ilmenite structures. The perovskite structure is the simplest crystal structure (Fig. 7.1) to exhibit ferroelectricity, and we shall devote the rest of this chapter primarily to barium titanate, which has this structure and is the crystal in the third group about which most experimental and theoretical information is available. The ilmenite structure, named

[4] J. Pirenne, Physica **15**, 1019 (1949). A detailed theory of the transition of potassium dihydrogen phosphate in terms of hydrogen bonds is given by J. C. Slater, J. Chem. Phys. **9**, 16 (1941); see also S. Yomosa and T. Nagamiya, Prog. Theor. Phys. **4**, 263 (1949); T. Nagamiya, Prog. Theor. Phys. **7**, 275 (1952).

from the mineral $FeTiO_3$, is quite complicated and we shall not discuss it here. The name perovskite comes from the mineral $CaTiO_3$.

THEORY OF BARIUM TITANATE

We consider first the general order of magnitude of the ferroelectric effects in barium titanate: It is observed that barium titanate has at room temperature a saturation polarization of 48,000 esu. As the volume of a unit cube is $(4 \times 10^{-8})^3$ cc, the dipole moment per unit cube is 3×10^{-18} esu. If, for example, all the polarization were

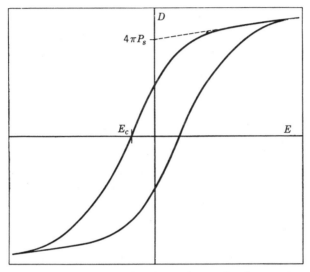

Fig. 7.2. Hysteresis loop in ferroelectric specimen, showing spontaneous polarization P_s and coercive field E_c. In barium titanate the value of $4\pi P_s$ may be of the order of 2×10^8 v/cm, and E_c of the order of 10^3 v/cm.

caused by a displacement of the central Ti^{4+} ion, we should require a displacement of $3 \times 10^{-18}/4(4.8 \times 10^{-10}) \approx 0.15 \times 10^{-8}$ cm, which is a reasonable magnitude.

We suppose that the Curie point is determined approximately by the interaction energy of a dipole with the local internal electric field caused by the polarization itself. The interaction energy is $-\frac{1}{2}(\mathbf{p} \cdot \mathbf{E})$; as E will be of the order of $-P_s$, the interaction energy is of the order of $\frac{1}{2}(3 \times 10^{-18})(5 \times 10^4) = 8 \times 10^{-14}$ ergs. We obtain the approximate transition temperature by setting the interaction energy equal to kT_c, giving $T_c \approx (8 \times 10^{-14})/(1.4 \times 10^{-16}) \approx 600°K$, which is of the order of magnitude of the observed $391°K$.

The most striking indication of ferroelectricity in barium titanate is provided by the hysteresis loops of the form shown in Fig. 7.2 as observed at temperatures below the transition temperature, 118°C; at temperatures above the transition the loop reduces to a straight line. The spontaneous polarization as a function of temperature is shown in Fig. 7.3. It is found by x-ray methods that the crystal structure becomes slightly deformed in the direction of the spontaneous polarization, and in the region between 0°C and 118°C the polarization is parallel to a side of the unit cube of the crystal structure, so that the crystal is elongated in this direction, which is called the c axis, and shortened in the directions of the a axes at right angles to the

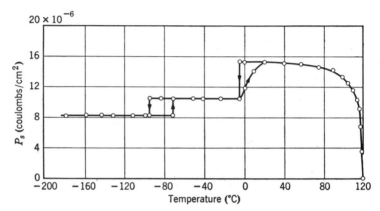

Fig. 7.3. Spontaneous polarization of barium titanate as a function of temperature. The discontinuities near 0°C and −80°C are caused by small changes in the crystal structure. The changes of the polarization measured along a cube edge at these two transition points is consistent with the assumption that the direction of spontaneous polarization, which is parallel to a cube edge above 0°C, becomes parallel to a face diagonal below 0°C and parallel to a body diagonal below −80°C, as the ratios of the P_s at the transition temperatures are approximately $1:1/2^{1/2}:1/3^{1/2}$. [After W. J. Merz, Phys. Rev. **76**, 1221 (1949).]

direction of the polarization (Fig. 7.4). The dielectric constant is usually very much larger when measured perpendicular to the c axis than when measured parallel to it (Fig. 7.5).

THE POLARIZATION CATASTROPHE IN FERROELECTRICS

The occurrence of ferroelectricty in barium titanate is believed to be the result of a polarization catastrophe in which the local electric fields arising from the polarization itself increase faster than the elastic restoring forces on the ions in the crystal, thereby leading ultimately to an asymmetrical shift in ionic positions; the shift is limited to a finite displacement by the onset of anharmonic restoring forces. The occurrence of ferroelectricity in an appreciable number of crystals

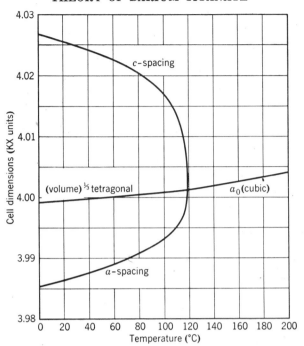

Fig. 7.4. Cell dimensions of barium titanate as a function of temperature. [After H. D. Megaw, Proc. Roy. Soc. (London) **A189,** 261 (1947).]

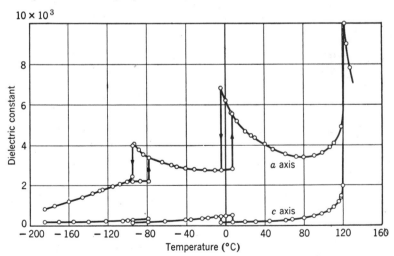

Fig. 7.5. Initial dielectric constants of barium titanate, parallel (c axis) and perpendicular (a axis) to the direction of the spontaneous polarization at room temperature. [After W. J. Merz, Phys. Rev. **76,** 1221 (1949); it is not known why ϵ_c and ϵ_a do not coincide below $-80°C$, as they should by symmetry.]

with the perovskite structure suggests that this structure is in some way favorably disposed to the production of a polarizability catastrophe; this suggestion is supported by the fact that the hexagonal modification of barium titanate is not ferroelectric, while the cubic (perovskite) form is ferroelectric. Calculations by Slater[5] and others have made clear the physical reason for the favored position of the perovskite structure. We give first the simple form of the catastrophe theory, supposing that the Lorentz factors are all $4\pi/3$.

We may rewrite (6.10) in the form

$$(7.1) \qquad \epsilon = \frac{1 + \dfrac{8\pi}{3} \, \Sigma N_i \alpha_i}{1 - \dfrac{4\pi}{3} \, \Sigma N_i \alpha_i},$$

where α_i is the polarizability of an ion of type i, and N_i the number of ions i per unit volume, noting that the numerical factors multiplying $\Sigma N_i \alpha_i$ are the consequence of the use of the Lorentz local field $E + (4\pi/3)P$. It is seen that the dielectric constant becomes infinite, corresponding to a finite polarization for zero applied field, when $\Sigma N_i \alpha_i = (4\pi/3)^{-1}$, and for this reason the polarization catastrophe is commonly known as the "$4\pi/3$ catastrophe." Onsager's objection to the Lorentz field, cited in the last chapter, applies only to the fields produced by permanent dipoles and not to the induced moments with which we are now concerned.

We note that the value of ϵ is sensitive to small departures of $\Sigma N_i \alpha_i$ from the critical value $3/4\pi$; if we write

$$(7.2) \qquad (4\pi/3)\Sigma N_i \alpha_i = 1 - s,$$

where $s \ll 1$, we have

$$(7.3) \qquad \epsilon \cong 3/s.$$

If we suppose that near the critical temperature the value of s varies with temperature in a linear fashion,

$$(7.4) \qquad s \cong \beta(T - T_c),$$

where β is a constant, we have above the transition temperature a Curie-Weiss law for the dielectric constant:

$$(7.5) \qquad \epsilon \cong \frac{3/\beta}{T - T_c},$$

[5] J. C. Slater, Phys. Rev. **78**, 748 (1950).

which is of the form of the observed temperature variation, as shown in Fig. (7.6):

$$(7.6) \qquad \epsilon \approx \frac{10^5}{T - T_c}.$$

If the ferroelectric state were the result of the dipolar interactions of freely rotating molecules bearing permanent moments, we should

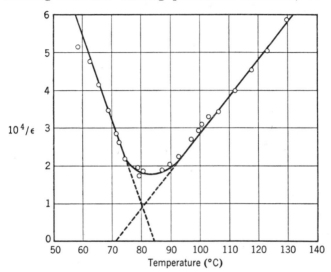

Fig. 7.6. Plot of reciprocal of the dielectric constant of barium titanate vs. temperature. [After B. Wul, J. Phys. (U.S.S.R.) **10**, 95 (1946); it is not known why Wul's Curie point is 40° below that reported by other workers.]

have, from (6.30),

$$(7.7) \qquad \epsilon \approx \frac{3T_c}{T - T_c};$$

the numerator $3T_c \approx 1200°\text{K}$ is two orders of magnitude smaller than the observed value of 10^5 in expression (7.6); this failure is a fairly strong indication, entirely apart from the x-ray evidence, that we are not concerned in barium titanate with the orientation of molecules bearing permanent dipole moments.

To account for the large value of the numerator observed in (7.6) we note that

$$(7.8) \qquad \beta = ds/dT = (4\pi/3)\Sigma[N_i(d\alpha_i/dT) + (dN_i/dT)\alpha_i];$$

now as N_i is the number of ions i per unit volume, the temperature coefficient $N_i^{-1}(dN_i/dT)$ will be of the order of magnitude of the volume expansion coefficient, which is $\approx 10^{-5}$ in barium titanate; the temperature coefficient of polarizability in ionic crystals is known to be of this same order of magnitude, so that β may reasonably be of the order of 10^{-5} as suggested by the observed variation of ϵ. This argument is probably over simplified.

The refractive index of barium titanate is 2.4; we estimate the electronic contribution to the polarizabilities from the relation

$$(7.9) \qquad \frac{n^2 - 1}{n^2 + 2} = \frac{4\pi}{3} \sum N_i \alpha_i \text{ (electronic)},$$

according to (6.11). Using Slater's values $\alpha(\text{Ba}) = 1.95 \times 10^{-24}$ cc; $\alpha(\text{O}) = 2.4 \times 10^{-24}$ cc; $\alpha(\text{Ti}) = 0.19 \times 10^{-24}$ cc, we find that $(4\pi/3) \sum N_i \alpha_i \text{ (electronic)} = 0.61$, so that a contribution of $1 - 0.61 = 0.39$ would be required from the ionic polarizabilities in order to explain the occurrence of a ferroelectric state. We saw earlier that, even if all the spontaneous polarization arose from the ionic displacement of the titanium ion in the center of each cube, a displacement of 0.15 $\times 10^{-8}$ cm would be required. There is nothing inherently unreasonable about an assumption that 39% of the total polarizability is ionic except that this is something of an *ad hoc* explanation; it does not give us any indication of why the perovskite structure is prone to ferroelectricity, nor does it suggest why crystals such as rutile (TiO_2) with an even higher refractive index [$n = 2.8$; $(4\pi/3) \sum N_i \alpha_i \text{(electronic)} = 0.70$] are not ferroelectric. We shall see in the following section that the actual local fields in the perovskite structure act to enhance the effect of the polarizability of the titanium ion by a factor of the order of 5 with respect to the situation when $E + 4\pi P/3$ is the local field.

LOCAL FIELD IN THE PEROVSKITE STRUCTURE

The Lorentz local field $E + 4\pi P/3$ holds for a crystal when all atoms have environments with cubic symmetry. In barium titanate the Ba and Ti ions see a cubic environment, but the O ions do not; there are, for example, only two nearest neighbor Ti ions adjacent to each O ion, so that the environment of the O ions cannot be cubic.. It is necessary in this circumstance to derive a generalized form of the Lorentz formula; this has been done by several authors,[5,6] and Slater[5] has actually carried out the calculations for barium titanate.

How we should go about obtaining an expression for the local field in barium titanate is quite obvious. We set up an expression for the

[6] G. J. Skanavi, Doklady Akad. Nauk S.S.S.R. **59**, 231 (1948); J. H. van Santen and W. Opechowski, Physica **14**, 545 (1948).

local field at each lattice point as the sum of the applied field and the polarization of the several types of ions. We take the applied field parallel to a particular cube side, which we call the z direction; there are then four types of ions to be considered: Ba, Ti, O', O'', where the O' ions are on lines parallel to the z direction and passing through the Ti ions; the remaining oxygen ions are the O'' ions. We have four simultaneous equations for the polarizations:

$$E(\text{Ba}) = P(\text{Ba})/N(\text{Ba})\alpha(\text{Ba})$$
$$= E_0 + q_{11}P(\text{Ba}) + q_{12}P(\text{Ti}) + q_{13}P(\text{O}') + q_{14}P(\text{O}'');$$

$$E(\text{Ti}) = P(\text{Ti})/N(\text{Ti})\alpha(\text{Ti})$$

(7.10)
$$= E_0 + q_{21}P(\text{Ba}) + q_{22}(\text{Ti}) + q_{23}P(\text{O}') + q_{24}P(\text{O}'');$$

$$E(\text{O}') = P(\text{O}')/N(\text{O}')\alpha(\text{O}')$$
$$= E_0 + q_{31}P(\text{Ba}) + q_{32}P(\text{Ti}) + q_{33}P(\text{O}') + q_{34}P(\text{O}'');$$

$$E(\text{O}'') = P(\text{O}'')/N(\text{O}'')\alpha(\text{O}'')$$
$$= E_0 + q_{41}P(\text{Ba}) + q_{42}P(\text{Ti}) + q_{43}P(\text{O}') + q_{44}P(\text{O}'').$$

The coefficient of the P's are lattice sums for dipole arrays and may be calculated by the methods given by Kornfeld and others,[7] which we discuss at the end of Appendix B. The q's have the following values:

$$q_{11} = q_{22} = q_{21} = q_{12} = q_{33} = 4\pi/3;$$

$$q_{13} = q_{31} = (4\pi/3) - 8.668;$$

$$q_{34} = q_{43} = q_{14} = q_{41} = (4\pi/3) + 4.334$$

$$q_{23} = q_{32} = (4\pi/3) + 30.080$$

$$q_{24} = q_{42} = (4\pi/3) - 15.040$$

$$q_{44} = (4\pi/3) - 4.334$$

It should particularly be noted that the interaction between the Ti and O' ions is especially strong, being $(4\pi/3) + 30.080$, which is approximately 8.2 times the ordinary value, $4\pi/3$. It is this factor which is responsible for the great enhancement of the field at the central ion of the perovskite structure.[8]

[7] H. Kornfeld, Z. Physik **22**, 27 (1924); L. W. McKeehan, Phys. Rev. **43**, 913 (1933); **72**, 78 (1947); J. M. Luttinger and L. Tisza, Phys. Rev. **70**, 954 (1946); **72**, 257 (1947).

[8] The Ba ions play a very minor role; in fact, in WO₃, which near room temperature is ferroelectric, the lattice sites corresponding to the sites occupied by Ba in barium titanate are left vacant. In the hexagonal modification of barium titanate the Ti-O lines are distorted, thereby reducing the interaction significantly. [J. R. Tessman, Phys. Rev. **83**, 677 (1951).]

The ferroelectric catastrophe occurs when the determinant of the coefficients of the P's in (7.10) vanishes, as this is the condition that the P's have nontrivial solutions for $E = 0$. We substitute the appropriate polarizabilities as used by Slater:

$$\alpha(\text{Ba}) = 1.95 \times 10^{-24} \text{ cc}$$

$$\alpha(\text{O}') \doteq \alpha(\text{O}'') = 2.4 \times 10^{-24} \text{ cc}$$

$$\alpha(\text{Ti}) = 0.19 \times 10^{-24} + \alpha_i(\text{Ti});$$

here we suppose that the polarizabilities are all electronic except for an ionic contribution $\alpha_i(\text{Ti})$ from the titanium ions. We then determine the value of $\alpha_i(\text{Ti})$ which makes the determinant vanish, and find

$$\alpha_i(\text{Ti}) = 0.95 \times 10^{-24} \text{ cc},$$

and $\qquad (4\pi/3)N(\text{Ti})\alpha_i(\text{Ti}) = 0.062,$

as compared with 0.39 on the elementary theory, the magnification of about 6 then being caused by the nature of the perovskite lattice. In particular the existence of lines of oxygen and titanium ions in the lattice is favorable for the high magnification, as exhibited explicitly in Problem 7.3.

It is not always valid to superpose ionic and electronic polarizabilities in quite the way we have done here, as Cohen[9] has emphasized.

DIELECTRIC CONSTANTS NEAR THE CURIE POINT

If there are non-linear interactions in the crystal (and there must be if the spontaneous polarization is to be contained at a finite value), we may write formally the local field as a power series in the polarization, omitting terms in even powers of P because we wish to consider the two ends of the crystal equivalent:

$$E_{\text{loc}} = g_1 P + g_2 P^3 + g_3 P^5 + \cdots,$$

where the g's may depend on temperature, and where g_1 is simply $(\Sigma N_i \alpha_i)^{-1}$. The local field may also be written

$$E_{\text{loc}} = E + fP,$$

so that, to terms in P^5,

(7.11) $\qquad E = (g_1 - f)P + g_2 P^3 + g_3 P^5.$

[9] M. H. Cohen, Phys. Rev. **84**, 368 (1951).

Above the Curie point in sufficiently weak applied fields the polarization will be small, and we may neglect the terms in P^3 and P^5, so that the susceptibility is

$$(7.12) \qquad \chi(+) = \frac{dP}{dE} = \frac{1}{g_1 - f},$$

where the $+$ sign denotes that the equation applies above the Curie point.

Below the Curie point the spontaneous polarization in zero field (P_s) is given by the stable solution of (7.11) with E set equal to zero:

$$(g_1 - f)P_s + g_2 P_s{}^3 + g_3 P_s{}^5 = 0.$$

There are two cases of particular interest:

Case A. $(g_1 - f)$ negative; g_2 positive; g_3 may be neglected. Then

$$(7.13) \qquad P_s{}^2 = (f - g_1)/g_2.$$

In this case there is a spontaneous polarization as long as $f > g_1$. For a small applied field ΔE, the additional polarization ΔP in the ferroelectric state is given by

$$\Delta E = (g_1 - f)\,\Delta P + 3g_2 P_s{}^2\,\Delta P$$

$$= 2(f - g_1)\,\Delta P,$$

so that the susceptibility below the Curie point is

$$(7.14) \qquad \chi(-) = \frac{1}{2(f - g_1)}.$$

If we make the quite plausible assumption, similar to (7.4), that the variation of $g_1 - f$ is linear about the Curie point:

$$g_1 - f = \beta(T - T_c),$$

then

$$\chi(+) = \frac{1}{\beta(T - T_c)};$$

$$(7.15) \qquad \chi(-) = -\frac{1}{2\beta(T - T_c)};$$

therefore the ratio of $d(1/\chi)/dT$ above and below the Curie point is $1 : -2$, in generally fair agreement with the experimental results in Fig. 7.6.

Case B. $(g_1 - f)$ positive; g_2 negative; g_3 positive.
The spontaneous polarization is given by a root of

$$(g_1 - f) + g_2 P_s{}^2 + g_3 P_s{}^4 = 0,$$

but to obtain the polarization at the transition we must consider the internal potential energy associated with the polarization. As illustrated in Fig. 7.7, the critical temperature in case B is attained when the depth of the potential energy minima corresponding to a finite polarization is equal to the depth at the central point for which the polarization is zero. We should strictly consider the thermodynamic free energy (Appendix T) rather than simply the internal energy in a

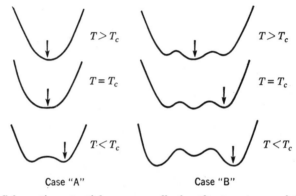

Case "A"   Case "B"

Fig. 7.7. Schematic potential energy wells for the two types of ferroelectric transitions, showing the variation of well shape with temperature.

discussion of this kind, but for elementary textbook purposes the loss in rigor in this particular problem is perhaps more than compensated by the gain in physical insight by speaking in terms of the internal energy. The internal energy associated with the polarization is given according to (G.5) by

$$(7.16) \qquad U_p = \int_0^P E \, dP = \tfrac{1}{2}(g_1 - f)P^2 + \tfrac{1}{4}g_2 P^4 + \tfrac{1}{6}g_3 P^6,$$

so that the Curie point is given by $U_p = 0$, or

$$(g_1 - f) + \tfrac{1}{2}g_2 P_s{}^2(T_c) + \tfrac{1}{3}g_3 P_s{}^4(T_c) = 0;$$

here also

$$(g_1 - f) + g_2 P_s{}^2(T_c) + g_3 P_s{}^4(T_c) = 0,$$

so that

$$P_s{}^2(T_c) = -\frac{3g_2}{4g_3};$$

$$P_s{}^4(T_c) = \frac{3(g_1 - f)}{g_3}.$$

Proceeding in the usual manner, we find for the susceptibility above the Curie point

(7.17)
$$\chi(+) = \frac{1}{g_1 - f},$$

as for case A, with the difference that now $f - g_1$ does not vanish at the Curie point. At the Curie point, but on the low temperature side, we find

(7.18)
$$\chi_{T_c}(-) = \frac{1}{4(g_1 - f)},$$

so that at the Curie point $\chi(+)/\chi(-) = 4$ on this model. In comparisons with experimental results it must be remembered that the

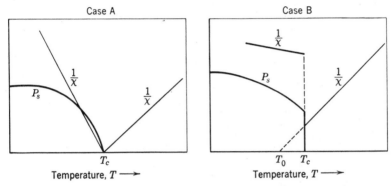

Fig. 7.8. Schematic variation of spontaneous polarization and reciprocal susceptibility for first order (case B) and second order (case A) transitions. The transition in barium titanate is first order, but is close to being second order.

observed susceptibility in polydomain crystals below the Curie point will usually include a contribution from domain movements, which are discussed later.

It is plausible to suppose here that we may express the temperature variation of $f - g_1$ approximately in the form

$$f - g_1 = \beta(T - T_0),$$

where T_0 is a parameter to be determined by experiment, but satisfying $T_0 < T_c$. Then

(7.19)
$$\chi(+) = \frac{1}{\beta(T - T_0)} \qquad (T > T_c).$$

The temperature dependences of P_s and $1/\chi$ for the two cases are shown in Fig. 7.8. We note here that it can be shown by standard thermodynamic methods that a case A transition does not have a latent heat of transition, but is rather accompanied by a discontinuity in the heat capacity; such a transition is known in thermodynamics as a second order transition; a case B transition is accompanied by a latent heat and is a first order transition. It is likely that ferroelectric transitions in perovskites are first order, but barium titanate probably comes very close to being second order in that T_0 is very close to T_c.

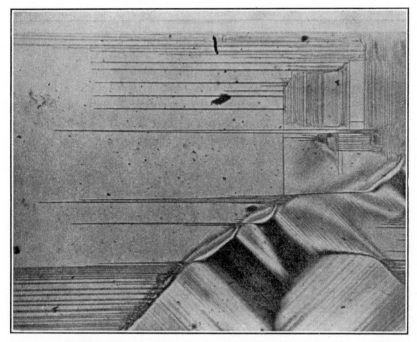

Fig. 7.9.   Wedge-shaped laminar domains in barium titanate single crystal.
(After Forsbergh.)

The transitions in Rochelle salt and in KH_2PO_4 are probably second order.

FERROELECTRIC DOMAINS

We have seen that a crystal of barium titanate has cubic symmetry above the Curie point and tetragonal symmetry below the Curie point.[10]   On cooling a crystal through the Curie point, it is usually found that the entire crystal does not have the same tetragonal axis, but that in one part of the crystal one of the formerly cubic axes has become the tetragonal axis, while in some other region in the crystal

[10] Below 5°C the symmetry changes from tetragonal to orthorhombic, and then near −70°C to trigonal, the crystal remaining ferroelectric.

another of the cubic axes has become the tetragonal axis. This means that different regions will have different directions of spontaneous polarization. A region within which the spontaneous polarization is in the same direction is called a *domain*. Crystals have been grown which consist entirely of a single domain, and this indeed is expected theoretically to be the stable configuration for a plate-like crystal between condenser plates which are connected. But crystals appear more commonly to grow with inhomogeneous concentrations of impurities leading to mechanical strains in the lattice which may often be reduced by the establishment of a domain structure.

Ferroelectric domains in barium titanate may be observed by optical means, as the crystals are transparent and exhibit different

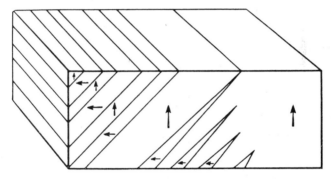

Fig. 7.10.   Directions of spontaneous polarization in polydomain barium titanate.

indices of refraction parallel and perpendicular to the tetragonal axis of a domain. In barium titanate the difference of the refractive indices at room temperature is $n_c - n_a = -0.055$. A detailed optical examination of various types of domain structures has been carried out by Forsbergh,[11] and we reproduce Fig. 7.9 from his paper. Schematic domain arrangements are shown in Fig. 7.10.

It is found that the domain structure can often be moved about by an applied electric field. Domains oriented unfavorably with respect to the direction of the electric field are diminished in volume, and favorably oriented domains increase in volume. The changes in domain volume are naturally accompanied by polarization changes; a part of the dielectric constant of ferroelectric crystals undoubtedly arises from domain movements, while the remainder is caused by the more ordinary polarization processes.

[11] P. W. Forsbergh, Jr., Phys. Rev. **76**, 1187 (1949); see also W. J. Merz, Phys. Rev. **88**, 421 (1952).

In general, in polydomain crystals there are three types of processes by which the polarization may change:

(a) increase in magnitude of polarization within a domain;
(b) change of direction of polarization within a domain;
(c) change of relative volume of different domains by means of displacement of the.domain boundaries.

In ferroelectric crystals all these processes are of importance, whereas in ferromagnetic crystals the first process does not occur to any significant extent at a constant temperature.

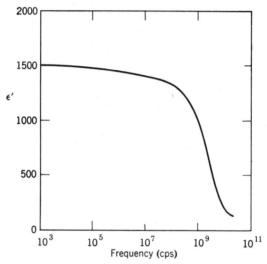

Fig. 7.11. Frequency dependence of the real part of the dielectric constant in barium titanate, from smoothed data of von Hippel and Powles and Jackson.

The theory of ferroelectric domains has not been worked out; the theory of ferromagnetic domains is well understood (Chapter 10) but would require modification to provide for charge neutralization and for high electromechanical coupling before it could be applied to ferroelectrics.

In Fig. 7.11 is shown the frequency dependence of the dielectric constant in polycrystalline barium titanate.[12]   The decrease in the dielectric constant at microwave frequencies is not yet understood, although it has been speculated[13] that the decrease is caused by the inertia of the domain boundaries.

[12] A. von Hippel, Revs. Modern Phys. **22**, 221 (1950); J. G. Powles and W. Jackson, Proc. Inst. Elec. Eng. (London) **96**, III, 383 (1949).
[13] C. Kittel, Phys. Rev. **83**, 458 (1951).

ANTIFERROELECTRIC CRYSTALS

Attention has recently been directed to the characteristics of anti-ferroelectric crystals,[14] which are usually defined as ionic crystals having lines of ions spontaneously polarized—but with neighboring lines polarized in antiparallel directions, as shown in Fig. 7.12a. There are also more general antiferroelectric arrangements, one of them being shown in Fig. 7.12b. It is also possible that ordered antiferroelectric arrangements or clusters of permanent electric dipole moments may occur in crystals such as the hydrogen halides at low temperatures, but this is not yet firmly established.

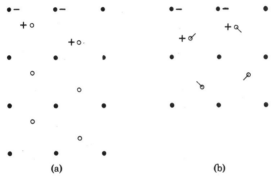

(a)   (b)

Fig. 7.12. Antiferroelectric arrangements: (a) antiparallel lines; (b) diagonal displacements.

There is x-ray evidence[15] that tungsten trioxide (WO_3) exists in an antiferroelectric form, with adjacent lines of tungsten ions displaced in opposite senses, at temperatures over 740°C. Evidence for an anti-ferroelectric structure in lead zirconate ($PbZrO_3$) has been presented by Japanese workers.[16] It is not unlikely that a number of crystals with the perovskite structure but with double-sized cells may be anti-ferroelectric, although this can only be determined by careful x-ray study. The occurrence of antiferroelectricity among the perovskites may be understood as the result of a local field catastrophe very similar to the ferroelectric catastrophe in other perovskites. Cohen[17] has

[14] C. Kittel, Phys. Rev. **82**, 729 (1951).

[15] Kehl, Hay, and Wahl, J. Appl. Phys. **23**, 212 (1952); for x-ray work on the ionic displacements in barium titanate, see W. Kaenzig, Helv. Phys. Acta **24**, 175 (1951).

[16] Sawaguchi, Maniwa, and Hoshino, Phys. Rev. **83**, 1078 (1951); G. Shirane, Phys. Rev. **86**, 219 (1952); Shirane, Sawaguchi, and Takagi, Phys. Rev. **84**, 476 (1951); for $ND_4D_2PO_4$, see Wood, Merz, and Matthias, Phys. Rev. **87**, 544 (1952).

[17] M. H. Cohen, Phys. Rev. **84**, 369 (1951).

in fact calculated that, on the basis of the Lorentz fields alone, barium titanate would be somewhat more likely to be antiferroelectric than ferroelectric. The experimental fact that tungsten trioxide is ferroelectric at low temperatures and antiferroelectric at high temperatures is in line with the prediction that the conditions for the two states in perovskite-like structures are not widely different.

PROBLEMS

7.1. Consider a system consisting of 2 dipoles separated by a fixed distance a, each dipole having a polarizability α. Find the relation between a and α for such a system to be ferroelectric.

7.2. Consider a system consisting of 2 dipoles separated by a fixed distance a along the x axis. Assume that the dipoles are so restrained that they may polarize only along the y axis, and let the polarizability along the y axis be α. Can such a system be ferroelectric? Find the relation between a and α for the system to be antiferroelectric.

7.3. Consider a three-dimensional structure consisting of lines separated by the distance a and parallel to the z direction. Every line contains oxygen and titanium ions alternating in position and separated by $a/2$. Neglect interactions between different lines and consider only interactions between atoms on the same line. Show that, if we have oxygen ions alone separated by a lattice constant a, the local field at an oxygen ion is

$$E_{loc} = E_0 + (4p/a^3) \sum_{n=1}^{\infty} n^{-3} \cong E_0 + 4.81P,$$

where E_0 is the applied electric field. Now insert the titanium ions on the lines at positions halfway between the oxygens. Taking $\alpha(O) = 2.4 \times 10^{-24}$ cc, and $a = 4.0 \times 10^{-8}$ cm, show that at an oxygen ion

$$E_{loc} = E_0 + 4.81P(O) + 33.7P(Ti),$$

and $$\frac{P(O)}{E_0} \propto \frac{1}{1 - 57\alpha(Ti)/a^3},$$

which exhibits the great sensitivity of a linear Ti-O structure to the ionic polarizability of the titanium ion.

7.4. Discuss the effect of an air gap between condenser plates and dielectric on the measurement of high dielectric constants. What is the highest apparent dielectric constant possible if the air gap thickness is 10^{-3} of the total thickness?

7.5. * Discuss the evidence for a first order transition at the Curie point of barium titanate. [See W. Känzig and N. Maikoff, Helv. Phys. Acta 24, 343 (1951).]

REFERENCES

P. W. Anderson, "Theory of the ferroelectric behavior of barium titanate," Ceram. Age (April, 1951).

Baumgartner, Jona, and Känzig, "Seignetteelektrizität," Ergebnisse der exacten Naturwissenschaften 23, 235 (1950).

M Born, "On the quantum theory of pyroelectricity," Revs. Modern Phys. **17**, 245 (1945).

W. G. Cady, *Piezoelectricity*, McGraw-Hill Book Co., New York, 1946.

A. F. Devonshire, "Theory of barium titanate," Phil. Mag. **60**, 1040 (1949); **62**, 1065 (1951).

E. T. Jaynes, *Ferroelectricity*, Princeton University Press, 1953.

A. von Hippel, "Ferroelectricity, domain structure, and phase transitions of barium titanate," Revs. Modern Phys. **22**, 221–237 (1950).

B. Wul, "High dielectric constant materials," J. Phys. (U.S.S.R.) **10**, 95 (1946).

8

Diamagnetism

Substances with a negative magnetic susceptibility are called *diamagnetic*. The magnetic susceptibility per unit volume is defined as

$$\chi = M/H,$$

where M is the magnetic moment per unit volume, or the *magnetization*, and H is the magnetic field intensity. Quite frequently the susceptibility may also be defined referred to unit mass or to a mole of the substance. The molar susceptibility is written χ_M.

Diamagnetism is associated with the tendency of electrical charges partially to shield the interior of a body from an applied magnetic field. In electromagnetism we are familiar with *Lenz's law*, which states that on attempting to change the flux through an electrical circuit an induced current is set up in such a direction as to oppose the flux change. In a resistanceless circuit, in a superconductor, or in an electron orbit within an atom, the induced current persists as long as the field is present, and the magnetic moment associated with the current is a diamagnetic moment.

DERIVATION OF THE LANGEVIN DIAMAGNETISM EQUATION

The usual derivation employs the Larmor theorem, which states that for an atom in a magnetic field the motion of the electrons is, to the first order in H, the same as a possible motion in the absence of H except for the superposition of a common precession of angular frequency

$$(8.1) \qquad \omega_L = -eH/2mc,$$

or $f_L = 1.40$ mc/oersted. Furthermore, if the field is applied slowly, the motion in the rotating reference system will be the same as the original motion in the rest system before the application of the field. The precession of the electron distribution is equivalent to diamagnetic current

$$(8.2) \qquad I = -(Ze)(eH/2mc)/2\pi c,$$

in electromagnetic units.   As the magnetic moment μ of a current loop is given by the product of the current by the area of the loop, we have

$$(8.3) \qquad \mu/H = -(Ze^2/4mc^2)\overline{\rho^2},$$

for Z electrons, where $\overline{\rho^2} = \overline{x^2} + \overline{y^2}$ is the average of the square of the perpendicular distance of the electron from the field axis.   In terms of the mean square distance $\overline{r^2} = \overline{x^2} + \overline{y^2} + \overline{z^2}$ from the nucleus, we have

$$(8.4) \qquad \overline{r^2} = \tfrac{3}{2}\overline{\rho^2}$$

for a distribution of charge which on the average is spherically symmetrical, so that $\overline{x^2} = \overline{y^2} = \overline{z^2}$.   Then the diamagnetic susceptibility per unit volume is, if N is the number of atoms per unit volume,

$$(8.5) \qquad \chi = -\frac{Ze^2N}{6mc^2}\overline{r^2},$$

which is the Langevin expression as corrected by Pauli.   A quantum-theoretical derivation of this result is given in Appendix E.

The problem of calculating the diamagnetic susceptibility is thus reduced to the calculation of $\overline{r^2}$; this means that we must determine the electron charge distribution within the atom.   The charge distribution can in principle be calculated by quantum mechanics, but exact solutions are available only for the hydrogen atom and isoelectronic ions.   The quality of the approximate solutions which have been worked out deteriorates as the number of electrons increases.   By and large, the best we can do is to use the charge distributions calculated by the "self-consistent field" method.   An index of wave functions obtained by this method has been prepared by Hartree[1]; Stoner[2] utilized Hartree functions in early susceptibility calculations.   Other approximate schemes have been devised by Slater,[3] Brindley,[4] Sommerfeld, and others.   A comparison of experimental and theoretical results is shown in Tables 8.1 and 8.2.

DERIVATION OF LARMOR THEOREM FOR A SPECIAL CASE

We consider an electron moving in a circular orbit of radius r about a fixed nucleus.   The balance of forces requires that

$$m\omega_0^2 r = e^2/r^2,$$

[1] D. R. Hartree, Repts. Prog. Phys. **11**, 113 (1946–47).
[2] E. C. Stoner, Proc. Leeds Phil. Lit. Soc. Sci. Sect. **1**, 484 (1929).
[3] J. C. Slater, Phys. Rev. **36**, 57 (1930).
[4] G. W. Brindley, Phil. Mag. **11**, 786 (1931).

TABLE 8.1. MOLAR DIAMAGNETIC SUSCEPTIBILITIES OF RARE GASES

(For literature references see Landolt-Börnstein, *Tabellen*, 6th ed., Vol. I.1, p. 394.)

	Probable Experimental Values (10^{-6} cc/mole)	Theoretical Values (10^{-6} cc/mole) Hartree-Stoner	Hartree-Fock
He	-1.9	-1.9	
Ne	-7.2	-8.6	
A	-19.4	-24.8	-20.6
Kr	$-28.$	......	
Xe	$-43.$	......	

TABLE 8.2. MOLAR DIAMAGNETIC SUSCEPTIBILITIES OF IONS IN CRYSTALS

	Experimental Values† (10^{-6} cc/mole)	Theoretical Values—Free Ions (10^{-6} cc/mole) Hartree‡	Hartree-Fock
F⁻	-9.4	-17.0	
Cl⁻	-24.2	-41.3	-30.4
Br⁻	-34.5		
I⁻	-50.6		
Li⁺	-0.7	-0.7	-0.7
Na⁺	-6.1	-5.6	-4.9
K⁺	-14.6	-17.4	-15.3§
Rb⁺	-22.0	-29.5	
Cs⁺	-35.1	-47.5	
Mg²⁺	-4.3	-4.2	
Ca²⁺	-10.7	-13.1	
Sr²⁺	-18.0		
Ba²⁺	-29.0		

† G. W. Brindley and F. E. Hoare, Trans. Faraday Soc. **33**, 268 (1937); Proc. Phys. Soc. (London) **49**, 619 (1937).

‡ D. R. Hartree, Proc. Cambridge Phil. Soc. **24**, 89 (1928).

§ D. R. Hartree and W. Hartree, Proc. Roy. Soc. (London) **A166**, 450 (1938).

so that

(8.6) $$\omega_0 = (e^2/mr^3)^{1/2}.$$

In a magnetic field H normal to the plane of the orbit we have the additional Lorentz force $\mathbf{F} = (e/c)\mathbf{v} \times \mathbf{H}$; therefore

$$m\omega^2 r = (e^2/r^2) - (e/c)r\omega H,$$

and

(8.7) $$\omega = -(eH/2mc) \pm [(eH/2mc)^2 + (e^2/mr^3)]^{1/2}.$$

Now, if $\omega_0 \gg eH/2mc$, we have approximately

(8.8) $$\omega = \pm\omega_0 - (eH/2mc),$$

in agreement with (8.1). We may note that for a free electron ($r \to \infty$), $\omega = eH/mc$; this is known as the magnetron or cyclotron frequency, and it is twice the Larmor frequency for a bound electron.

DIAMAGNETISM OF MOLECULES

The derivation of the Larmor equation assumes implicitly that the field direction is an axis of symmetry of the system. In most molecular systems this condition is not satisfied, and the general theory of Van Vleck (Appendix F) must be applied. For a polyatomic molecule with spin quantum number zero we have, according to (F.6), the total molar susceptibility

$$(8.9) \qquad \chi_M = - \frac{Le^2}{6mc^2} \sum \overline{r^2} + 2L \sum_n \frac{|(n|\mu_z|0)|^2}{W_n - W_0},$$

where L is the Avogadro number, $(n|\mu_z|0)$ is the matrix element of the z component of the orbital magnetic moment connecting the ground state with the excited state n, and $W_n - W_0$ is the energy separation of the two states. The susceptibility in this case is independent of temperature, but the material is diamagnetic or paramagnetic according to whether the first or second term of (8.9) is greater.

For the normal state of the H_2 molecule Van Vleck and Frank[5] calculate using Wang's wave functions, and measuring r from the center of mass,

$$\chi_M = -4.71 \times 10^{-6} + 0.51 \times 10^{-6} = -4.20 \times 10^{-6},$$

per mole. The experimental values are between -3.9 and -4.0×10^{-6}, per mole.

Pascal has studied empirically the influence of chemical combination on diamagnetic susceptibility and has formulated a set of rules for estimating susceptibilities, particularly of organic liquids. He expresses the susceptibility of the molecule as a sum of the atomic susceptibilities of the constituents plus a correction factor which depends on the nature of the bonds (such as single or double bonds) between the atoms. In the book listed at the end of the chapter, Stoner discusses the Pascal rules.

DIAMAGNETIC ANISOTROPY OF AROMATIC MOLECULES

It has been observed[6] that crystals with layer-like lattices exhibit a marked anisotropy in the diamagnetic susceptibility, the susceptibility being abnormally large when measured in a direction normal to the layers. The effect is particularly marked in antimony, bismuth,

[5] J. H. Van Vleck and A. Frank, Proc. Natl. Acad. Sci. U.S. **15**, 539 (1929).

[6] See, for example, the review by K. S. Krishnan, Strasbourg conference 1939, *Le magnétisme*, vol. III, 247–285; also K. Lonsdale, Repts. Prog. Phys. **4**, 368 (1937).

graphite, and in aromatic molecules (see Table 8.3). It was pointed out by Ehrenfest and by Raman and Krishnan that the abnormal sus-

TABLE 8.3. DIAMAGNETIC ANISOTROPY OF AROMATIC MOLECULES
(From Krishnan and collaborators, quoted by L. Pauling.[7])

Molecule	Molar Molecular Susceptibility $(10^{-6}$ cc/mole$)$		
	K_1	K_2	$K_\perp$
Benzene:	-37	-37	-91
Napthalene:	-39	-43	-187
Anthracene:	-46	-53	-273
Terphenyl:	-98	-98	-260

The diamagnetic susceptibilities K_1 and K_2 are the principal susceptibilities in the plane of the molecule; $K_\perp$ is taken normal to the plane.

ceptibilities probably arise from the Larmor precession of electrons in orbits including many nuclei. Pauling[7] has worked out a very ingenious semiclassical theory of the effect, using electrical circuit theory, and F. London[8] has given a quantum-theoretical treatment.

We may easily estimate on the Pauling model the molar diamagnetic anisotropy, $\Delta K = K_\perp - K_1$, of benzene (C_6H_6). There are three unsaturated linkages in benzene, suggesting that there are six electrons more or less free to move around the ring. As the contribution of the orbital motion of these electrons to the susceptibility will be felt only in $K_\perp$, by (8.3) the molar anisotropy will be given by

$$(8.10) \qquad \Delta K = -(Le^2/4mc^2)\overline{a^2},$$

the usual statistical factor $\frac{2}{3}$ not being needed here. If we use for $\overline{a^2}$ the value R^2, where R is the distance from the axis to the carbon nuclei, 1.39 A, we have

$$\Delta K = -49 \times 10^{-6} \text{ cm}^3 \text{ per mole,}$$

[7] L. Pauling, J. Chem. Phys. **4**, 673(1936).

[8] F. London, J. phys. radium **8**, 397 (1937); H. Brooks, J. Chem. Phys. **8**, 939 (1940); **9**, 463 (1941).

in good agreement with the experimental value $\Delta K = -54 \times 10^{-6}$ for benzene.

METHOD OF MEASUREMENT OF SUSCEPTIBILITIES

The usual methods of measuring diamagnetic and paramagnetic susceptibilities depend in one way or another on the force exerted on a specimen by a non-uniform magnetic field. The force $\mathbf{F}$ is given by

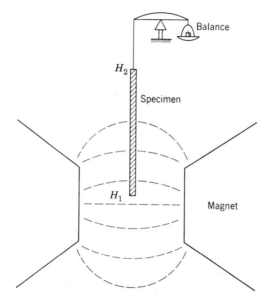

Fig. 8.1.   Gouy method for measuring susceptibilities.

minus the gradient of the magnetic energy, so that, by (G.6),

$$(8.11) \qquad \mathbf{F} = \tfrac{1}{2} \, \mathrm{grad} \int \chi H^2 \, dV,$$

where now χ is the volume susceptibility.

If we suppose that the specimen is in the form of a thin rod, as in the Gouy method shown in Fig. 8.1, we may write for the downward pull

$$(8.12) \qquad F_z = \frac{1}{2} \chi A \int \frac{d}{dz} H^2 \, dz = \frac{1}{2} \chi A (H_1{}^2 - H_2{}^2),$$

where A is the sectional area of the specimen. Other methods of measurement are discussed, for example, in the book by Stoner cited in the references. A high sensitivity method has been described by Lewis, Calvin, and Kasha.[9]

[9] Lewis, Calvin, and Kasha, J. Chem. Phys. **17,** 804 (1949).

PROBLEMS

8.1.* Given an atom with a spherically symmetrical charge distribution in an external field H, show that the field at the nucleus caused by the diamagnetic current is

$$\Delta H = -(eH/3mc^2)v(0),$$

where $v(0)$ is the electrostatic potential produced at the nucleus by the atomic electrons [W. E. Lamb, Jr., Phys. Rev. **60**, 817 (1941).] This diamagnetic correction to the magnetic field at the nucleus is of some importance in connection with the accurate determination of nuclear moments [W. C. Dickinson, Phys. Rev. **81**, 717 (1951).] Estimate very roughly the magnitude of $\Delta H/H$ for an atom with $Z = 50$, and show that the result may be of the order of 10^{-3}.

8.2. The wave function of the hydrogen atom in its ground state $(1s)$ is

$$\psi = (\pi a_0^3)^{-\frac{1}{2}} e^{-r/a_0},$$

where $a_0 = \hbar^2/me^2 = 0.529 \times 10^{-8}$ cm. The charge density is $\rho(x,y,z) = e |\psi|^2$, according to the statistical interpretation of the wave function. Show that for this state

$$\overline{r^2} = 3a_0^2,$$

and calculate the molar diamagnetic susceptibility of atomic hydrogen (8.5 $\times$ 10^{-6} cm^3/mole).

8.3. Pauling has shown that, starting with the result for the diamagnetic anisotropy of benzene, the anisotropy of related aromatic molecules may be derived from the following model: a structure having the form of the molecule is constructed of wire and placed with its plane perpendicular to a magnetic field which increases linearly with time. The magnetic moment of the structure is proportional to the diamagnetic anisotropy. Show that for the napthalene molecule the induced current is $\frac{9}{5}$ that for benzene, so that the estimated anisotropy in the magnetic moment is $\frac{12}{5}$ that for benzene. Using Kirchhoff's laws apply the same scheme to anthracene, and show that the moment is $\frac{60}{17}$ that for benzene. Compare the ΔK values calculated using these ratios with the observed values in Table 8.3.

8.4. Given a plane slab of a metal containing N resistanceless electrons per unit volume, find an expression for the distance below the surface at which an applied static magnetic field H_0 parallel to the surface is reduced in intensity by e^{-1}.

REFERENCES

W. R. Meyers, "Diamagnetism of ions," Revs. Modern Phys. **24**, 15 (1952).

P. W. Selwood, *Magnetochemistry*, Interscience Publishers, London, New York, 1943.

E. C. Stoner, *Magnetism and matter*, Methuen and Co., Ltd., London, 1934.

J. H. Van Vleck, *Theory of electric and magnetic susceptibilities*, Clarendon Press, Oxford, 1932.

9

Paramagnetism

The chapter begins with the classical Langevin theory of the paramagnetic susceptibility of gases, followed by a quantum-mechanical treatment. The properties of paramagnetic ions in solids are discussed, and an account is given of the attainment of very low temperatures by the adiabatic demagnetization of paramagnetic salts. Then there is a brief discussion of nuclear and electronic spin resonance absorption at radio and microwave frequencies.

Electronic paramagnetism is found in:

(a) All atoms and molecules possessing an odd number of electrons, as here the total spin of the system cannot be zero. Examples: free sodium atoms; gaseous nitric oxide (NO); organic free radicals such as triphenylmethyl, $C(C_6H_5)_3$.

(b) All free atoms and ions with an unfilled inner shell: transition elements; ions isoelectronic with transition elements; rare earth and actinide elements. Examples: Mn^{2+}, Gd^{3+}, U^{4+}. Paramagnetic properties are exhibited by many of these ions when incorporated into solids, and as ions in solution, but not invariably.

(c) A few miscellaneous compounds with an even number of electrons, including molecular oxygen and organic biradicals.

(d) Metals: the paramagnetism of conduction electrons is treated in Chapters 12 and 13.

THEORY OF PARAMAGNETIC SUSCEPTIBILITIES

LANGEVIN THEORY OF PARAMAGNETISM

We treat a medium containing N atoms per unit volume, each bearing a magnetic moment $\mathbf{\mu}$. The energy of interaction (G.1) with an applied magnetic field $\mathbf{H}$ is

$$(9.1) \qquad V = -\mathbf{\mu} \cdot \mathbf{H}.$$

For thermal equilibrium the magnetization is calculated by following exactly the steps (6.23) to (6.28) in the derivation of the Debye orien-

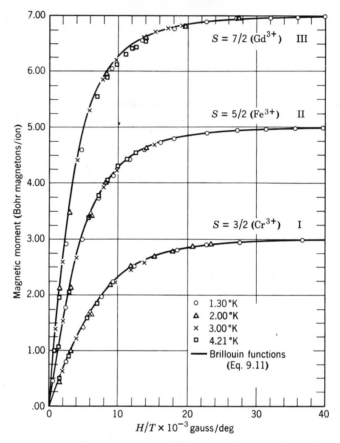

Fig. 9.1.   Plot of magnetic moment vs. H/T for spherical samples of (I) potassium chromium alum, (II) ferric ammonium alum, and (III) gadolinium sulfate octahydrate.   Over 99.5% magnetic saturation is achieved for 1.3°K and about 50,000 gauss.   [After W. E. Henry, Phys. Rev. **88**, 559 (1952).]

tational polarizability, with $\mathbf{\mu}$ written for $\mathbf{p}$ and $\mathbf{H}$ for $\mathbf{E}$.   The magnetization is then given by

$$(9.2) \qquad\qquad M = N\mu L(a),$$

where $a = \mu H/kT$, and the Langevin function $L(a)$ is

$$L(a) = \operatorname{ctnh} a - \frac{1}{a}\cdot$$

For $a \ll 1$, $L(a) = a/3$, and

$$(9.3) \qquad\qquad M \cong N\mu^2 H/3kT.$$

For an electron $\mu \approx 10^{-20}$; at room temperature in a field of 10^4 oersteds we have $\mu H/kT \approx \frac{1}{400}$, so that here we may safely approximate the Langevin function by $\mu H/3kT$. At low temperatures saturation effects have been observed, as shown in Fig. 9.1.

The magnetic susceptibility in the limit $\mu H/kT \ll 1$ is

$$(9.4) \qquad \chi = M/H = N\mu^2/3kT = C/T,$$

where the Curie constant C is equal to $N\mu^2/3k$. The $1/T$ temperature dependence is known as the Curie law, and the whole expression is known as the Langevin equation.

QUANTUM THEORY OF PARAMAGNETISM

We treat first the paramagnetism caused by electron spins with angular momentum $\frac{1}{2}$ as measured in units of $\hbar$. In a magnetic field

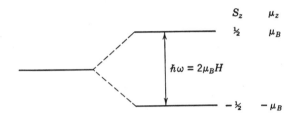

Fig. 9.2. Energy level splitting scheme for one electron, with only spin angular momentum, in a magnetic field H directed along the positive z axis. Note that the Bohr magneton $\mu_B = e\hbar/2mc$ is a negative number as used here.

H the energy levels are separated according to (9.1), and as in the elementary theory of the Zeeman effect, by

$$(9.5) \qquad \Delta W = 2|\mu_z|H = g\,\frac{e\hbar}{2mc}\,H = g\mu_B H,$$

where for an electron spin the g factor or *spectroscopic splitting factor* is equal to 2.00; $\mu_B = e\hbar/2mc = -0.927 \times 10^{-20}$ erg/oersted is the Bohr magneton. The splitting for an electron spin is shown in Fig. 9.2. For free atoms where orbital angular momentum may also be present, the g factor is given by the Landé equation

$$(9.6) \qquad g = 1 + \frac{J(J + 1) + S(S + 1) - L(L + 1)}{2J(J + 1)},$$

where J, S, L refer, respectively, to the total, spin, and orbital angular momentum quantum numbers.

Where there are only two levels in the magnetic field the populations in thermal equilibrium are

(9.7)
$$\frac{N_1}{N} = \frac{e^{\mu H/kT}}{e^{\mu H/kT} + e^{-\mu H/kT}};$$

$$\frac{N_2}{N} = \frac{e^{-\mu H/kT}}{e^{\mu H/kT} + e^{-\mu H/kT}};$$

here N_1, N_2 are the populations of the lower and upper levels, and $N = N_1 + N_2$ is the total number of atoms. The projection of the magnetic moment of the upper state along the field direction is $g\mu_B/2$, and of the lower state is $-g\mu_B/2$, so that the resultant magnetization for N atoms per unit volume is

(9.8)
$$M = \frac{Ng\mu_B}{2} \cdot \frac{e^x - e^{-x}}{e^x + e^{-x}} = \frac{Ng\mu_B}{2} \tanh x,$$

where $x = g\mu_B H/2kT$. For $x \ll 1$, $\tanh x \cong x$, and

$$M \cong \frac{Ng\mu_B}{2} \cdot \frac{g\mu_B H}{2kT}.$$

The susceptibility in this limit is

(9.9)
$$\chi = N(g^2/4)\mu_B{}^2/kT.$$

This equation for an electron spin with $g = 2$ appears to differ from the classical result (9.3) by a factor of 3; however, in quantum mechanics the total spin angular moment is given by $[S(S + 1)]^{1/2} = (\frac{3}{4})^{1/2}$ rather than by $S = \frac{1}{2}$; accordingly the total magnetic moment must be given by $\mu = (3)^{1/2}\mu_B$; therefore (9.9) becomes

$$\chi = N\mu^2/3kT,$$

in accord with the classical result.

An atom with angular momentum quantum number J has $2J + 1$ equally spaced energy levels in a magnetic field. It is left as a problem (9.3) to show that the magnetization is given by

(9.10)
$$M = NgJ\mu_B B_J(x),$$

where $x = gJ\mu_B H/kT$, and the Brillouin function B_J is given by

(9.11)
$$B_J = \frac{2J + 1}{2J} \text{ ctnh} \left(\frac{(2J + 1)x}{2J}\right) - \frac{1}{2J} \text{ ctnh} \left(\frac{x}{2J}\right)$$

For $x \ll 1$, the susceptibility is

(9.12)
$$\chi = NJ(J + 1)g^2\mu_B{}^2/3kT = Np^2\mu_B{}^2/3kT,$$

where the effective number of Bohr magnetons is defined as

(9.13) $$p = g[J(J + 1)]^{\frac{1}{2}}.$$

The order of magnitude of the volume susceptibility for $N \approx 10^{22}$ atoms/cc as in a solid and $\mu \approx 10^{-20}$ cgs is $\sim 1/(400\ T)$. For $T = 300°$K, $\chi \sim 10^{-5}$; for $T = 0.3°$K, $\chi \sim 10^{-2}$.

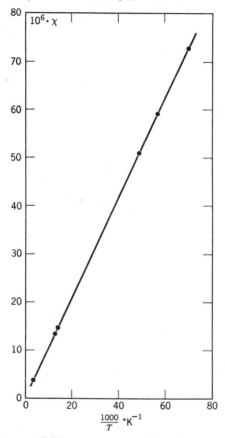

Fig. 9.3. Plot of susceptibility per gm vs. reciprocal temperature for powdered $CuSO_4 \cdot K_2SO_4 \cdot 6H_2O$, showing the Curie law temperature dependence. [Measurements by J. C. Hupse, Physica **9**, 633 (1942).]

In Fig. 9.3 we show susceptibility measurements on copper potassium sulfate, which obeys the Curie law quite well.

RARE EARTH IONS

The discussion above applies principally to atoms which in the absence of a magnetic field have a $(2J + 1)$-fold degenerate ground state, the degeneracy being lifted upon application of a magnetic field; the influence of all higher energy states of the system is neglected. These conditions appear from Table 9.1 to be satisfied by a number of

TABLE 9.1. EFFECTIVE MAGNETON NUMBERS FOR TRIVALENT RARE EARTH
IONS
(Near room temperature)

Ion	Configuration	Basic Level	$p(\text{calc}) =$ $g[J(J+1)]^{\frac{1}{2}}$	$p(\exp)$ approx.
Ce^{3+}	$4f^1 5s^2 p^6$	$^2F_{\frac{5}{2}}$	2.54	2.4
Pr^{3+}	$4f^2 5s^2 p^6$	$^3H_4.$	3.58	3.5
Nd^{3+}	$4f^3 5s^2 p^6$	$^4I_{\frac{9}{2}}$	3.62	3.5
Pm^{3+}	$4f^4 5s^2 p^6$	$^5I_4$	2.68	....
Sm^{3+}	$4f^5 5s^2 p^6$	$^6H_{\frac{5}{2}}$	0.84	1.5
Eu^{3+}	$4f^6 5s^2 p^6$	$^7F_0$	0	3.4
Gd^{3+}	$4f^7 5s^2 p^6$	$^8S_{\frac{7}{2}}$	7.94	8.0
Tb^{3+}	$4f^8 5s^2 p^6$	$^7F_6$	9.72	9.5
Dy^{3+}	$4f^9 5s^2 p^6$	$^8H_{\frac{15}{2}}$	10.63	10.6
Ho^{3+}	$4f^{10} 5s^2 p^6$	$^5I_8$	10.60	10.4
Er^{3+}	$4f^{11} 5s^2 p^6$	$^4I_{\frac{15}{2}}$	9.59	9.5
Tm^{3+}	$4f^{12} 5s^2 p^6$	$^3H_6$	7.57	7.3
Yb^{3+}	$4f^{13} 5s^2 p^6$	$^2F_{\frac{7}{2}}$	4.54	4.5

the rare earth ions. The calculated magneton numbers are obtained by using g values from the Landé formula (9.6) for the ground state level assignment predicted by the Hund theory of spectral terms, which tells us that for equivalent electrons the ground state has the maximum multiplicity $2S + 1$ allowed by the Pauli principle and the maximum L consistent with this multiplicity; furthermore, the J value is equal to $L - S$ when the shell is less than half full and $L + S$ when the shell is more than half full.

The discrepancy between the experimental magneton numbers and those calculated on our present assumptions is quite marked for Eu^{3+} and Sm^{3+} ions. In these ions it is necessary to consider the influence of the higher states of the $L - S$ multiplet,[1] as the intervals here are not very large compared to kT. Van Vleck and Frank have shown that the experimental facts are accounted for in a satisfactory way when the higher levels are considered.

The full theoretical expression for the susceptibility as a function of temperature when higher states are to be considered may be quite complicated. In Appendix F we consider two limiting cases, when the level splitting is $\ll kT$ or $\gg kT$. Levels $\gg kT$ above the ground state may contribute to the susceptibility a term which is independent of temperature over the appropriate range. This term is known as Van

[1] A multiplet is the set of levels of different J values arising out of a given L and S.

Vleck paramagnetism; it is in addition to the $1/T$ and diamagnetic terms already discussed.

IRON GROUP IONS

Table 9.2 shows that, for salts of the iron transition group of the periodic table the experimental magneton numbers are in poor agreement with (9.13), but instead, as noted by Sommerfeld, Bose, and Stoner, agree quite well with magneton numbers

$$(9.14) \qquad p = 2[S(S + 1)]^{1/2}$$

calculated as if the orbital moment were not there at all.   One expresses this situation by saying that the orbital moments are "quenched."

TABLE 9.2.   EFFECTIVE MAGNETON NUMBERS FOR IRON GROUP IONS

Ion	Config- uration	Basic Level	p(calc) = $g[J(J + 1)]^{1/2}$	p(calc) = $2[S(S + 1)]^{1/2}$	p(exp)[†]	g(exp)[‡]
Ti^{3+}, V^{4+}	$3d^1$	$^2D_{3/2}$	1.55	1.73	1.8	......
V^{3+}	$3d^2$	$^3F_2$	1.63	2.83	2.8	(1.98)
Cr^{3+}, V^{2+}	$3d^3$	$^4F_{3/2}$	0.77	3.87	3.8	(1.97)
Mn^{3+}, Cr^{2+}	$3d^4$	$^5D_0$	0	4.90	4.9	2.0
Fe^{3+}, Mn^{2+}	$3d^5$	$^6S_{5/2}$	5.92	5.92	5.9	2.0
Fe^{2+}	$3d^6$	$^5D_4$	6.70	4.90	5.4	2.2
Co^{2+}	$3d^7$	$^4F_{9/2}$	6.54	3.87	4.8	2.5
Ni^{2+}	$3d^8$	$^3F_4$	5.59	2.83	3.2	2.3
Cu^{2+}	$3d^9$	$^2D_{5/2}$	3.55	1.73	1.9	2.2

† Representative values.
‡ In this column $g = p$ (exp)$/[S(S + 1)]^{1/2}$.

The basic reason for the difference in behavior of the rare earth and iron group salts is that the $4f$ shell responsible for paramagnetism in the rare earth ions lies deep inside the ions, being partly shielded from the environment by the outer $5s$ and $5p$ shells, whereas in the iron group the $3d$ shell responsible for paramagnetism is the outermost shell in the ionic state.   The $3d$ shell is thus exposed to the intense local electric fields produced by neighboring ions and the dipole moments of water of hydration in the crystal.   The interaction of the paramagnetic ions with the crystalline electric fields has two major effects: the coupling of L and S vectors is largely broken up, so that the states are no longer specified by their J values; furthermore, the $2L + 1$ sublevels belonging to a given L which are degenerate in the free ion may now be split up, in some cases with important effects on the contribution of the orbital motion to the magnetic moment.

QUENCHING OF THE ORBITAL ANGULAR MOMENTUM

In an electric field directed toward a fixed center such as a nucleus, the plane of a classical orbit remains fixed in space, so that the orbital angular momentum components L_x, L_y, L_z are constant. In quantum theory only one angular momentum component (usually taken as L_z) and the square of the total orbital angular momentum L^2 are constant in a central field. If an inhomogeneous electric field is superposed on the central field, the plane of the orbit will move about; the angular momentum components are no longer constant and may average to zero. In quantum theory, as shown in detail in Appendix H, L_z will no longer be a constant of the motion, although to a good approximation L^2 may continue to be constant. If L_z averages to zero, it is said to be quenched.

The magnetic moment of a state is given by the average value of the magnetic moment operator $\mu_B(\mathbf{L} + 2\mathbf{S})$ over the state. For a magnetic field in the z direction the orbital contribution to the magnetic moment is proportional to the expectation value of L_z, so that the orbital magnetic moment is quenched if the mechanical moment L_z is quenched.

When the spin orbit interaction energy is introduced as an additional perturbation on the system, the quenching may be partially lifted as the spin may carry some orbital moment along with it. If the sign of the spin orbit interaction favors parallel orientation of the spin and orbital magnetic moments, the total magnetic moment will be larger than for the spin alone, and the g value as defined in Table 9.2 will be greater than 2. The experimental results in the table suggest, in good agreement with the known variation of sign[2] of the spin orbit interaction, that $g > 2$ when the $3d$ shell is more than half full, $g = 2$ when the shell is half full, and $g < 2$ when the shell is less than half full. The effect of spin orbit coupling is worked out in Appendix I for a simple model, with particular reference to the results of electron spin resonance experiments discussed below.

NUCLEAR PARAMAGNETISM

The magnetic moments of nuclei are smaller than the magnetic moment of the electron by a factor $\sim 10^{-3}$; therefore according to (9.4) the susceptibility of a nuclear paramagnetic system for the same number of particles will be smaller by a factor $\sim 10^{-6}$ than that of an electronic paramagnetic system. The susceptibility of solid hydrogen, which is diamagnetic with respect to electrons but para-

---

[2] See E. U. Condon and G. H. Shortley, *Theory of Atomic Spectra*, Cambridge University Press, 1935, p. 210; the spin orbit interaction of a single electron is such that the lowest energy state of a multiplet has **S** oppositely directed to **L**; in shells more than half full we think of the motion as that of positive holes in the shell, so that the sign of the interaction is reversed.

magnetic with respect to protons, has been measured at very low temperatures by Laserew and Schubnikow,[3] who found results consistent with the known magnitude of the proton magnetic moment. This is the only static nuclear susceptibility measurement that has been made. Values of the magnetic moments of several nuclei[4] are given in Table 9.3.

TABLE 9.3. NUCLEAR MAGNETIC MOMENTS

(Magnetic moments in units of the nuclear magneton

$\mu_p = e\hbar/2M_pc = 5.05 \times 10^{-24}$ ergs/oersted)

Nucleus	Spin (units $\hbar$)	Magnetic Moment
Neutron	$\frac{1}{2}$	-1.913
H^1	$\frac{1}{2}$	2.793
D^2	1	0.857
Li^7	$\frac{3}{2}$	3.256
Na^{23}	$\frac{3}{2}$	2.217
Mn^{55}	$\frac{5}{2}$	3.468
Co^{59}	$\frac{7}{2}$	4.648
Ta^{181}	$\frac{7}{2}$	2.1

COOLING BY ADIABATIC DEMAGNETIZATION OF A PARAMAGNETIC SALT

The universal method for attaining temperatures below 1°K is that of adiabatic demagnetization.[5] By its use temperatures near 10^{-3} °K have been reached. The method rests on the fact that at a fixed temperature the entropy of a system of magnetic moments is lowered by a magnetic field. The entropy is always a measure of the order of a system; the greater the disorder, the higher the entropy. In the field the moments will be partly lined up, or partly ordered, so that the entropy is lowered by the field. The entropy is also lowered by lowering the temperature, as more of the moments line up. If the field can be removed without the entropy of the spin system changing, the disorder of the spin system will look as it should at a lower temperature. When the specimen is demagnetized adiabatically, heat can flow into the spin system only from the system of lattice vibrations. At the temperatures of interest the entropy of the lattice system is quite negligible, so that the entropy of the spin system alone is essentially constant during adiabatic demagnetization of the specimen.

[3] B. Lasarew and L. Schubnikow, Physik. Z. Sowjetunion 11, 445 (1937).

[4] For a large compilation of nuclear moments, see J. E. Mack, Rev. Modern Phys. 22, 64 (1950). Nuclear moments are at present determined principally by nuclear resonance methods, as discussed below in this chapter.

[5] The method was suggested independently by P. Debye, Ann. Physik 81, 1154 (1926); and W. F. Giauque, J. Am. Chem. Soc. 49, 1864 (1927).

We now derive an expression for the field dependence of the entropy. As the entropy is a function of H and T, we have

(9.15) $$dS = \left(\frac{\partial S}{\partial H}\right)_T dH + \left(\frac{\partial S}{\partial T}\right)_H dT.$$

In an isothermal process the second term may be set equal to zero, so that

(9.16) $$dS = \left(\frac{\partial S}{\partial H}\right)_T dH.$$

We note that, by a modified Maxwell thermodynamic relation, $(\partial S/\partial H)_T = (\partial M/\partial T)_H$, so that

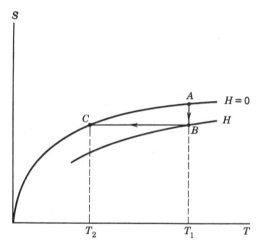

Fig. 9.4.   Entropy-temperature plot for adiabatic demagnetization.

$$dS = \left(\frac{\partial M}{\partial T}\right)_H dH.$$

Therefore in isothermal magnetization, using the Maxwell relation,

(9.17) $$S(H,T) - S(O,T) = \int_0^H (\partial M/\partial T)_H \, dH.$$

In the Curie law region, using (9.12) and (9.13),

(9.18) $$S = S_0 - \tfrac{1}{6}Nk(p\mu_B H/kT)^2.$$

The steps carried out in the cooling process are shown in Fig. 9.4. The field is applied at temperature T_1 with the specimen in good thermal contact ($\Delta T = 0$) with the surroundings, giving the isothermal path AB.   The specimen is then insulated ($\Delta S = 0$) and the field removed, so that the specimen follows the isoentropic path BC, ending up at temperature T_2.

The lowest temperature reached in adiabatic demagnetization is largely limited by the natural splitting of the spin energy levels occurring even in the absence of external magnetic fields. The zero field splitting may be caused by electrostatic effects (Appendix H), by the interaction of the magnetic moments with each other, or by nuclear interactions. The zero field splitting causes the entropy at T_2 in Fig. 9.5 to be less than it would be (T_2') for a smaller splitting, so that the final temperature is not as low as it might otherwise be.

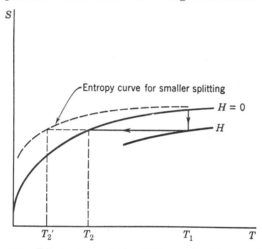

Fig. 9.5.   Effect of zero field splitting on final temperature.

Kürti and Simon[6] have given an approximate formula for estimating the final temperature reached, starting at an initial temperature T_1 and a field H. We take a simple model of the zero field splitting, supposing that the ground level of each ion is split into $2J + 1$ sublevels separated by *equal* energy differences $k\theta_0$. In the field H we suppose that $g\mu_B H$ is the splitting of each of the $2J + 1$ sublevels. At the initial temperature the distribution on the various sublevels, and hence the entropy is determined by the ratio $g\mu_B H/kT_1$, provided that $T_1 \gg \theta_0$ and $g\mu_B H \gg k\theta_0$. The entropy of the final state at temperature T_2 will be the same function of $k\theta_0/kT_2$ as the initial entropy was of $g\mu_B H/kT_1$, because the entropy depends only on the occupation of the sublevels, and these ratios determine the occupation. As the

[6] N. Kürti and F. Simon, Proc. Roy. Soc. (London) **A149**, 152 (1935).

entropy remains constant during adiabatic demagnetization, we have for this model

$$(9.19) \qquad \frac{T_2}{T_1} = \frac{k\theta_0}{g\mu_B H} = 7.5 \frac{\theta_0}{H_i},$$

where H_i is in kilo-oersteds, θ_0 in degrees Kelvin, and we have set $g = 2$.

For the salt iron ammonium alum, $FeNH_4(SO_4)_2 \cdot 12H_2O$, we may estimate $\theta_0 = 0.061°K$ from heat capacity data. Starting with $T_1 = 1.2°K$ and $H = 14,000$ oersteds, a final temperature $T_2 = 0.038°K$ was reached. From (9.19) we would have estimated $T_2(\text{est}) = (7.5)(1.2)(0.061)/14 = 0.039°K$.

ENTROPY OF THE SPIN SYSTEM

At temperatures $T \gg \theta_0$, where $k\theta_0$ is the zero field level splitting, the entropy of a system of N ions each of spin J is given by

$$(9.20) \qquad S = Nk \log (2J + 1).$$

We establish this directly from the Boltzmann definition of the entropy of a distribution of objects as

$$(9.21) \qquad S = k \log W,$$

where W is the number of independent arrangements of the elements of the system according to the prescribed distribution. At a temperature so high that all sublevels are nearly equally populated, the number of arrangements W is the number of ways of arranging N spins on $2J + 1$ sublevels, as nearly all arrangements will be possible energetically. Thus

$$(9.22) \qquad W = (2J + 1)^N,$$

and

$$(9.23) \qquad S = k \log (2J + 1)^N = Nk \log (2J + 1).$$

NUCLEAR AND ELECTRONIC SPIN RESONANCE ABSORPTION

Spin resonance absorption studies have made important contributions to our understanding of interactions in solids and liquids and of the magnetic properties of nuclei. We consider first a free particle of spin S in a magnetic field H. The $2S + 1$ magnetic sublevels labeled by the magnetic quantum number $m_s = S, S - 1, \ldots, -S + 1, -S$ are separated in the field by equal energy differences $g\mu_0 H$ between adjacent sublevels. Here μ_0 is usually taken for electrons as the Bohr magneton and for nuclei as the nuclear magneton; g is the appropriate factor which makes the energy come out correctly, and it is called the *g factor* or *spectroscopic splitting factor*. The level scheme for a single electron spin is shown in Fig. 9.2. Electromagnetic radiation of frequency such that

$$(9.24) \qquad \hbar\omega = g\mu_0 H$$

will induce transitions between neighboring magnetic levels according to the selection rule $\Delta m_s = \pm 1$ for magnetic dipole transitions. The transition occurs between the Zeeman components of a single spectral level. Energy is absorbed from the radiation field when (9.24) is satisfied. A schematic experimental set-up is shown in Fig. 9.6.

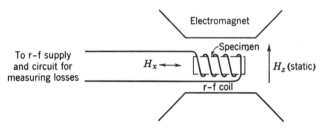

Fig. 9.6.   Schematic arrangement for spin resonance absorption experiments.

The specimen is placed in the static magnetic field H_z of an electromagnet. An r-f magnetic field H_x of fixed angular frequency ω is applied perpendicular to the static field. The r-f power absorbed in the specimen is determined by electrical measurements, as by measuring the Q of the coil. The resonance effect for electrons was found first by Zavoisky,[7] that for nuclei by Purcell, Torrey, and Pound[8] and by Bloch, Hansen, and Packard.[9]

Experimental results for electron spin resonance in a paramagnetic organic compound are shown in Fig. 9.7, and for proton spin resonance in water (with some dissolved ferric nitrate) in Fig. 9.8. The electron spin resonance relation for $g = 2.00$ is

$$(9.25) \qquad f(\text{mc/sec}) = 2.80 \, H \text{ (oersteds)},$$

and the proton resonance relation is

$$(9.26) \qquad f(\text{kc/sec}) = 4.26 \, H \text{ (oersteds)}.$$

[7] E. Zavoisky, J. Phys. (U.S.S.R.) **9**, 211, 245, 447 (1945).
[8] Purcell, Torrey, and Pound, Phys. Rev. **69**, 37 (1946).
[9] Bloch, Hansen, and Packard, Phys. Rev. **70**, 474 (1946).

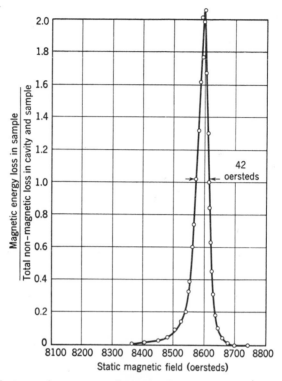

Fig. 9.7.   Electron spin resonance absorption in an organic free radical compound at 24,446 mc/sec.   [After Holden *et al.*, Phys. Rev. **75,** 1614 (1949).]

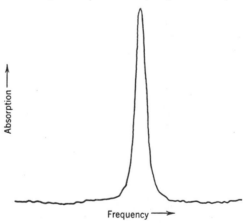

Fig. 9.8.   Proton spin resonance absorption in ferric nitrate solution; fixed magnetic field, varying frequency.   For a frequency of 30 mc/sec the resonance occurs at 7050 oersteds.   [After Bloembergen, Purcell, and Pound, Phys. Rev. **73,** 679 (1948).]

For $H \sim 5000$ oersteds, the electron resonance frequency falls in the microwave range, and the proton resonance frequency in the short wave communications range. For technical reasons the electron experiments are usually performed at fixed frequency and varying field, while the nuclear experiments are often done at fixed field and varying frequency. Nuclear resonance is becoming the most important laboratory method for the accurate measurement of magnetic field intensity.

MACROSCOPIC EQUATIONS

It is sometimes useful to consider the resonance process in terms of the magnetic moment of the entire specimen[10] rather than in terms of the levels of an individual ion. Writing **M** for the magnetization (magnetic moment/volume) and **J** for the angular momentum density, the classical equation of motion

$$d\mathbf{J}/dt = \text{torque/volume}$$

becomes

(9.27) $$d\mathbf{J}/dt = \mathbf{M} \times \mathbf{H}.$$

Now, if we may consider the spin system free with respect to lattice interactions, we may write

(9.28) $$\mathbf{M} = \gamma \mathbf{J},$$

where for electrons

(9.29) $$\gamma = ge/2mc.$$

We have then as the equation of motion for the magnetization

(9.30) $$d\mathbf{M}/dt = \gamma \mathbf{M} \times \mathbf{H}.$$

We obtain very simply an approximate solution of this equation. We take the static field as H_z and the r-f field as H_x. The component equations may be written, for time dependence $e^{i\omega t}$,

$$i\omega M_x = \gamma M_y H_z;$$

(9.31) $$i\omega M_y = \gamma(M_z H_x - M_x H_z);$$

$$i\omega M_z = -\gamma M_y H_x \cong 0.$$

The third equation may be neglected as long as $H_x \ll H_z$ and $M_y \ll M_z$. We may then solve for M_x, finding

$$-\omega^2 M_x = \gamma^2 (M_z H_z H_x - M_x H_z{}^2),$$

10 F. Bloch, Phys. Rev. **70**, 460 (1946).

or, for the r-f susceptibility χ_x,

$$(9.32) \qquad \chi_x = M_x/H_x = \frac{\gamma^2 M_z H_z}{(\gamma H_z)^2 - \omega^2}.$$

Setting the resonance frequency $\omega_0 = \gamma H_z$, in agreement with (9.24), and writing $\chi_0 = M_z/H_z$ for the static susceptibility, we have

$$(9.33) \qquad \chi_x = \frac{\chi_0}{1 - (\omega/\omega_0)^2}$$

We may picture the magnetization vector as precessing about the static field at an angle which depends on the amplitude of the r-f field, on the proximity to resonance, and on damping factors which we have not introduced here.

LINE WIDTH

The width of the resonance line is caused usually by the interactions of the spins with each other and by their interaction with the crystal lattice.

If we have N spins per unit volume, of moment μ, oriented more or less at random, the magnetic field any one spin will see is the sum of the external field plus a random field of the order of $\Delta H \approx \mu/a^3 \approx \mu N$, where a is the nearest neighbor distance. We may therefore expect a line width of the order of $\Delta H \approx \mu N$, which for electrons may be $\approx (10^{-20})(10^{23}) = 1000$ oersteds, and for nuclei may be $\approx (10^{-23})$ $(10^{23}) = 1$ oersted. These values are of the order of magnitude of the observed widths in many cases. If, however, the electrons have a strong exchange interaction with each other, the lines may be much sharper.[11] In liquids[12] the nuclear lines are sharpened when the neighboring nuclei are in rapid thermal motion with respect to the reference nucleus. Here the perturbing field caused by neighboring nuclei does not look like a random addition to the static field, but rather like a high frequency perturbation, to which the spin does not respond when the frequency of the random field is higher than the frequency corresponding to the unperturbed width of the resonance.

ZERO FIELD ELECTRONIC SPLITTING

In many solids, as we have previously mentioned, the ground state of the paramagnetic ion is split by the crystalline electric field, and it is

[11] C. J. Gorter and J. H. Van Vleck, Phys. Rev. **72**, 1128 (1947); J. H. Van Vleck Phys. Rev. **74**, 1168 (1948).

[12] Bloembergen, Purcell, and Pound, Phys. Rev. **73**, 679 (1948).

possible to observe r-f transitions between the sublevels without necessarily applying a static magnetic field. This was first done by Bleaney and co-workers. Usually, however, a static field is applied and the zero field separation of the levels is deduced from a theoretical interpretation of the several absorption lines observed under these conditions of combined crystalline and Zeeman splittings. Results for ammonium chrome alum at room temperature are shown in Fig. 9.9; the spectrum is interpreted by a zero field splitting of 0.143

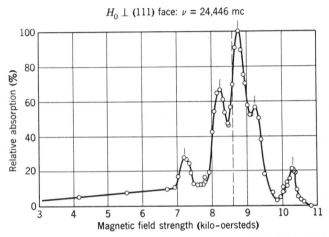

Fig. 9.9. Absorption in ammonium chrome alum, $NH_4Cr(SO_4)_2 \cdot 12H_2O$ near 1 cm wavelength. [After Yager, Merritt, Holden, and Kittel, Phys. Rev. **75**, 1630 (1949).]

cm^{-1} and a g value of 1.99. The theory for this crystal is discussed by Broer[13] and Weiss.[14]

FURTHER REMARKS

Paramagnetic relaxation effects observed when the r-f field is parallel to the static field, or when there is no static field, are discussed in Gorter's book cited at the end of the chapter. The relaxation frequencies are of the order of 10^6 to 10^9 cps, or higher.

A review of hyperfine structure effects in electronic resonance has been prepared by Bleaney.[15] In paramagnetic salts which have been diluted with a non-magnetic isomorphous salt it is often possible to resolve a line structure caused by the interaction of electrons with

[13] L. J. F. Broer, Physica **9**, 547 (1942).
[14] P. R. Weiss, Phys. Rev. **73**, 470 (1948).
[15] B. Bleaney, Physica **17**, 175 (1951).

nuclear spins.   The hyperfine structure of Mn^{2+} ions in aqueous solution is shown in Fig. 9.10 (from work by Tinkham, Weinstein, and Kip).

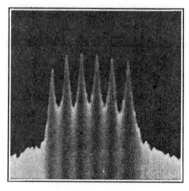

Fig. 9.10.   Hyperfine structure of Mn^{2+} ions in water. [After Tinkham, Weinstein, and Kip, Phys. Rev. **84**, 848 (1951).]   The nuclear spin is $I = \frac{5}{2}$, and the electronic spin is $S = \frac{5}{2}$.

PROBLEMS

9.1. Show that on the Langevin theory the first two terms in a series expansion of the differential susceptibility are

$$\chi = dM/dH = (N\mu^2/3kT)\{1 - [(\mu H/kT)^2/5] + \cdots \}.$$

9.2. Bohr (and also van Leeuwen) has shown that, in any dynamical system to which classical statistical mechanics can be applied, the diamagnetic and paramagnetic susceptibilites cancel, so that classically one always has zero susceptibility in thermal equilibrium.   Consider a moving charge e constrained to remain at a fixed distance r from an attracting center; show that the magnetic dipole moment is

$$\mu = (e/2mc)mr\dot\theta^2.$$

The kinetic energy of the rigid rotator has the average value kT on Boltzmann statistics, as the particle has two degrees of freedom.   Calculate the mean square dipole moment and substitute in the Langevin paramagnetic susceptibility equation.   Compare the result with the diamagnetic equation, (8.5), and show that the total susceptibility vanishes.   Quantization completely modifies the picture and makes magnetization possible.

9.3.* There are N atoms per unit volume, each with total angular momentum quantum number J and spectroscopic splitting factor g.   Show that the magnetization is given by

$$M = NgJ\mu_B B_J(x)$$

where $x = gJ\mu_B H/kT$ and B_J is the Brillouin function:

$$B_J = \frac{2J + 1}{2J} \operatorname{ctnh} \left[\frac{(2J + 1)x}{2J} \right] - \frac{1}{2J} \operatorname{ctnh} \left(\frac{x}{2J} \right).$$

Show also that, for $x \ll 1$,

$$B_J \cong (J' + 1)x/3J,$$

and

$$M \cong Ng^2\mu_B{}^2J(J + 1)H/3kT.$$

Show that in the limit $J \to \infty$ the Brillouin function goes over into the Langevin function. Note that the classical magnetic moment μ is defined so that

$$\lim_{J \to \infty} (gJ\mu_B) \to \mu.$$

9.4. Some organic molecules have a triplet $(S = 1)$ excited state not far above a singlet $(S = 0)$ ground state. Plot the susceptibility as a function of temperature for a zero field splitting $\Delta/k = 100°K$, where k is the Boltzmann constant. Show that the susceptibility for $kT \gg \Delta$ is approximately independent of Δ.

9.5.* Following the discussion in Appendix I, show that to the first order in λ/Δ the g value measured in the x direction of the system discussed there is equal to 2. The anisotropy in the g value leads to an anisotropy in the susceptibility. Actual paramagnetic salts may exhibit quite large anisotropies in the susceptibility, amounting, for example, to 30 % in $Co(NH_4)_2(SO_4)_2 \cdot 6H_2O$.

9.6. Making *rough* calculations, compare the entropy (for $H = 0$) at 2°K of 1 cm^3 of the salt iron ammonium alum, $FeNH_4(SO_4)_2 \cdot 12H_2O$, with that of 1 cm^3 of lead at the same temperature. This result shows that one may use the salt to cool other substances. At 2°K, $T/\theta_0 > 10$ for iron ammonium alum, where $k\theta_0$ is the zero field splitting.

9.7. A paramagnetic salt contains 10^{22} ions/cm^3 with magnetic moment 1 Bohr magneton. Calculate the surplus fraction, i.e., the percentage indicating how many more are parallel rather than antiparallel to a magnetic field of 10,000 gauss at 300°K.

9.8.* Derive (I.1) in Appendix I, neglecting terms of order $(\lambda/\Delta)^2$.

REFERENCES

L. F. Bates, *Modern magnetism*, Cambridge University Press, Cambridge, 3rd ed., 1951.

B. Bleaney and K. W. H. Stevens, "Paramagnetic resonance," Rept. Prog. Phys. **16**, 108 (1953).

H. B. G. Casimir, *Magnetism and very low temperatures*, Cambridge University Press, Cambridge, 1940.

K. K. Darrow, "Magnetic resonance," Bell System Tech. J. **32**, 74–99, 384–405 (1953).

C. J. Gorter, *Paramagnetic relaxation*, Elsevier, Amsterdam, 1947.

International Conference on Spectroscopy at Radiofrequencies, Physica **17**, 169 (1951).

C. Kikuchi and R. D. Spence, "Microwave methods in physics: II. Microwave absorption in paramagnetic substances," Am. J. Phys. **18**, 167 (1950).

G. E. Pake, "Fundamentals of nuclear magnetic resonance absorption," Am. J. Phys. **18**, 438, 473 (1950).

J. H. Van Vleck, "Quelques aspects de la théorie du magnétisme," Ann. inst. Henri Poincaré **10**, 57 (1947).

J. H. Van Vleck, *The theory of electric and magnetic susceptibilities*, Clarendon Press, Oxford, 1932.

10

Ferromagnetism
and Antiferromagnetism

We discuss first in this chapter the physical origin and properties of the saturation magnetization in ferromagnetics, and the interpretation of gyromagnetic and spin resonance experiments. The properties of ferromagnetic materials of interest in technical applications are closely related to the domain structure. We develop for simple situations the theory of ferromagnetic domains. An introduction to the behavior of antiferromagnetic substances and ferrites is presented.

CURIE POINT AND THE EXCHANGE INTEGRAL

We call a substance ferromagnetic if it possesses a spontaneous magnetic moment, that is, a magnetic moment even in the absence of an applied magnetic field. The saturation magnetization M_s is defined as the spontaneous magnetic moment per unit volume. In technical literature the saturation flux density $B_s = 4\pi M_s$ is often used. The Curie point T_c is the temperature above which the spontaneous moment vanishes.

If we could add to a paramagnetic substance an interaction tending to make the ionic and atomic magnetic moments line up the same way, we would have a ferromagnetic substance. Let us postulate such an interaction and call it the Weiss field.[1] The orienting effect of the Weiss field is opposed by the motion of thermal agitation of the elementary moments. We consider the Weiss field the equivalent of an effective magnetic field H_E acting on the electron spins. The interaction energy of a spin with the Weiss field must be of the order of magnitude of the thermal energy of a spin at the Curie point. Hence

$$(10.1) \qquad gS\mu_B H_E \approx kT_c,$$

or

$$(10.2) \qquad H_E \approx kT_c/gS\mu_B.$$

[1] Also called the molecular field or the exchange field; Weiss was the first to imagine such a field.

For iron we have $T_c \approx 1000°\text{K}$, $g \approx 2$, $S \approx 1$; therefore $H_E \approx 10^{-13}/2 \times 10^{-20} = 5 \times 10^6$ oersteds. This field is much stronger than that produced by the magnetic moments of the other ions in the crystal, as the magnetic interaction is only $\sim \mu_B/a^3 \sim 10^3$ oersteds, where a is the lattice constant.

Pierre Weiss (1907), inventor of this concept, showed that it will account for several important attributes of ferromagnetism provided that one assumes that the Weiss field H_E is proportional to the magnetization:

$$(10.3) \qquad H_E = \lambda M,$$

where λ stands for a constant called the Weiss field constant. The susceptibility above the Curie point is deduced by postulating that the Curie law (9.4) holds if we take as the magnetic field the sum of the applied field H and the Weiss field H_E. Then

$$(10.4) \qquad \frac{M}{H + \lambda M} = \frac{C}{T},$$

or

$$(10.5) \qquad \chi = \frac{M}{H} = \frac{C}{T - C\lambda}.$$

This gives a non-zero magnetization for zero applied field at the Curie point expressed by

$$(10.6) \qquad T_c = C\lambda,$$

so that

$$(10.7) \qquad \chi = \frac{C}{T - T_c}.$$

This expression, known as the Curie-Weiss law, describes quite well the observed susceptibility variation in the paramagnetic region above the Curie point.[2] From (10.6) and the definition (9.4) and (9.12) of the Curie constant C we may determine the value of the Weiss field constant:

$$(10.8) \qquad \lambda^{-1} = C/T_c = Ng^2 S(S + 1)\mu_B{}^2/3kT_c,$$

so that for iron, $\lambda \approx (4 \times 10^{-13})/(8 \times 10^{-17}) \approx 5000$, in agreement with the earlier estimate of H_E.

[2] Experimentally the susceptibility well above the Curie point is given quite accurately by $C/(T - \theta)$, where θ, called the paramagnetic Curie point, may be slightly greater than the actual transition temperature (ferromagnetic Curie point) T_c.

The physical origin of the Weiss field is in the quantum-mechanical exchange integral, as pointed out by Heisenberg (1928). On certain assumptions it can be shown[3] that the energy of interaction of atoms i, j bearing spins S_i, S_j contains a term

(10.9) $$W_{ex} = -2J S_i \cdot S_j,$$

where J is the exchange integral and is related to the overlap of the charge distributions i, j. The exchange energy has no classical analogue. It expresses the difference in Coulomb interaction energy of the systems when the spins are parallel or antiparallel. It is a consequence of the Pauli exclusion princple that in quantum mechanics one cannot usually change the relative direction of two spins without making changes in the spatial charge distribution in the overlap region. The resulting changes in the coulomb energy of the system may conveniently be written in the form[4] (10.9), so that it appears *as if* there were a direct coupling between the spins S_i, S_j.

We establish an approximate connection between the exchange integral J and the Weiss field constant λ. Suppose that the atom under consideration has z nearest neighbors, each connected with the central atom by the interaction J; for more distant neighbors we take J as zero. Then the interaction energy may be written, neglecting components of S perpendicular to the average magnetization,

$$W_{ex} \cong -2Jz\bar{S}^2 = -g\bar{S}\mu_B H_E = -g\bar{S}\mu_B\lambda(g\bar{S}\mu_B\Omega^{-1}),$$

where the term in parentheses is equal to M_s; here Ω is the atomic volume. Then

(10.10) $$J = \lambda g^2\mu_B^2/2z\Omega,$$

and, using (10.8) and recalling that $N = 1/\Omega$,

(10.11) $$J = \frac{3kT_c}{2zS(S+1)},$$

This is the connection, as given by the Weiss field theory, between the exchange integral and the Curie point. More exact quantum statistics give somewhat different results. For a simple cubic lattice ($z = 6$)

---

[3] This is shown in most texts on quantum theory; see also J. H. Van Vleck, Revs. Modern Phys. **17**, 27 (1945).

[4] Equation (10.9) is really an operator equation in the spin operators S_i, S_j, but for many purposes in ferromagnetism it is a good approximation to treat the spins as classical vectors.

with $S = \frac{1}{2}$ various calculations give the results below.

	J/kT_c
P. Weiss theory (10.11)	0.333
Opechowski[5]	0.518
P. R. Weiss[6]	0.540

For a body-centered cubic lattice with spin 1, P. R. Weiss calculates $J/kT_c = 0.1502$; substituting $T_c = 1043°K$ for iron, we have $J = 160k$.

TEMPERATURE DEPENDENCE OF THE SPONTANEOUS MAGNETIZATION

On the Weiss theory we must use the complete expression (9.10) for the magnetization in calculating the spontaneous magnetization

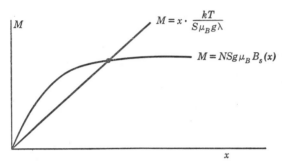

Fig. 10.1. Method for finding the spontaneous magnetization at a temperature T, according to the Weiss theory. The value of M_s is given by the intersection of the two curves.

as a function of temperature. We have

(10.12) $$M_s = NSg\mu_B B_s(x),$$

where now in the absence of an applied magnetic field

(10.13) $$x = Sg\mu_B\lambda M_s/kT.$$

At a temperature $T < T_c$ we obtain M_s by plotting M_s vs. x as given by both (10.12) and (10.13) and looking for the intercept of the two curves, as shown in Fig. 10.1. The Curie point is the highest temperature for which the curves have an intercept; as defined in this way it is consistent with the earlier result (10.6).

The curves of M_s vs. T obtained in this way reproduce the general features of the experimental results, as shown in Fig. 10.2 for nickel.

[5] W. Opechowski, Physica **4**, 181 (1937); **6**, 1112 (1939); V. Zehler, Z. Naturforsch. **5A**, 344 (1950).

[6] P. R. Weiss, Phys. Rev. **74**, 1493 (1948).

At low temperatures, $T/T_c \ll 1$, a quantum treatment using the method of spin waves (Appendix J) predicts

$$(10.14) \qquad M_s(T) = M_s(0)[1 - CT^{3/2} - \cdots],$$

where, for a body-centered cubic structure and spin S,

$$(10.15) \qquad C = (0.0587/2S)(k/2SJ)^{3/2};$$

the constant C should not be confused with the Curie constant. For a face-centered cubic structure the right side of (10.15) is multiplied by

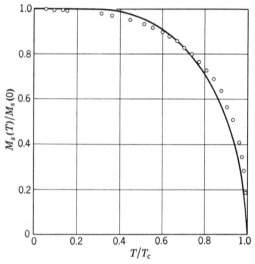

Fig. 10.2.   Saturation magnetization of nickel as a function of temperature, together with the theoretical curve for $S = \frac{1}{2}$ on the Weiss theory.   [Experimental values by P. Weiss and R. Forrer, Ann. phys. **5**, 153 (1926).]

$\frac{1}{2}$.   Expression (10.14) is known as the Bloch $T^{3/2}$ law; it is in quite good agreement with observation in the very low temperature region.   At somewhat higher temperatures a T^2 term is dominant, and it is explained by Stoner[7] on a collective electron theory.   Experimental values[8] of C follow:

Substance	C $(°K)^{-3/2}$	J	
Iron	3.5×10^{-6}	$205k$	$(S = 1)$
Nickel	8.6×10^{-6}	$230k$	$(S = \frac{1}{2})$

[7] E. C. Stoner, Repts. Prog. Phys. **11**, 43 (1948); Proc. Roy. Soc. (London) **A165**, 372 (1938).

[8] M. Fallot, Ann. Phys. **6**, 305 (1936).

In Table 10.1 are representative values of the spontaneous magnetization, effective magneton number, and Curie point. The effective magneton number n_{eff} relates to the saturation magnetization, and must not be confused with the paramagnetic effective magneton number p defined by (9.13). Observed magneton numbers are usually considerably smaller than the theoretical values calculated from the free ions and also are frequently non-integral. It is possible to modify ionic models to account for the results by allowing mixtures of various ionicity. However, perhaps the most natural way of accounting for the non-integral magneton numbers is to abandon the ionic model and to adopt instead a band or collective electron model[9] on which the $3d$ electrons, for example, are visualized as being in two energy bands,[10] as in Fig. 10.3, one for electrons with spin up and the other for electrons with spin down. The bands are separated in energy by the exchange interaction.

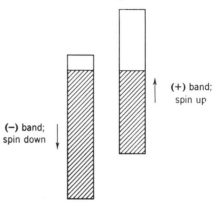

Fig. 10.3. Schematic explanation (for $3d$ electrons) of non-integral magneton numbers, on the band model. The $+$ and $-$ bands contain 5 states per atom each. The case of 7 electrons, 4.25 in one band and 2.75 in the other, is shown; the effective magneton number is 1.5.

GYROMAGNETIC AND SPIN RESONANCE EXPERIMENTS

GYROMAGNETIC EXPERIMENTS

Gyromagnetic experiments identify the magnetization in ferromagnetics as arising largely from the electron spin, rather than from the orbital moment. The magnetomechanical ratio is defined as the ratio of the magnetic moment to the angular momentum. It is useful to equate the ratio to $g'e/2mc$, where g' is called the *magnetomechanical factor*.[11] For an electron spin the magnetic moment is $\mu_B = e\hbar/2mc$,

[9] J. C. Slater, Phys. Rev. **49**, 537 (1936); E. C. Stoner, Proc. Roy. Soc. (London) **A165**, 372 (1938); **A169**, 339 (1939); M. F. Manning, Phys. Rev. **63**, 190 (1943); for a recent attempt at an alternative explanation, see C. Zener, Phys. Rev. **81**, 440 (1951); **83**, 299 (1951); **85**, 324 (1952).

[10] The concept of energy bands is discussed in Chapter 13.

[11] This quantity, which is useful for comparison with the microwave resonance experiments, is sometimes called the gyromagnetic ratio, but strictly speaking the gyromagnetic ratio is the reciprocal of the magnetomechanical ratio.

and the angular momentum is $\hbar/2$; the ratio is e/mc, so that $g_{\text{spin}}' = 2$. For orbital motion of an electron the magnetic moment z component is $L_z(e\hbar/2mc)$ and the angular momentum is $L_z\hbar$; therefore $g_{\text{orbit}}' = 1$. The experimental values of g' in ferromagnetic substances are usually between 1.85 and 2.0, showing that the major contribution comes from electron spin.

TABLE 10.1.   EFFECTIVE NUMBER n_{eff} OF BOHR MAGNETONS PER MAGNETIC ATOM, AND DATA ON SATURATION MAGNETIZATION AND CURIE POINTS

(General reference: R. M. Bozorth, *Ferromagnetism*, Van Nostrand, New York, 1951.)

Substance	Saturation magnetization M_s		n_{eff} (0°K)	Ferromagnetic Curie Temperature (°K)
	Room temperature	0°K		
Fe	1707	1752	2.221	1043
Co	1400	1446	1.716	1400
Ni	485	510	0.606	631
Gd	....	1980	7.10	289
Dy	....	....	.....	105
MnBi	600	675	3.52	630
Cu$_2$MnAl	430	(580)	(4.0)	603
Cu$_2$MnIn	500	(600)	(4.0)	506
MnAs	670	870	3.40	318
MnB	147	....	.....	533
Mn$_4$N •	183	....	0.24	745
MnSb	710	....	3.53	587
CrTe	240	....	2.39	336
CrO$_2$	....	....	2.07	....
MnOFe$_2$O$_3$	358	....	5.0†	783
FeOFe$_2$O$_3$	485	....	4.2†	848
CoOFe$_2$O$_3$	....	....	3.3†	793
NiOFe$_2$O$_3$	240	....	2.3†	863
CuOFe$_2$O$_3$	290	....	1.3†	728
MgOFe$_2$O$_3$	143	....	1.1†	583

† Calculated per molecule MOFe$_2$O$_3$, where M is the bivalent cation.

The two principal gyromagnetic methods are (1) the *Einstein-de Haas method*, in which one reverses the magnetization of a freely suspended specimen and observes the resulting rotation; and (2) the *Barnett method*, in which one rotates the specimen and observes the resulting magnetization.

We shall discuss the Einstein-de Haas method, which is illustrated in Fig. 10.4.   If no external torques act on the system during magnetization reversal, and if the system does not radiate, the total angular momentum change must be zero:

(10.16) $\Delta \mathbf{J} = 0$.

The total angular momentum is the sum of contributions from spin, orbit, and crystal lattice motions:

(10.17) $\mathbf{J} = \mathbf{J}_{\text{spin}} + \mathbf{J}_{\text{orbit}} + \mathbf{J}_{\text{lattice}}$.

We actually observe $\Delta J_{\text{lattice}}$. The magnetic moment change is

(10.18) $\Delta \mathfrak{M} = \Delta(\mathfrak{M}_{\text{spin}} + \mathfrak{M}_{\text{orbit}} + \mathfrak{M}_{\text{lattice}})$,

but the lattice contribution here may be neglected because of the relatively large mass of the positive ions composing the lattice—the positive ions rotate too slowly to produce a significant magnetic moment. Thus what we measure in an experiment is

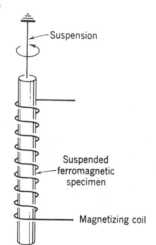

(10.19) $\dfrac{g'e}{2mc} = \dfrac{\Delta(\mathfrak{M}_{\text{spin}} + \mathfrak{M}_{\text{orbit}})}{-\Delta J_{\text{lattice}}}$

$\qquad\qquad = \dfrac{\Delta(\mathfrak{M}_{\text{spin}} + \mathfrak{M}_{\text{orbit}})}{\Delta(J_{\text{spin}} + J_{\text{orbit}})}$,

from (10.16) and (10.17). If we suppose that

(10.20) $J_{\text{orbit}}/J_{\text{spin}} = 2\varepsilon$,

we must have

(10.21) $\mathfrak{M}_{\text{orbit}}/\mathfrak{M}_{\text{spin}} = \varepsilon$,

so that, for $\varepsilon \ll 1$,

(10.22) $g' \cong 2(1 - \varepsilon)$.

We see that ε is a measure of the extent to which the orbital moment participates in the magnetization. If the orbital moment were completely quenched in the sense of Chapter 9, then $\varepsilon = 0$ and $g' = 2$. Experimental values of g' and ε are given in Table 10.2.

Fig. 10.4. Einstein-de Haas gyromagnetic experiment. When the current in the magnetizing coil is reversed, the magnetization in the specimen is reversed and the specimen rotates.

FERROMAGNETIC RESONANCE ABSORPTION

Spin resonance absorption experiments at microwave frequencies in ferromagnetic substances are closely similar in princple to the nuclear and electronic spin resonance experiments described in Chapter 9. The total magnetic moment of the specimen precesses about the direction of the static magnetic field, and energy is absorbed strongly from the r-f transverse field when its frequency is equal to the precessional frequency. We may equally well think of the macroscopic vector representing the total spin of the entire saturated ferromagnet as quantized in the large static field, with energy levels separated by the order of the usual Zeeman frequencies; the selection rule $\Delta m_s = \pm 1$ allows transitions only between adjacent levels.

TABLE 10.2. SUMMARY OF RESULTS OF GYROMAGNETIC EXPERIMENTS

[Reference: S. J. Barnett, Proc. Am. Acad. Arts Sci., **75**, 109 (1944); the experimental situation is not yet stabilized: cf. G. G. Scott, Phys. Rev. **82**, 542 (1951); **87**, 697 (1952); and A. J. P. Meyer, J. phys. et radium **12**, 303 (1951)].

Substance	g'	ε (Eq. 10.22)
Iron	1.93	0.04
Cobalt	1.87	0.07
Nickel	1.92	0.04
Magnetite, Fe_3O_4	1.93	0.04
Heusler alloy, Cu_2MnAl	2.00	0.00
Permalloy, 78% Ni, 22% Fe	1.91	0.05

Ferromagnetic resonance was discovered first in experiments by Griffiths.[12] An unusually sharp resonance line (Fig. 10.5) was found in the Ni-Fe alloy Supermalloy by Yager and Bozorth.[13] A schematic experimental arrangement is shown in Fig. 10.6. In the experiments it is found that the apparent g values are often very much higher than the free electron g value 2.00 when the results are interpreted in terms the usual resonance relation (9.24):

$$(10.23) \qquad \omega = (ge/2mc)H.$$

It has been shown,[14] when all demagnetizing effects are included, that, with the usual experimental arrangement—a thin disk specimen with the static field H parallel to the disk—the resonance relation becomes

$$(10.24) \qquad \omega = (ge/2mc)(BH)^{\frac{1}{2}},$$

where $B = H + 4\pi M_s$. Several g values obtained in this way are given in Table 10.3. The values are close to the free spin value and are independent of the frequency at which the experiments are performed, when the appropriate B and H values are used.

[12] J. H. E. Griffiths, Nature **158**, 670 (1946).
[13] W. A. Yager and R. M. Bozorth, Phys. Rev. **72**, 80 (1947).
[14] C. Kittel, Phys. Rev. **71**, 270 (1947); **73**, 155 (1948).

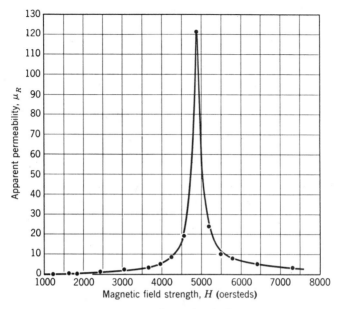

Fig. 10.5. Ferromagnetic resonance absorption in Supermalloy, near 24,000 mc. (After W. A. Yager.)

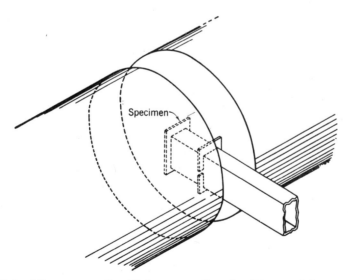

Fig. 10.6. Microwave cavity with ferromagnetic end wall in gap of electromagnet.

The derivation of (10.24) is straightforward. We start with (9.30):

$$d\mathbf{M}/dt = \gamma \mathbf{M} \times \mathbf{H},$$

with $\gamma = ge/2mc$. If the sample is thin in the y direction, the demagnetizing factors are $N_x = 0$, $N_y = 4\pi$, $N_z = 0$. The components of $\mathbf{H}$ are $(H_x, -4\pi M_y, H)$, where H_x is the r-f field; $H_y = -4\pi M_y$ is the demagnetizing field which arises when in the course of the precession the magnetization vector acquires a component M_y in the y direction; and H is the static field in the z direction. Then, for time dependence $e^{i\omega t}$ and neglecting squares and products of small quantities on the assumption H_x, M_x, $M_y \ll H_z$, we have

$$i\omega M_x = \gamma(M_y H + 4\pi M_y M_z);$$

(10.25) $$i\omega M_y = \gamma(M_z H_x - M_x H);$$

$$i\omega M_z \cong 0.$$

On substituting for M_y in the first equation, we find

(10.26) $$\chi_x = M_x/H_x = \frac{\chi_0}{1 - (\omega/\omega_0)^2},$$

where

$$\chi_0 = M_z/H.$$

The resonance frequency is

(10.27) $$\omega_0 = \gamma(BH)^{1/2},$$

with

(10.28) $$\gamma = ge/2mc,$$

and $B = H + 4\pi M_z$, where M_z may be taken as M_s.

The constant g as used here is called the *spectroscopic splitting factor;* it is quite similar to the Landé factor used in optical spectroscopy. A theoretical relationship[15] connects g and g', where g' is defined by (10.19) as the result of a gyromagnetic experiment:

(10.29) $$g - 2 \cong 2 - g',$$

as it can be shown (Appendix I) that

(10.30) $$g \cong 2(1 + \varepsilon)$$

[15] J. H. Van Vleck, Phys. Rev. **78**, 266 (1950); D. Polder, Phys. Rev. **73**, 1116 (1948); C. Kittel, Phys. Rev. **76**, 743 (1949).

where ε is defined by (10.21). However, the values of ε given in Table 10.3 as determined by microwave experiments are appreciably higher than the values found in Table 10.2 from gyromagnetic experiments, and the reason for the discrepancy is not yet understood.

TABLE 10.3. SUMMARY OF RESULTS OF FERROMAGNETIC RESONANCE EXPERIMENTS

[For references see C. Kittel, J. phys. et radium **12**, 291 (1951).]

Substance	g	ε (Eq. 10.30)
Iron	2.12–2.17	0.06–0.09
Çobalt	2.22	0.11
Nickel	2.2	0.1
Magnetite, Fe_3O_4	2.2	0.1
Heusler alloy, Cu_2MnAl	2.01	0.005
Permalloy, 78% Ni, 22% Fe	2.07–2.14	0.04–0.07
Supermalloy, 79% Ni, 5% Mn, 16% Fe	2.12–2.20	0.06–0.10

FERROMAGNETIC DOMAINS[16]

At temperatures well below the Curie point the electronic magnetic moments of a ferromagnetic specimen are essentially all lined up, when regarded on a microscopic scale. Yet, looking at a specimen as a whole, the overall moment may be very much less than that corresponding to saturation, and the application of an external magnetic field may be required to saturate the specimen. The behavior observed in single crystals is similar to that in polycrystalline specimens.

F i g . 1 0 . 7 . Schematic domain arrangement for zero resultant magnetic moment in a single crystal.

Weiss explained this phenomenon, the existence of the technical magnetization curve, by assuming that actual specimens are composed of a number of small regions called domains, within each of which the local magnetization is saturated; the directions of magnetization of different domains need not necessarily be parallel, however. A schematic arrangement of domains with zero resultant magnetic moment is shown in Fig. 10.7 for a single crystal.

The increase in the value of the resultant magnetic moment of the specimen under the action of an applied magnetic field may be imagined to take place, according to the domain theory, by two independent processes, as suggested by R. Becker: by an increase in the volume of domains which are favorably oriented with respect to the

[16] Domain theory is reviewed in the article by C. Kittel cited at the end of the chapter. A 16mm motion picture of actual domain movements, entitled "Action pictures of ferromagnetic domains," is available on loan from the Publications Department, Bell Telephone Laboratories, 463 West St., New York 14, N.Y.

field at the expense of unfavorably oriented domains; or by rotation of the directions of magnetization toward the direction of the field. These two methods by which the resultant magnetization may change are shown in Fig. 10.8.

Closer examination reveals that in weak fields the magnetization changes usually proceed by means of domain boundary displacements,

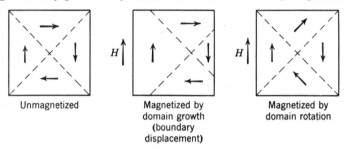

| Unmagnetized | Magnetized by domain growth (boundary displacement) | Magnetized by domain rotation |

Fig. 10.8.   Fundamental magnetization processes.

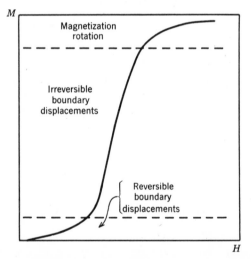

Fig. 10.9.   Representative magnetization curve, showing the dominant magnetization processes in the different regions of the curve.   In some sintered ferrites the regions appear to be divided up in another fashion, with reversible rotation effective at low H.

so that the domains change in size.   In strong fields the magnetization usually changes by means of rotation of the direction of magnetization. A typical magnetization curve is shown in Fig. 10.9; the regions in which each process is dominant are designated.

The domain structure of ferromagnetic materials affects closely the technically important properties, which in a transformer core include high permeability, and in a permanent magnet include high coercive force.[17] By suppressing the possibility of boundary displacement we may achieve a high coercivity; the suppression may be accomplished by using very fine powders or, as in Alnico V, by precipitating a second metallurgical phase so that the specimen is heterogeneous on a very fine scale. By making the material pure, homogeneous, and well-oriented we facilitate boundary displacement and thereby attain high permeability; values of the permeability up to 3.8×10^6 have been reported.[18]

ORIGIN OF DOMAINS

Now we shall show that domain structure is a natural consequence[19] of the various contributions to the energy—exchange, anisotropy, and magnetic—of a ferromagnetic body. The existence of domains may be inferred from the character of the magnetization curve itself. But the most direct evidence of domain structure is furnished by photomicrographs of domain boundaries obtained by the technique of magnetic powder patterns. This method, applied originally by Bitter (1931), has, in the hands of W. C. Elmore and H. J. Williams and his collaborators, provided convincing proof that domains exist and behave as expected theoretically. The powder pattern method consists in placing a drop of a colloidal suspension of finely divided ferromagnetic material, such as magnetite, on the carefully prepared surface of the ferromagnetic crystal under study. It is found on observation through a microscope that the colloid particles in the suspension become strongly concentrated about certain well-defined lines which represent the boundaries between domains magnetized in different directions. The reason why the colloid particles concentrate near these boundaries is that in their vicinity there exist very strong local magnetic fields which attract the magnetic particles. A photograph of a relatively simple domain structure in iron is shown in Fig. 10.10; along with the interpretation derived from the photograph and from certain auxiliary experiments.

[17] The *coercive force* is defined as the reverse field needed to reduce the induction B or the magnetization M to zero, starting in a saturated condition. Usually the definition is understood to refer to B, except in theoretical work. When referred to M, one writes $_IH_c$ or $_MH_c$.

[18] M. Goertz, Phys. Rev. **82**, 340 (1951).

[19] L. Landau and E. Lifshitz, Physik. Z. Sowjetunion **8**, 153 (1935); L. Néel, J. phys. radium **5**, 241, 265 (1944), has extended the calculations to other geometries, and his results have been verified experimentally by L. F. Bates and F. E. Neale, Physica **15**, 220 (1949).

We may understand the origin of domains by considering the structures shown in Fig. 10.11, each representing a cross section through a ferromagnetic single crystal.   In (a) we have a saturated configuration consisting of a single domain; as a consequence of the magnetic "poles" formed on the surfaces of the crystal this configuration will have a high value of the magnetic energy $(1/8\pi)\int H^2\, dV$.   The magnetic energy for a square cross section will be of the order of $M_s{}^2 \approx 10^6$ ergs/cc; here M_s denotes the saturation magnetization.

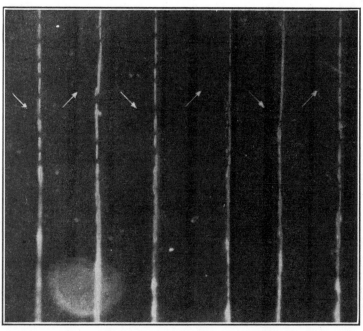

Fig. 10.10.   Simple domain structure in Si-Fe single crystal.   [After Williams, Bozorth, and Shockley, Phys. Rev. **75**, 155 (1949).]

In (b) the magnetic energy has been reduced by a factor of roughly one-half as a result of dividing the crystal into two domains magnetized in opposite directions.   The subdivision process may be carried further as in (c): with N domains it turns out that the magnetic energy is reduced (because of the reduced spatial extension of the field) to approximately $1/N$ of the magnetic energy of the saturated configuration (a).

The subdivision process continues until the energy required to establish an additional boundary layer or interface, separating two domains magnetized oppositely, is greater than the reduction in magnetic field energy consequent on the finer subdivision.   A boundary layer does have a certain amount of energy associated with it: on opposite sides of the boundary the magnetization is directed in anti-parallel directions; as the exchange forces favor parallel and oppose antiparallel orientations of the magnetization, energy will be required to establish a boundary layer. Later we shall calculate this energy and we shall find that it is of the order of 1 erg/cm^2. If then we suppose tentatively that there are $N = 10^3$ domains/cm, the total boundary energy in a crystal cube 1 cm on each edge will be of the order of 10^3 ergs and the magnetic energy will also be of the order of 10^3 ergs.

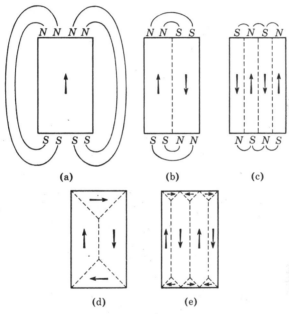

Fig. 10.11.   The origin of domains.

This situation represents approximately the equilibrium number of domains for the particular geometrical arrangement shown.

It is possible to devise domain arrangements such as (d) and (e) for which the magnetic energy is zero. Here the boundaries of the triangular prism domains (termed "domains of closure") near the end faces of the crystal make equal angles—45°—with the magnetization in the rectangular domains and with the magnetization in the domains of closure: therefore the component of magnetization normal to the boundary is continuous across the boundary, and no poles are formed anywhere in the crystal. As there are no poles there is no magnetic field associated with the magnetization, and we may speak of the flux circuit being completed within the crystal—thus giving rise to the phrase "domains of closure" for the domains near the surfaces of the crystal which act to complete the flux circuit.

The energy required to form a domain of closure in a uniaxial crystal such as cobalt comes principally from what is called the *crystalline anisotropy energy*. The anisotropy energy tends to make the magnetization of a domain line up along certain crystallographic axes. The axes thus favored are known as preferred axes, or axes of easy magnetization. Such axes are well-established experimentally, and it is known that a considerably larger amount of energy may be required to saturate a specimen along an arbitrary axis than along one of the preferred axes. In cobalt the hexagonal axis of the crystal

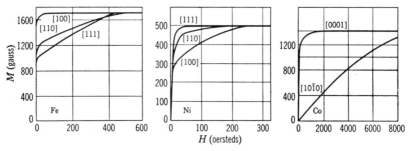

Fig. 10.12.   Magnetization curves for single crystals of iron, nickel, and cobalt. (After Honda and Kaya.)

is the only preferred axis, and cobalt is accordingly referred to as uniaxial. In iron, which is cubic, the preferred axes are the cube edges; in nickel, which is also cubic, the preferred axes are the body diagonals. Figure 10.12 shows magnetization curves for iron, nickel, and cobalt in directions of easy and hard magnetization.

In cobalt, if the basic rectangular domains are magnetized along the easy axis of magnetization, the domains of closure will by necessity be magnetized in hard directions. In a cubic crystal such as iron it is possible for both the basic domains and the closure domains to be magnetized along different easy axes. The energy expenditure in this case arises from magnetostriction: since the closure domains are magnetized along different axes from the basic domains, they will tend to be elongated by magnetostriction along different axes, and in order to fit the various domains together in the crystal structure we have to do work against elastic forces. Magnetostriction is the change of length with magnetization direction.

The termination structures revealed by powder patterns are often more complicated than the simple cases we have discussed, but *domain structure always has its origin in the possibility of lowering the energy*

*of a system by going from a saturated configuration with high magnetic
energy to a domain configuration with a lower energy.*

A particularly simple type of domain structure is shown in Fig.
10.13; this structure has been obtained by Williams and Shockley[20]
with a single crystal of silicon iron which was cut to the form of a
hollow rectangle with legs accurately parallel to [001] and [010] crystal
axes. When the crystal is saturated entirely in one sense the domain
boundaries are the 45° lines shown in (a); when part of the crystal is
magnetized clockwise and part counterclockwise, the square-shaped
boundary in (b) is formed in addition. Magnetization changes are
then found to take place by the movement of the square-shaped

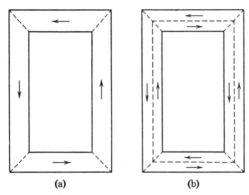

(a)   (b)

Fig. 10.13. Simple domain structures in single crystal of iron in form of rectangular loop, with legs parallel to [001] and [010] axes.

boundary, the flux changes corresponding quantitatively to the displacements of the domain wall.

COERCIVE FORCE AND HYSTERESIS

The coercive force is perhaps the most sensitive property of ferromagnetic materials which is subject to our control, and it is one of the
most important criteria in the selection of ferromagnetic materials for
practical application. The essential difference between material for
permanent magnets and material for transformer cores lies in the
coercive force, which may range from the value of 600 oersteds in a
loudspeaker magnet (Alnico V) and 20,000 in a special high stability
magnet (Fe-Pt) to the value of 0.5 in a commercial power transformer
(Si-Fe) or 0.004 in a pulse transformer (Supermalloy). Thus the
coercive force may be varied over a range of 5×10^6.

[20] H. J. Williams and W. Shockley, Phys. Rev. **75**, 178 (1949).

The problem of the theory is to interpret the observed values of the coercivity in terms of the physical state of the material. A certain amount of progress has been made, although the problem is beset with the usual difficulty in determining quantitatively the relevant physical factors such as impurities, lattice imperfections, and internal strains. The saturation hysteresis loss at low frequencies is closely related to the coercive force, since the area enclosed by the hysteresis loop is approximately given by the product of the saturation induction B_s and the coercive force.

The coercive force in "magnetically soft" (low H_c) materials may be understood from the following: The total energy of a given specimen

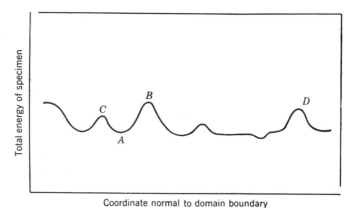

Coordinate normal to domain boundary

Fig. 10.14.   Variation in energy of specimen as a function of the position of the boundary.

may vary with the position of a domain boundary because of local variations in internal strains, impurities, crystallite dimensions, etc.; the variation is indicated schematically in Fig. 10.14. In the absence of an applied magnetic field the boundary will be situated at some minimum position such as A in the figure. In the presence of a field the boundary will be unable to make a large displacement to the extreme right (D) unless the energy is increased by a sufficient amount to enable the boundary to pass over the point B corresponding to the maximum boundary energy. The increase in energy must be furnished by the reorientation of the local magnetization M_s in the applied field H, and the value of H which suffices to reverse about one-half of the magnetization of the specimen will be the coercive field H_c.

Qualitatively this picture of the coercive process explains the fact that the coercive force diminishes as the precipitate or impurity content decreases and also as internal strains are removed through annealing (slow cooling); it also explains why it is that alloys containing a precipitated phase may be magnetically hard.

The coercive force of one type of magnetically hard material may be understood from a quite different picture; we refer to materials composed of very small grains or fine powders where each particle is always magnetized to saturation as a single domain. The fact that a sufficiently small particle, with diameter less than 10^{-4} or 10^{-5} cm, is composed of a single domain is a result of domain theory which has been confirmed by experiment. It can be shown[21] that with such very small particles the formation of a domain boundary is energetically unfavorable, frequently because too large a proportion of the volume of a small particle would be contained within the wall, the wall thickness being independent of the particle size.

If a small particle is constrained to remain as a single domain, it will not be possible for magnetization reversal to take place by means of the process of boundary displacement which usually requires relatively weak fields; instead the magnetization of the particle must rotate as a whole, a process which may require large fields depending on the anisotropy energy of the material or the shape of the particle: the reason is that we must rotate the magnetization over the energy hump corresponding to a direction of hard magnetization.

The coercive force of fine iron particles is expected theoretically to be about 250 oersteds on the basis of rotation opposed by the crystalline anisotropy energy, and this is of the order of the value reported by several observers. Similarly the high coercivity of powders of MnBi ($_tH_c > 12{,}000$), according to Guillaud, seems to be in line with the rotation concept, with anisotropy energy as the factor opposing rotation.

REVERSIBLE PERMEABILITY

The extent of the range of field strength over which the permeability is reversible is determined by the distance through which a domain boundary may move without passing over a peak in the curve of wall energy vs. distance; with reference to Fig. 10.14, one such region of reversible permeability is the region CAB; when the domain boundary leaves this region it moves irreversibly to the extreme right or extreme left of the figure.

The reversible permeability is determined by the irregularities of the curve of boundary energy vs. displacement, and thus is determined by

[21] C. Kittel, Phys. Rev. 70, 965 (1946); E. C. Stoner and E. P. Wohlfarth, Trans. Roy. Soc. (London) A240, 599 (1948); L. Néel, Compt. rend. 224, 1488 (1947).

essentially the same physical conditions as the coercive force. A comparison of the initial permeability μ_0 and the coercive force H_c for a wide range of magnetic materials is shown in Fig. 10.15. There is a very close correlation, materials with high coercivities having low permeabilities, and vice versa.

ANISOTROPY ENERGY

The anisotropy energy'or, as it is sometimes called, the magnetocrystalline energy of a ferromagnetic crystal acts in such a way that

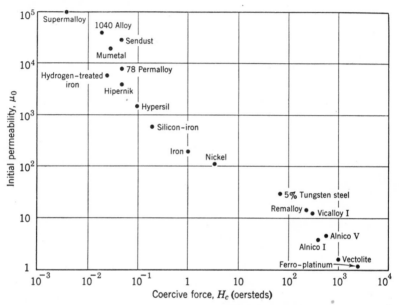

Fig. 10.15.   Correlation between the initial permeability and coercive force of a wide range of magnetic materials.

the magnetization tends to be directed along certain definite crystallographic axes which, accordingly, are called directions of easy magnetization; the directions along which it is most difficult to magnetize the crystal are called hard directions.   It is found experimentally to require the expenditure of a certain, and often considerable, amount of energy to magnetize a crystal to saturation in a hard direction, referred to the lower energy required to saturate along a direction of easy magnetization.   The excess energy required in the hard direction is the anisotropy energy.

As an example of anisotropy energy we may consider cobalt, which is a hexagonal crystal.   The direction of the hexagonal axis is the direction of easy magnetization (at room temperature), while all directions in the basal plane, normal to the axis, are hard directions. The magnetization curves of a single crystal of cobalt are shown in Fig. 10.12. The energy represented by the magnetization curve in the hard direction is given by $\int H \, dI$ per unit volume and amounts to an excess energy of about 5×10^6 ergs/cc for the curve shown.

The origin of the anisotropy energy is believed to be largely the result of the combined effects of spin orbit interaction and the partial quenching of the orbital angular momentum (by inhomogeneous crystalline electric fields and by orbital exchange interaction with neighboring atoms). The magnetization of the crystal "sees" the crystal lattice through the agency of the orbital motion of the electrons; the spin interacts with the orbital motion by means of the spin orbit coupling, and the orbital motion in turn interacts with the crystal structure by means of the electrostatic fields and overlapping wave functions associated with neighboring atoms in the lattice. The theory as developed along these lines is quite complicated. The present theoretical position has been reviewed by Van Vleck.[22]

In cobalt it is found that a very good representation of the experimental observations is given by the two terms:

$$(10.31) \qquad f_k = K_1' \sin^2 \theta + K_2' \sin^4 \theta,$$

where θ is the angle the magnetization makes with the hexagonal axis. At room temperature

$$K_1' = 4.1 \times 10^6 \text{ ergs/cm}^3; \qquad K_2' = 1.0 \times 10^6 \text{ ergs/cm}^3.$$

Iron is a cubic crystal, and the magnetization curves (Fig. 10.12) show that the cube edges [100], [010], and [001] are the directions of easy magnetization, while the body diagonals ([111] and equivalent axes) are hard directions. The excess work done in magnetizing along [111] is about 1.4×10^5 ergs/cm^3 room temperature.

In attempting to represent the anisotropy energy of iron in an arbitrary direction with direction cosines α_1, α_2, α_3 referred to the cube edges, we are guided by the restrictions imposed by cubic symmetry. For example, the expression for the anisotropy energy must be an even power of each α_i, and it must be invariant under interchanges of the α_i among themselves. The lowest order combination satisfying the symmetry requirements is $\alpha_1^2 + \alpha_2^2 + \alpha_3^2$, but this is identically equal to unity and does not describe anisotropy effects. The next

[22] J. H. Van Vleck, Quelques aspects de la théorie du magnétisme, Ann. inst. Henri Poincaré 10, 57 (1947); H. Brooks, Phys. Rev. 58, 909 (1940).

combination is of the fourth degree: $\alpha_1{}^2\alpha_2{}^2 + \alpha_1{}^2\alpha_3{}^2 + \alpha_3{}^2\alpha_2{}^2$, and then of the sixth degree: $\alpha_1{}^2\alpha_2{}^2\alpha_3{}^2$. As this is as far as one usually needs to go,

$$(10.32) \quad f_K = K_1(\alpha_1{}^2\alpha_2{}^2 + \alpha_2{}^2\alpha_3{}^2 + \alpha_3{}^2\alpha_1{}^2) + K_2\alpha_1{}^2\alpha_2{}^2\alpha_3{}^2,$$

where, at room temperature,

$$K_1 = 4.2 \times 10^5 \text{ ergs/cm}^3; \quad K_2 = 1.5 \times 10^5 \text{ ergs/cm}^3.$$

Results for iron at other temperatures are shown in Fig. 10.16. For nickel at room temperature $K_1 = -5 \times 10^4$ ergs/cm^3. An excellent

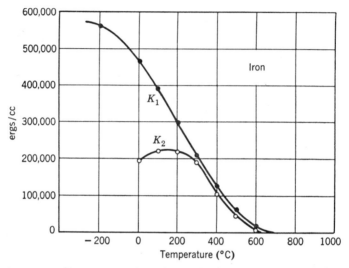

Fig. 10.16.   Temperature dependence of anisotropy constants of iron.

review of anisotropy data is included in the book by Bozorth cited at the end of the chapter.

MAGNETOSTRICTION

It is observed in ferromagnetic single crystals that the length of the crystal in a given direction relative to the crystal axes depends in general on the direction of the magnetization relative to the crystal axes. In cubic crystals the dimensional changes may be expressed approximately by the relation

$$(10.33) \quad \delta l/l = \tfrac{3}{2}\lambda_{100}(\alpha_1{}^2\beta_1{}^2 + \alpha_2{}^2\beta_2{}^2 + \alpha_3{}^2\beta_3{}^2 - \tfrac{1}{3})$$
$$+ 3\lambda_{111}(\alpha_1\alpha_2\beta_1\beta_2 + \alpha_2\alpha_3\beta_2\beta_3 + \alpha_3\alpha_1\beta_3\beta_1),$$

where α_1, α_2, α_3 are the direction cosines of the magnetization direction referred to the cubic axes, and β_1, β_2, β_3 are the direction cosines of the direction in which δl is measured; λ_{100} and λ_{111} are the saturation values of the longitudinal magnetostriction in the directions [100] and [111], respectively. It may be shown that λ_{100} and λ_{111} are simply related to the magnetoelastic coupling constants B_1 and B_2 introduced in Problem 10.3:

$$(10.34) \qquad \lambda_{100} = -\frac{2}{3}\frac{B_1}{c_{11} - c_{12}};$$

$$\lambda_{111} = -\frac{1}{3}\frac{B_2}{c_{44}}.$$

Experimental values are:

	$\lambda_{100} \times 10^6$	$\lambda_{111} \times 10^6$	$B_1 \times 10^6$ ergs/cc	$B_2 \times 10^6$ ergs/cc
Fe	19.5	−18.8	−29	64
Ni	−46	−25	62	90

For nickel, expression (10.33) does not give a very good fit to the observations, and an expression involving four parameters instead of two is often used, as discussed by Becker and Döring in the book cited at the end of the chapter.

Physically it is useful to think of magnetostriction as arising from the dependence of the crystalline anisotropy energy on the state of strain of the lattice: thus it may be energetically favorable for the crystal to deform slightly from the exactly cubic condition if doing so will lower the anisotropy energy by more than the elastic energy is raised.

In devising high permeability materials an effort is often made to find an alloy composition with low magnetostriction (low coupling constants B_1, B_2) so that internal strains will not induce a local anisotropy energy. In Permalloy, for example, both the anisotropy energy and the magnetostriction are very low.

THE BLOCH WALL

The term "Bloch wall" denotes the transition layer which separates adjacent domains magnetized in different directions.

The essential idea of the Bloch wall is that the entire change in spin direction between domains magnetized in different directions does not occur in one discontinuous jump across a single atomic plane. Rather, the change of direction will take place in a gradual way over many atomic planes (Fig. 10.17). The reason for the gradual nature of the change is the fact that for a given total change of spin direction the exchange energy is lower when the change is distributed over many spins than when the change occurs abruptly.

This behavior may be understood from the expression

$$(10.35) \qquad w_{\text{ex}} = JS^2\phi^2$$

for the exchange energy between two spins making a small angle ϕ with each other; here J is the exchange integral and S is the spin quantum number. We obtain this equation by interpreting (10.9) classically, and replacing $\cos \phi$ by $1 - \frac{1}{2}\phi^2$. Let the total desired change of angle be ϕ_0; if the change occurs in N equal steps, the angle

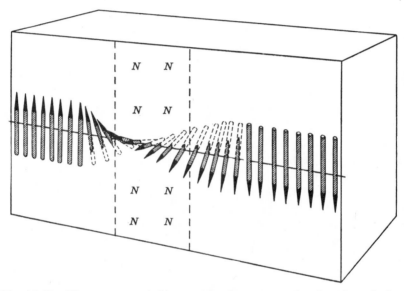

Fig. 10.17.   The structure of the transition layer separating domains.   In iron the thickness of the transition region is about 300 lattice constants.

change between neighboring spins is ϕ_0/N, and the exchange energy between each pair of neighboring atoms is

$$(10.36) \qquad w_{\text{ex}} = JS^2(\phi_0/N)^2.$$

The total exchange energy of the line of $N + 1$ atoms is thus

$$(10.37) \qquad W_{\text{ex}} = JS^2\phi_0{}^2/N.$$

If the total change of angle between domains is $\phi_0 = \pi$, corresponding to a reversal of magnetization direction on passing through the wall, the exchange energy of a line of atoms through a wall 100 atoms in thickness is of the order of $kT_c/100$, as compared with kT_c for a wall only one atom layer in thickness.

Since the exchange energy of a wall is inversely proportional to the thickness (10.37), the wall might spread out until it filled a sizable proportion of the crystal, were it not for the restraining effect of the anisotropy energy, which acts to limit the width of the transition layer. As the spins contained within the wall are largely directed away from the axes of easy magnetization, there is a certain amount of anisotropy energy associated with the wall, roughly proportional to the thickness.

The actual thickness and energy of the transition layer is the result of a balance between the competing claims of exchange energy and anisotropy energy, the former tending to increase the thickness and the latter tending to decrease the thickness.

We proceed to make a rough order-of-magnitude estimate of the thickness and energy of a Bloch wall. Let us consider a wall parallel to the cube face of a simple cubic lattice and separating domains magnetized in opposite directions. We wish to determine the thickness of the wall in terms of the number N of atomic planes contained within the wall, and also to determine the energy per unit surface area, σ_w.

The energy may be represented to a good approximation as the sum of contributions from exchange and anisotropy energies:

$$(10.38) \qquad \sigma_w = \sigma_{\text{ex}} + \sigma_{\text{anis}}.$$

The exchange energy is given approximately by (10.37) for each line of atoms through the wall and normal to the plane of the wall. There are $1/a^2$ such lines per unit area, where a is the lattice constant; whence

$$(10.39) \qquad \sigma_{\text{ex}} = \pi^2 J S^2 / N a^2.$$

The anisotropy energy is of the order of the anisotropy constant times the volume, or

$$(10.40) \qquad \sigma_{\text{anis}} \approx K N a;$$

therefore

$$(10.41) \qquad \sigma_w \approx (\pi^2 J S^2 / N a^2) + K N a,$$

which is a minimum with respect to N when

$$(10.42) \qquad \partial \sigma_w / \partial N = 0 = -(\pi^2 J S^2 / N^2 a^2) + K a$$

or

$$(10.43) \qquad N = (\pi^2 J S^2 / K a^3)^{1/2}.$$

For order of magnitude, in iron,

$$N \approx (k T_c / K a^3)^{1/2} \approx (10^{-13} / 10^5 10^{-23})^{1/2} \approx 300 \text{ lattice constants}$$
$$\approx 1000 \text{ A.}$$

The total wall energy per unit area is

(10.44) $$\sigma_w = 2\pi(JKS^2/a)^{\frac{1}{2}},$$

which in iron is of the order of magnitude

$$\sigma_w = (kT_cK/a)^{\frac{1}{2}} \approx 1 \text{ erg/cm}^2.$$

In the above estimate we have rather arbitrarily supposed that the total change in spin direction is shared equally by each of the N atoms on a line through the wall; we have also used a very rough estimate of the anisotropy energy of the spin system within the wall. More

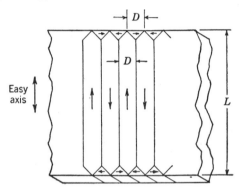

Fig. 10.18.   Flux-closure domain configuration in a uniaxial crystal.

accurate calculation for a 180° wall in a (100) plane gives

(10.45) $$\sigma_w = 2(2K_1JS^2/a)^{\frac{1}{2}},$$

which gives for iron 1.8 ergs/cm².

DOMAIN DIMENSIONS

We carry through, following the original treatment by Landau and Lifshitz, the calculation of the domain width for a flux-closure arrangement of domains (Fig. 10.18) in a uniaxial crystal. The wall energy per unit area of the crystal surface is approximately

$$w_{\text{wall}} = \sigma_w L/D.$$

The volume contained within the domains of closure is oriented in a direction of hard magnetization and involves an energy K per unit volume, where K is the anisotropy constant. Per unit area of crystal surface on one side, the volume in the domains of closure on both sides is $D/2$, so that

(10.46) $$w_{\text{anis}} = KD/2.$$

The wall energy tends to increase the domain width, while the anisotropy energy tends to decrease the width.

The total energy is

$$(10.47) \qquad w = (\sigma_w L/D) + (KD/2)$$

per unit area, and this is a minimum with respect to the domain width D when

$$\partial w/\partial D = -(\sigma_w L/D^2) + (K/2) = 0.$$

The condition for the minimum is then

$$(10.48) \qquad D = (2\sigma_w L/K)^{1/2},$$

and the corresponding energy per unit area is

$$(10.49) \qquad w = (2\sigma_w LK)^{1/2}.$$

The energy per unit volume is

$$(10.50) \qquad f_{\text{domain}} = (2\sigma_w K/L)^{1/2}.$$

If we arbitrarily substitute the approximate values of the constants for iron, and take the length L as 1 cm, we have

$$(10.51) \qquad D = [(2)(2)(1)/4 \times 10^5]^{1/2} \approx 3 \times 10^{-3} \text{ cm}$$

and

$$(10.52) \qquad f \approx 1.3 \times 10^3 \text{ ergs/cm}^3.$$

ANTIFERROMAGNETISM

The antiferromagnetic state is characterized by an ordered antiparallel arrangement of electron spins. When the exchange integral J

Fig. 10.19. Comparison of spin ordering in the ferromagnetic and antiferromagnetic states.

in (10.9) is positive, we have ferromagnetism; when J is negative, we have antiferromagnetism. On passing below the Curie point of an antiferromagnetic the spins lock in (Fig. 10.19) with antiparallel orientations, and at the Curie point the susceptibility attains its maximum value, as shown in Figs. 10.20 and 10.21. We recognize antiferromagnetism by a well-defined kink in the susceptibility vs. temperature curve. The transition is also marked by anomalies in the heat capacity and thermal expansion coefficient.

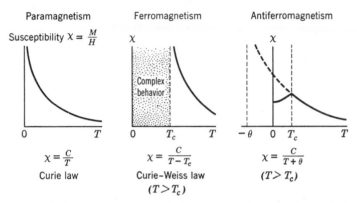

Fig. 10.20. Distinguishing features of the temperature dependence of the magnetic susceptibility in paramagnetism, ferromagnetism, and antiferromagnetism.

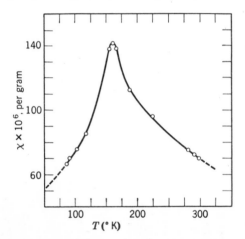

Fig. 10.21. Magnetic susceptibility per gram vs. temperature for manganese selenide. [After C. F. Squire, Phys. Rev. **56**, 922 (1939).]

Antiferromagnetism was first discovered in 1938 by Bizette, Squire, and Tsai,[23] while working with manganese oxide, which has a Curie temperature of 116° to 120°K. Néel[24] and Bitter[25] had presented

[23] Bizette, Squire, and Tsai, Compt. rend. **207**, 449 (1938).
[24] L. Néel, Ann. phys. **18**, 5 (1932); **5**, 232 (1936).
[25] F. Bitter, Phys. Rev. **54**, 79 (1937).

theoretical discussions of the antiferromagnetic state earlier, and Van Vleck[26] gave the first detailed treatment. Table 10.4 summarizes important data regarding antiferromagnetics. The effective magneton numbers, as deduced from the Curie constant C in the high temperature susceptibility, are not tabulated as the

TABLE 10.4. SUMMARY OF ANTIFERROMAGNETIC DATA
The Curie points often vary by considerable amounts between samples, and in some cases there is large thermal hysteresis. For a bibliography relating to experimental data on antiferromagnetic substances, see H. Bizette, J. phys. et radium **12**, 161 (1951). The values for metallic chromium and manganese are from neutron diffraction work by C. Shull (unpublished), and for CrSb from Haraldsen, Rosenquist, and Gronwold, Arch. Math. Naturvidenskab, No. 4, 1948. The value of θ is obtained by fitting an expression of the form $\chi = C/(T + \theta)$ to the susceptibility above the actual transition temperature T_c. In recent literature the transition or Curie temperature is sometimes referred to as the Néel temperature.

Substance	Paramagnetic Ion Lattice	Transition Temperature $T_c(°K)$	Curie-Weiss $\theta(°K)$	θ/T_c	$\dfrac{\chi(0)}{\chi(T_c)}$
MnO	fcc	122	610	5.0	$\frac{2}{3}$
MnS	fcc	165	528	3.2	0.82
MnSe	fcc	~150(?)	~ 435	~3	
MnTe	fcc	307			
MnF$_2$	bc rect.	72	113	1.57	0.76
FeF$_2$	bc rect.	79	117	1.48	0.72
FeCl$_2$	hex. layer	23.5	48	2.0	<0.2
FeO	fcc	198	570	2.9	0.8
CoCl$_2$	hex. layer	24.9	38.1	1.53	
CoO	fcc	291			
NiCl$_2$	hex. layer	49.6	68.2	1.37	
NiO	fcc	523			
α-Mn	complex	~100			
Cr	bcc	475			
CrSb	hex. layer	725	~1000	1.4	$\sim\frac{1}{4}$
Cr$_2$O$_3$	complex	310			
TiCl$_3$	complex	~100			
FeCO$_3$	complex	57			$\sim\frac{1}{4}$

values are generally in close agreement with the values obtaining in ordinary paramagnetic salts (Table 9.2). However, the moments for metallic manganese and chromium are much smaller than the free ion values; Shull finds by neutron diffraction that chromium has 0.4 μ_B and α-manganese 0.5 μ_B.

[26] J. H. Van Vleck, J. Chem. Phys. **9**, 85 (1941).

TWO-SUBLATTICE MODEL

The simplest situation in antiferromagnetism arises when the lattice of paramagnetic ions can be divided into two interpenetrating sublattices A, B such that all nearest neighbors of an ion on sublattice A lie on sublattice B. This condition is, for example, satisfied by the sc and bcc lattices, but not by the fcc lattice. If the only interactions are antiferromagnetic interactions between nearest neighbors, we may write for the magnetization above the Curie point on the Weiss field theory:

$$(10.53) \qquad TM_A = C'(H - \lambda M_B);$$

$$TM_B = C'(H - \lambda M_A).$$

Here C' is the Curie constant for one sublattice, and the effective field on sublattice A is written as $H - \lambda M_B$, which for positive λ corresponds to antiferromagnetic interactions between A and B. Adding,

$$(10.54) \qquad TM = T(M_A + M_B) = 2C'H - C'\lambda M,$$

so that

$$(10.55) \qquad \chi = \frac{2C'}{T + C'\lambda},$$

or

$$(10.56) \qquad \chi = \frac{C}{T + \theta}$$

with

$$(10.57) \qquad C = 2C'; \qquad \theta = C'\lambda.$$

The transition temperature is that below which each sublattice A and B possesses a magnetic moment even without a field. Below the Curie point it is not legitimate to treat the moment as a linear function of the effective field, but, as saturation is not important close to the Curie point, linearity may be assumed in the equations for the Curie point.

The transition temperature T_c is then the temperature at which equations (10.53) have a non-trivial solution for $H = 0$. The condition for this is that the determinant of the coefficients of the unknowns M_A, M_B should be zero:

$$\begin{vmatrix} T & \theta \\ \theta & T \end{vmatrix} = 0$$

or

$$(10.58) \qquad T_c = \theta.$$

On this model the transition temperature T_c should be equal to the constant θ in the Curie-Weiss law (10.56). The experimental values in Table 10.4 indicate that values of θ/T_c are usually of the order 1.5 to 5. Values of θ/T_c of the observed magnitude may be obtained when next nearest neighbor interactions[27] are provided for, and when more general kinds of sublattice arrangements[28] are considered. It is shown in Problem 10.6 that, if a molecular field constant $-\varepsilon$ is introduced to describe interactions within a sublattice, then

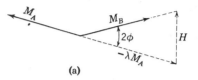

(a)

$$(10.59) \quad \theta/T_c = (\lambda + \varepsilon)/(\lambda - \varepsilon).$$

SUSCEPTIBILITY BELOW THE CURIE POINT

We consider two cases on a two-sublattice model: first, with the applied magnetic field perpendicular to the axis of the spins; and, second, with the field parallel to the axis of the spins. At the Curie point the susceptibility is nearly independent of the direction of the field relative to the domain axis.

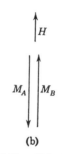

(b)

For $\mathbf{H} \perp \mathbf{M}_A$, $\mathbf{M}_B$ we can calculate the susceptibility on elementary considerations. If the spin systems A, B are turned by the field H so as to make an angle 2ϕ with each other (Fig. 10.22a), the component of the molecular field acting on B in a direction parallel to H will be, for small angles, $-2\lambda M_A\phi$, and at equilibrium this is equal to but opposite H. The total magnetization component parallel to H is $M\phi = (M_A + M_B)\phi = 2M_A\phi$, so that

Fig. 10.22. Calculation of (a) parallel and (b) perpendicular susceptibilities at 0°K, on the molecular field theory.

$$(10.60) \qquad H = \lambda M,$$

or

$$(10.61) \qquad \chi_\perp = \frac{1}{\lambda} \qquad (T \leq T_c).$$

[27] L. Néel, Ann. phys. **3**, 137 (1948).

[28] P. W. Anderson, Phys. Rev. **79**, 350, 705 (1950); J. M. Luttinger, Phys. Rev. **81**, 1015 (1951).

Now, from (10.56) (10.57), and (10.58),

(10.62) $$\chi(T_c) = \frac{1}{\lambda},$$

so that

(10.63) $$\chi_\perp(0) = \chi(T_c).$$

On quantum-mechanical treatments $\chi_\perp(0)$ is somewhat larger than $\chi(T_c)$; therefore (10.61) need not hold.

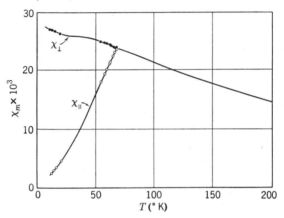

Fig. 10.23. Molar magnetic susceptibility of manganese fluoride, MnF_2, paralle perpendicular to the c axis of the crystal. (After Griffel and Stout.)

In the parallel orientation (Fig. 10.22b) the susceptibility at $T = 0°K$ is zero:

(10.64) $$\chi_\parallel(0) = 0;$$

the spins being at absolute zero all parallel or antiparallel to the field, no torque is exerted on them, and there is no net magnetization. Van Vleck's calculations show that the parallel susceptibility increases smoothly until it reaches the value

(10.65) $$\chi_\parallel(T_c) = \chi_\perp(T_c) = \chi(T_c).$$

Stout and Griffel[29] have verified the anisotropy of χ below the Curie point with measurements on a single crystal of manganese fluoride, as shown in Fig. 10.23.

In a polycrystalline specimen at $0°K$ the mean susceptibility is given by

(10.66) $$\overline{\chi(0)} = \overline{\sin^2 \theta}\,\chi_\perp(0) + \overline{\cos^2 \theta}\,\chi_\parallel(0) = \tfrac{2}{3}\chi(T_c),$$

[29] J. W. Stout and M. Griffel, J. Chem. Phys. **18**, 1455 (1950).

assuming (10.63) and (10.64). The average of $\sin^2 \theta$ over a sphere is $\frac{2}{3}$. The factor $\frac{2}{3}$ is in fair agreement with some of the experimental ratios in Table 10.4. The calculated values will depend on the actual arrangement of the spin lattices.

ANTIFERROMAGNETIC RESONANCE

Spin resonance absorption in antiferromagnetic crystals at temperatures above the Curie point is similar to that observed in para-

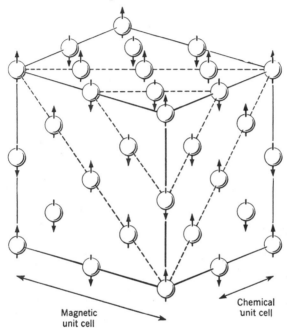

Fig. 10.24. Arrangement of spins of the Mn^{2+} ions in manganese oxide, MnO, as determined by neutron diffraction methods by Shull, Strauser, and Wollan.

magnetic crystals, but below the Curie point there is a strong effective field leading to a zero field splitting of the resonance line. In the simplest situation at 0°K the effective field, apart from the applied magnetic field, is given by[30]

$$(10.67) \qquad H_{\text{eff}} = [H_A(2H_E + H_A)]^{\frac{1}{2}},$$

where H_A is the effective anisotropy field of one sublattice and H_E is the exchange field. For manganese fluoride the effective field amounts

[30] T. Nagamiya, Prog. Theor. Phys. **6**, 342 (1951); C. Kittel, Phys. Rev. **82**, 565 (1951); F. Keffer and C. Kittel, Phys. Rev. **85**, 329 (1952); F. Keffer, Phys. Rev. **87**, 608 (1952).

to 1.0 × 10⁵ oersteds, corresponding to a zero field splitting of 1 mm wavelength. No experiments have as yet been performed on the normal antiferromagnetic salts at wavelengths short enough to detect the predicted effect, but Gorter and co-workers[31] have observed antiferromagnetic resonance in $CuCl_2 \cdot 2H_2O$ with a Curie point near 4°K.

DETERMINATION OF SPIN LATTICES BY NEUTRON DIFFRACTION

Shull[32] and his collaborators have had remarkable success in the determination of the arrangement of spins into lattices in ferromagnetic and antiferromagnetic substances by neutron diffraction experiments. The experimental spin structure of manganese oxide in the antiferromagnetic state is shown in Fig. 10.24. The most surprising feature about the observed spin lattice structure is that it suggests a strong next nearest neighbor interaction. The strength of the next nearest neighbor interaction may be interpreted[28] on the Kramers[33] picture of superexchange, according to which the possibility of excited paramagnetic states of the intervening anion (oxygen in this case) serves to carry the exchange interaction diametrically across the anion, thereby linking the spin systems of two Mn ions situated too far apart for direct exchange to be important.

MAGNETIC PROPERTIES OF FERRITES

The ferrites of magnetic interest belong to the group of compounds of composition represented by the chemical formula $MOFe_2O_3$, where M is a divalent metal ion such as Mn, Co, Ni, Cu, Mg, Zn, Cd, Fe^{2+}, or a mixture of these ions. These ferrites are cubic and have the spinel structure, after the mineral spinel ($MgAlO_4$). Ferrites may be imagined as derived from magnetite, Fe_3O_4, by replacing the ferrous ions by the divalent ions listed above.

Ferrites have acquired great practical interest because their high electrical resistivities are useful in magnetic applications at high frequencies. The resistivities of commercial ferrites are in the range 10^2 to 10^6 ohm-cm, as compared with 10^{-5} ohm-cm for iron. The commercial development is due to Snoek, Verwey, and others at the Philips Laboratories; of most interest are Ferroxcube 3 (Zn-Mn ferrite) and Ferroxcube 4 (Zn-Ni ferrite).

[31] Poulis, van den Handel, Ubbink, Poulis, and Gorter, Phys. Rev. **82**, 552 (1951); Ubbink, Poulis, Gerritsen, and Gorter, Physica **18**, 361 (1951).

[32] Shull, Strauser, and Wollan, Phys. Rev. **83**, 333 (1951)· Shull, Wollan, and Koehler, Phys. Rev. **84**, 912 (1951).

[33] H. A. Kramers, Physica **1**, 182 (1934).

The properties of ferrites are reviewed in the papers by Went and Gorter and by Fairweather *et al.*, cited at the end of the chapter. We mention here several aspects of the Néel theory[34] of the saturation magnetization of ferrites. We note first from Table 10.1 that the value 485 for the saturation magnetization of Fe_3O_4 corresponds only to 4.2 Bohr magnetons per molecule Fe_3O_4, whereas the value expected if the one Fe^{2+} and two Fe^{3+} ions per molecule are lined up parallel to one another is about $14\mu_B$ per molecule. Néel accounts for the discrepancy by supposing that the Fe^{3+} ions are antiparallel to each

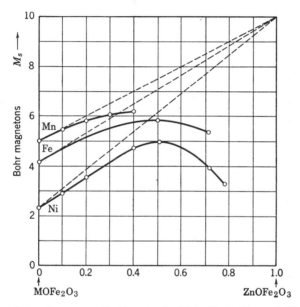

Fig. 10.25. Saturation magnetization of mixed Mn-Zn, Fe-Zn, and Ni-Zn ferrites, as a function of the zinc content. [After J. J. Went and E· W. Gorter, Philips Tech. Rev. **13**, 181 (1952).]

other, so that the resultant moment arises only from the Fe^{2+} ion. This has a moment of $4\mu_B$ corresponding to a spin of 2; the agreement with the observed moment of magnetite is quite satisfactory. Néel terms a situation of this type *ferrimagnetism*; the basic idea was somewhat anticipated by the work of Guillaud on manganese compounds such as MnBi. Néel suggests that all the interactions in ferrites are antiferromagnetic, but shows that the condition of minimum free energy may often require, when two types of ions are involved, that the total magnetization be different from zero.

[34] L. Néel, Ann. phys. **3**, 137 (1948).

The Néel theory accounts in a natural way for the variation with zinc content of the saturation magnetization curves shown in Fig. 10.25. The moments for zero zinc content agree quite well with the idea that the Fe^{3+} ions do not contribute, and the trend of the moments toward zero for $ZnO \cdot Fe_2O_3$ is also plausible, zinc ions being diamagnetic. In the intermediate region the zinc ions cause an unbalance in the system, increasing the total moment. The situation is discussed by Went and Gorter.

The spinel structure may be visualized as a cubic close packing of oxygen ions with the Fe^{3+} and M^{2+} ions distributed among the various interstices between the O^{2-} ions. The unit cell is about 8.4 A on a side and contains 16 tetrahedral interstices (A) each with four O^{2-} nearest neighbors and 32 octahedral interstices (B) each with six O^{2-} nearest neighbors. Half of the tetrahedral and half of the octahedral sites are occupied, thus accommodating 24 metal ions in the unit cell. The exchange interactions $A - A$, $B - B$, and $A - B$ are all antiferromagnetic, but the $A - B$ interaction is usually considerably the strongest, so that the A and B lattices are individually ferromagnetic but with the magnetizations M_A, M_B oppositely directed. If, however, $M_A = O$ as in zinc ferrite, the only effective exchange interaction is $B - B$, so that the B ions will be antiferromagnetically ordered and $M_B = 0$.

The circumstance that three antiferromagnetic interactions can result in ferromagnetism is worth looking into more closely. The molecular fields acting on the A and B spin lattices may be written

(10.68) $$H_A = -\lambda M_A - \mu M_B;$$

$$H_B = -\mu M_A - \nu M_B;$$

taking λ, μ, ν to be positive. The interaction energy is then

(10.69) $$w = -\tfrac{1}{2}(H_A \cdot M_A + H_B \cdot M_B)$$

$$= \tfrac{1}{2}\lambda M_A{}^2 + \mu M_A \cdot M_B + \tfrac{1}{2}\nu M_B{}^2,$$

which is lower when M_A is antiparallel than when it is parallel to M_B. The energy when antiparallel must be compared with zero, the energy for $M_A = M_B = 0$. Thus when

(10.70) $$\mu M_A M_B > \tfrac{1}{2}(\lambda M_A{}^2 + \nu M_B{}^2)$$

the ground state will have M_A directed oppositely to M_B.

PROBLEMS

10.1. Discuss the way the band theory of ferromagnetism accounts for the fact that the addition of small amounts of manganese to nickel increases the saturation moment, while the addition of small amounts of copper decreases the moment (Fig. 10.26). References: J. C. Slater, J. Appl. Phys. **8**, 385 (1937); R. M. Bozorth, Phys. Rev. **79**, 887 (1950); for an ionic model explanation, see W. J. Carr, Jr., Phys. Rev. **85**, 590 (1952).

10.2. Show that the condition for ferromagnetic resonance in a general ellipsoid with demagnetizing factors N_x, N_y, N_z is

$$\omega = \gamma\{[H + (N_x - N_z)M][H + (N_y - N_z)M]\}^{\frac{1}{2}},$$

where the static field H is in the z direction. It is assumed that the ellipsoid is small in comparison with the wavelength and is made of an insulating ferromagnetic substance, such as a ferrite, so that eddy current effects may be neglected.

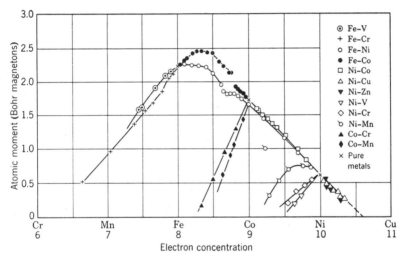

Fig. 10.26.   Average atomic moments of binary alloys of the elements in the iron group.   (After Bozorth.)

10.3. In a cubic crystal the elastic energy density is, according to (3.22),

$$U_e = \tfrac{1}{2}c_{11}(e_{xx}^2 + e_{yy}^2 + e_{zz}^2) + \tfrac{1}{2}c_{44}(e_{xy}^2 + e_{yz}^2 + e_{zx}^2) + c_{12}(e_{yy}e_{zz} + e_{xx}e_{zz} + e_{xx}e_{yy}),$$

and the magnetic anisotropy energy density is, from (10.32),

$$U_a \cong K(\alpha_1^2\alpha_2^2 + \alpha_2^2\alpha_3^2 + \alpha_3^2\alpha_1^2).$$

Coupling between elastic strain and magnetization direction may be taken formally into account by adding to the total energy density a term

$$U_c \cong B_1(\alpha_1^2 e_{xx} + \alpha_2^2 e_{yy} + \alpha_3^2 e_{zz}) + B_2(\alpha_1\alpha_2 e_{xy} + \alpha_2\alpha_3 e_{yz} + \alpha_3\alpha_1 e_{zx}),$$

which may be regarded as a first order correction to U_a arising from the strain dependence of U_a; here B_1 and B_2 are constants and are called *magnetoelastic coupling constants.* Show that the total energy is a minimum when

$$e_{ii} = B_1[c_{12} - \alpha_i^2(c_{11} + 2c_{12})]/[(c_{11} - c_{12})(c_{11} + 2c_{12})];$$

$$e_{ij} = -B_2\alpha_i\alpha_j/c_{44} \quad (i \neq j).$$

This is a formal explanation of the origin of magnetostriction.

10.4. Show that the magnetic energy of a saturated sphere of diameter d is $\approx M_s d^3$. The domain wall energy of an arrangement with appreciably less magnetic energy will be $\pi\sigma_w d^2/4$, where σ_w is the wall energy per unit area, and the wall is taken as passing through the center of the sphere. Estimate for cobalt the critical radius below which the particles are stable as single domains, taking JS^2/a as for iron.

10.5. Consider a small sphercial single-domain particle. Show that the effective permeability for a weak field applied perpendicular to the easy axis is

$$\mu = 1 + 2\pi(M_s^2/K),$$

and show that $2K/M_s$ may be regarded as an effective anisotropsy field. Show also that the reverse field along the axis required to reverse the magnetization is

$$H = 2K/M_s.$$

The coercive force for a single-domain particle is of this magnitude. Estimate H_c for iron single-domain particles.

10.6. Taking the effective fields on the two sublattice model of an antiferromagnetic as

$$H_A = H - \lambda M_B - \varepsilon M_A,$$

$$H_B = H - \lambda M_A - \varepsilon M_B,$$

show that

$$\theta/T_c = (\lambda + \varepsilon)/(\lambda - \varepsilon).$$

10.7. Show that, for spins on a face-centered cubic lattice with antiferromagnetic nearest neighbor interactions only,

$$\theta/T_c = 3.$$

10.8. Explain in terms of domain magnetization processes the values of the magnetization at which the curves for nickel in Fig. 10.12 diverge from each other at low fields. Show that the turning points are given approximately by $M = M_s$, $M_s/2^{1/2}$, $M_s/3^{1/2}$ for the [111], [110], and [100] directions, respectively.

REFERENCES

L. F. Bates, *Modern magnetism*, Cambridge University Press, Cambridge, 3rd ed., 1951.

R. Becker and W. Döring, *Ferromagnetismus*, J. Springer, Berlin, 1939.

R. M. Bozorth, *Ferromagnetism*, Van Nostrand, New York, 1951.

Fairweather, Roberts, and Welch, "Ferrites," Repts. Prog. Phys. **15**, 142 (1952).

C. Kittel, "Physical theory of ferromagnetic domains," Revs. Modern Phys. **21**, 541 (1949).

ONR Maryland Magnetism Conference, Revs. Modern Phys. (January, 1953).

J. L. Snoek, *New developments in ferromagnetic materials*, Elsevier, Amsterdam, 2nd ed., 1949.

E. C. Stoner, "Ferromagnetism," Rept. Prog. Phys. **11,** 43 (1948); **13,** 83 (1950).

E. C. Stoner, *Magnetism and matter*, Methuen and Co., Ltd., London, 1934.

J. H. Van Vleck, "A survey of the theory of ferromagnetism," Revs. Modern Phys. **17,** 27 (1945).

J. H. Van Vleck, "Recent developments in the theory of antiferromagnetism," J. phys. et radium, **12,** 262 (1951).

J. J. Went and E. W. Gorter, "Magnetic and electrical properties of Ferroxcube materials," Philips Tech. Rev. **13,** 181 (1952).

11

Superconductivity

We first survey the central experimental facts concerning superconductivity, and then discuss the theoretical situation and supplementary experiments bearing on the theory. There is not yet a satisfactory quantum theory of superconductivity, but we do have a fairly satisfactory macroscopic theory of the electrodynamics of superconductivity. The direction which the ultimate quantum theory may take is gradually becoming apparent.

EXPERIMENTAL SITUATION

Zero resistance. Superconductivity was discovered in 1911 when Kamerlingh Onnes observed at Leiden that the resistivity of mercury

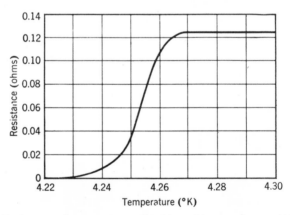

Fig. 11.1. Resistance of mercury as a function of temperature. (After Kamerlingh Onnes, 1911.)

(Fig. 11.1) vanished completely below 4.2°K, the transition from normal conductivity occurring over a very narrow range of temperature of the order of 0.05°K.

Persistent currents. A ring of superconducting material is cooled in a magnetic field from a temperature above the transition temperature T_c to below T_c; the field is then switched off, thereby inducing cur-

200

rents in the ring. The currents have been observed by the associated magnetic field to persist with undiminished strength for days. In experiments at Leiden[1] using a coil of 700 meters of lead wire it was impossible in a run of about 12 hr to detect any decrease of the current. From the sensitivity of the apparatus and the decay formula $i \sim e^{-Rt/L}$ it was calculated that $R < 10^{-17}R_0$, where R_0 is the resistance at room temperature, or $R < 10^{-15}R_0'$, where R_0' is the extrapolated residual resistance at 0°K, extrapolated as if superconductivity did not set in.

Effect of magnetic fields. It is possible to destroy superconductivity by the application of a sufficiently strong magnetic field. The thresh-

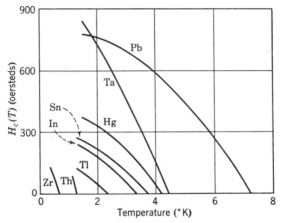

Fig. 11.2. Threshold field curves for several superconductors. (From F. London, *Superfluids*, John Wiley & Sons, 1950.)

old or critical value of the magnetic field for the destruction of superconductivity is denoted by $H_c(T)$ and is a function of the temperature; at $T = T_c$, $H_c = 0$. The variation of the critical field with temperature for several superconducting elements is shown in Fig. 11.2. The threshold curves separate the superconducting state in the lower left region of the figure from the normal state in the upper right region.

The original observation on destruction was made by Kamerlingh Onnes in 1913; he found that the passage of an electric current down a superconducting wire led to the destruction of superconductivity when a certain critical current was exceeded. This circumstance prevents the use of superconducting electromagnets to produce intense magnetic fields. Silsbee (1916) suggested that the important factor in causing the transition back to the normal state was the magnetic field associ-

[1] Unpublished; quoted by H. B. G. Casimir, Ann Arbor Lectures, 1948.

ated with the current, rather than the value of the current itself. Thus superconductivity in a long circular wire of radius a should be destroyed when the current I exceeds the value determined by the equation $H_c = 2I/a$ for the field at the surface of the wire. The Silsbee hypothesis has been confirmed experimentally for pure unstrained metallic elements; however, complex compounds and alloys, or impure and strained elements, do not satisfy the Silsbee relationship, and such specimens are termed *non-ideal*.

Flux exclusion. Meissner and Ochsenfeld[2] (1933) showed that, if a long superconductor is cooled in a longitudinal magnetic field from above the transition temperature, the lines of induction are pushed out (Fig. 11.3) at the transition. The Meissner effect shows that a super-

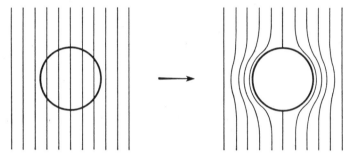

Fig. 11.3.   Meissner effect in a sphere cooled in a constant applied magnetic field; on passing below the transition temperature the lines of induction are ejected from the sphere.   (From F. London, *Superfluids*, John Wiley & Sons, 1950.)

conductor behaves as if inside the specimen $B = 0$ or $\chi = -1/4\pi$; that is, a superconductor exhibits perfect diamagnetism. This very important result cannot be derived merely from the characterization of a superconductor as a medium of zero resistivity ρ: from $E = \rho j$ we see that, if ρ is zero while j is finite, then E must be zero and with it curl E must be zero. Therefore from Maxwell's equations

(11.1) $$\frac{dB}{dt} = -c \text{ curl } E = 0,$$

so that the flux through the metal cannot change on cooling through the transition. The Meissner effect contradicts this result and suggests that perfect diamagnetism and zero resistivity are two independent essential properties of the superconducting state.

[2] W. Meissner and R. Ochsenfeld, Naturwiss. **21**, 787 (1933).

Intermediate state. The magnetization curve for a *sphere* in the superconducting state (Fig. 11.4) show that superconductivity is partially destroyed for $\frac{2}{3}H_c < H < H_c$. This region is called the intermediate state, although it is really a mixture of domains of normal and superconducting states. The magnetization curve for $H < \frac{2}{3}H_c$ is in good agreement with an apparent diamagnetic susceptibility $\chi = -(1/4\pi)$, provided that demagnetization effects are taken into account.

Entropy increase on going to normal state. There is a difference between the heat capacities in the normal and superconducting states

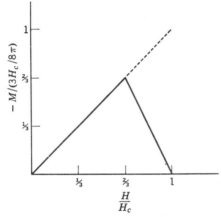

Fig. 11.4. Magnetization curve of a sphere below T_c, showing the onset of the intermediate state at $H/H_c = \frac{2}{3}$. The initial part of the curve is determined by the relations $H_i = H - (4\pi/3)M$; $B_i = 0 = H_i + 4\pi M = H + (8\pi/3)M$. (From F. London, *Superfluids*, John Wiley & Sons, 1950.)

(Fig. 11.5). Below the transition temperature there is an increase of entropy on going from the superconducting state to the normal state. That is, the superconducting state is more ordered than the normal state. The difference in entropy is of the order of $10^{-3} R$ per mole, instead of the order of R as in an ordinary transition of the second kind (such as in ferromagnetism). The small difference suggests that the rearrangement of the system on becoming superconducting is relatively small.

Frequency effects. In d-c measurements the resistivity in the superconducting state is zero. At infrared frequencies the resistivity is that of the normal state; that is, no change in the resistivity, as measured by the reflection coefficient, is observed on passing through the critical magnetic field. The transition between low frequency behavior and high frequency behavior occurs gradually, but is well along at microwave frequencies (Fig. 11.6).

Gyromagnetic ratio. Kikoin and Gubar[3] performed a gyromagnetic experiment on a superconductor and found the magnetomechanical

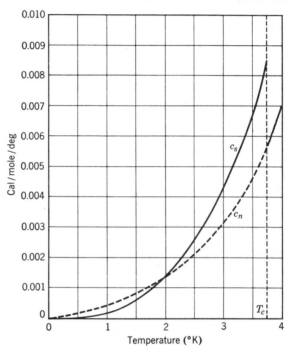

Fig. 11.5. Heat capacity of tin in the normal and superconducting states. [After Keesom and Van Laer, Physica **5**, 193 (1938).] The heat capacity in the normal state below T_c is measured in the presence of a magnetic field strong enough to destroy superconductivity.

factor (see Eq. 10.19) $g' = 1.0$, as expected if the superconducting currents are caused by the motion of electrons.

Isotope effect. It has been observed that the critical temperature of superconductors varies with isotopic mass. The observation was first made by Maxwell[4] and by Reynolds and co-workers,[5] who used mercury isotopes; the effect has since been found by workers using

[3] I. K. S. Kikoin and S. W. Gubar, J. Phys. (U.S.S.R.) **3**, 333 (1940); the experiment has been repeated by Houston and a co-worker.

[4] E. Maxwell, Phys. Rev. **78**, 477 (1950).

[5] Reynolds, Serin, Wright, and Nesbitt, Phys. Rev. **78**, 487 (1950).

tin[6] and lead[7] isotopes.   To give an idea of the magnitude of the effect, for mercury T_c varies from 4.185°K to 4.146°K as the isotopic mass M varies from 199.5 to 203.4.

The experimental results are generally in agreement with a relation of the form

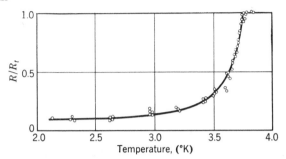

Fig. 11.6.   Surface resistance of tin in the superconducting state, at 24,000 mc/sec. [After Maxwell, Marcus, and Slater, Phys. Rev. **76**, 1332 (1949).]

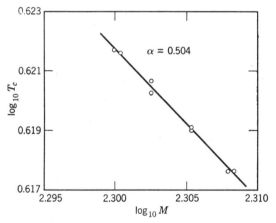

Fig. 11.7.   Log-log plot of transition temperature vs. average mass number for separated isotopes of mercury. [After Reynolds, Serin, and Nesbitt, Phys. Rev. **84**, 691 (1951.)] The line drawn is a fit of the equation $M^\alpha T_c = $ const; α as determined from these data by a least squares fit equals 0.504.

$$(11.2) \qquad\qquad M^{\frac{1}{2}}T_c = \text{constant}$$

within each series of isotopes, as shown for mercury in Fig. 11.7. This leads to the very suggestive relation

[6] E. Maxwell, Phys. Rev. **79**, 173 (1950); **86**, 235 (1952); D. Shoenberg et al., Nature **166**, 1071 (1950); K. Mendlessohn et al., Nature **166**, 1071 (1950).

[7] M. Olsen, Nature **168**, 245 (1951); Serin, Reynolds, and Lohman, Phys. Rev. **86**, 162 (1952).

(11.3) $$T_c/\Theta = \text{constant,}$$

where Θ is the Debye temperature; (11.3) follows from (11.2) on observing from (5.17) that Θ is proportional to the sound velocity v, which in turn from (4.4) is proportional to $M^{-\frac{1}{2}}$. The constancy of T_c/Θ implies that lattice vibrations have an important bearing on superconductivity and gives a clear guide to theory by suggesting that electron lattice interactions must be taken into account.

Occurrence of superconductivity. The superconducting elements and their transition temperatures are listed in Table 11.1. The features to be noted are:

(a) Monovalent metals are not superconductors.

(b) The ferromagnetic and antiferromagnetic metals are not superconductors.

(c) Superconducting metals are not as good conductors at room temperature as the normal metals at room temperature. For example; titanium, zirconium, and hafnium have resistivities at room temperature of 89, 45, and 32 microhm-cm, respectively, while copper, silver and gold have 1.6, 1.5, and 2.4 microhm-cm.

It is always possible that metals not reported as superconducting may become so at lower temperatures than attained during the tests, but in a number of cases runs have been made to $\sim 0.07°\text{K}$ without finding superconductivity.

Non-ideal superconductors. A number of chemical compounds are superconducting, including several compounds composed of elements none of which is superconducting, such as molybdenum carbide, MoC, with $T_c = 7.6 - 8.3°\text{K}$. The superconducting compounds and alloys are often characterized by a high transition temperature, high critical field, incomplete Meissner effect, breakdown of Silsbee's rule, and a broad transition region; because of these properties they are known as non-ideal or hard superconductors. The anomalous properties have not yet found a complete explanation. Data on compounds are given in Table 11.2. Niobium nitride, NbN, has the highest transition temperature yet reported, 14.7°K.

Lasarew and Galkin[8] have shown that all the characteristic features of a superconductive alloy can be reproduced in a chemically pure specimen of a nominally ideal or soft superconductor by application of a severe inhomogeneous strain. They found that, for tin on going from the unstrained to the strained condition, T_c increased from 3.72° to 9.0°K, while H_c at 2°K increased from 210 to 15,000 oersteds; at the

[8] B. Lasarew and A. Galkin, J. Phys. (U.S.S.R.) **8**, 371 (1944).

Table 11.1. Superconducting Elements in the Periodic System

(Transition temperatures given below superconductors)

																H	He
Li	Be											B	C	N	O	F	Ne
Na	Mg											Al 1.14°	Si	P	S	Cl	A
K	Ca	Sc	Ti 0.53°	V 5.1°	Cr	Mn	Fe	Co	Ni	Cu	Zn 0.79°	Ga 1.07°	Ge	As	Se	Br	Kr
Rb	Sr	Y	Zr 0.7°	Nb 9.22°	Mo	Tc 11.2°	Ru 0.47°	Rh	Pd	Ag	Cd 0.54°	In 3.37°	Sn† 3.69°	Sb	Te	I	Xe
Cs	Ba	La 4.71° Lu	Hf 0.35°	Ta 4.38°	W	Re 2.4°	Os 0.71°	Ir	Pt	Au	Hg 4.12°	Tl 2.38°	Pb 7.26°	Bi	Po	At	Rn
Fr	Ra	Ac	Th 1.32°	Pa	U 0.8°												

† White tin.

same time the critical current at 2°K dropped from 3.0 to 0.067 amp, demonstrating the breakdown of Silsbee's rule.

Superconductivity of small particles. The diamagnetic susceptibility of small particles is less than that of bulk superconductors. A large mercury sphere (Fig. 11.4) exhibits an effective volume susceptibility of $\chi_0 = -3/8\pi$, whereas Shoenberg[9] finds $\chi/\chi_0 < 0.005$ for mercury particles of diameter about 10^{-5} cm suspended in an albumen colloid. Mercury particles of diameter about 10^{-4} cm have $\chi/\chi_0 \approx 0.4$.

Thermoelectric effects. Daunt and Mendlessohn[10] found that the Thomson coefficient of superconductive lead was zero within their accuracy, which meant less than 2×10^{-3} of the Thomson coefficient just above the transition. It was concluded from this result that the entropy of the superconducting electrons is effectively zero.

TABLE 11.2. TRANSITION TEMPERATURES OF SUPERCONDUCTING COMPOUNDS
Results are variable from specimen to specimen, and in some cases the pure metal present as a precipitate may be responsible for the superconductivity. For data on alloys, see Shoenberg's book cited at the end of the chapter.

Compound	$T_c(°K)$	Compound	$T_c(°K)$
Pb_2Au	7.0	ZrB	2.8– 3.2
$PbTl_2$	3.8	CuS	1.6
Pb_5Na_2	7.2	TaSi	4.4
SnSb	3.9	MoC	7.6– 8.3
Sn_3Sb_2	4.0	Mo_2C	2.4– 3.2
Sn_2Au	2.5–2.75	MoB	4.4
Sn_4Au	2.5–2.75	Mo_2N	5
Tl_3Bi_5	6.4	MoN	12.0
Tl_2Hg_5	3.8	NbN	14.7
Tl_7Sb_2	5.2	NbB	6
Au_2Bi	1.7	NbC	10.1–10.5
WC	2.5– 4.2	TaC	9.3– 9.5
ZrC	2.3	W_2C	2.0– 3.5
VN	1.5–3.2	ZrN	9.3– 9.6
		$CoSi_2$	1.27

Thermal conductivity. Hulm, and Mendelssohn and Olsen,[11] have discussed results on thermal conductivity in superconductors. In ideal superconductors there is a marked drop in the thermal conductivity when superconductivity sets in, suggesting that the electronic contribution drops, the superconducting electrons possibly playing no part in heat transfer. Results for a specimen of tin are given in Fig. 11.8. In impure or non-ideal superconductors an increase in thermal

[9] D. Shoenberg, Nature **143**, 434 (1939).

[10] J. G. Daunt and K. Mendlessohn, Proc. Roy. Soc. London, **A185**, 225 (1946).

[11] K. Mendlessohn and J. L. Olsen, Proc. Phys. Soc. (London) **A63**, 2 (1950); J. K. Hulm, Proc. Roy. Soc. (London) **A204**, 98 (1950).

conductivity on becoming superconducting has been observed in a few specimens. Hulm suggests that the increase is due to decreased scattering of lattice waves by electrons.

THEORETICAL SITUATION

There is at present no quantum theory of superconductivity which is generally accepted, although recent work by Fröhlich and Bardeen

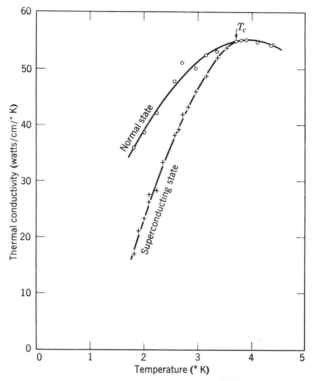

Fig. 11.8. Thermal conductivity of a specimen of tin in the normal and super-conducting states; results vary considerably among different specimens according to their purity. (After Hulm.)

gives the impression that a period of progress may be close at hand. We first discuss several theoretical topics, including the London equations, which help define the problems requiring solution.

THERMODYNAMICS OF THE SUPERCONDUCTING TRANSITION

It has been demonstrated experimentally by van Laer and Keesom[12] that the transition between the normal and superconducting states is

[12] P. H. van Laer and W. H. Keesom, Physica 5, 993 (1938).

thermodynamically reversible, in the same sense that with slow evaporation the transition between liquid and vapor phases of a substance is reversible. The Meissner effect also suggests that the transition is reversible, which it would not be were the superconducting currents to die away with the production of Joule heat when superconductivity is destroyed. As the transition is reversible we may, following Gorter and Casimir,[13] apply thermodynamics to the transition, obtaining an expression for the entropy difference between normal and superconducting states in terms of the critical field curve H_c vs. T.

The Gibbs free energy per unit volume in a magnetic field is

$$(11.4) \qquad G = U - TS - HM;$$

here M is the magnetization and S the entropy; the pV term is neglected. We may verify (11.4) by observing that the internal energy density in the presence of a magnetic field is given, from Appendices G and T, by

$$(11.5) \qquad dU = T \, dS + H \, dM,$$

which may be compared with the familiar

$$(11.6) \qquad dU = T \, dS - p \, dV.$$

We see that the substitution

$$(11.7) \qquad p \to -H, \qquad V \to M$$

in the standard expression

$$(11.8) \qquad G = U - TS + pV$$

gives us (11.4) directly. Then, from (11.4) and (11.5),

$$(11.9) \qquad dG = -S \, dT - M \, dH.$$

Substituting $M = -H/4\pi$ and integrating (11.9), we have for the superconducting state

$$(11.10) \qquad G_s(H) = G_s(0) + \frac{1}{8\pi} H^2.$$

The central result of the thermodynamic theory of equilibria is that the Gibbs free energies must be equal for two phases to be in equilib-

---

[13] C. Gorter and H. B. G. Casimir, Physica **1**, 306 (1934); for a discussion of the "two-fluid" model of the superconducting state, see C. Gorter and H. B. G. Casimir, Physik. Z. **35**, 963 (1934).

rium (at constant T, P, H). Thus, along the critical field curve where the superconducting and normal states are in equilibrium,

$$(11.11) \qquad G_n = G_s(0) + \frac{1}{8\pi} H_c{}^2,$$

where G_n is the Gibbs free energy density of the normal state and is essentially independent of the magnetic field. From (11.9),

$$(11.12) \qquad (\partial G/\partial T)_H = -S,$$

so that (11.10) and (11.11) give the important result

$$(11.13) \qquad S_n - S_s = -\frac{H_c}{2\pi} \frac{dH_c}{dT},$$

where S_s is taken in zero field. As dH_c/dT is found to be always negative, the entropy of the normal state is always greater than the superconducting state.

The difference in heat capacity is given by

$$(11.14) \quad \Delta C = C_s - C_n = T \frac{d}{dT}(S_s - S_n) = \frac{TH_c}{4\pi} \frac{d^2H_c}{dT^2} + \frac{T}{4\pi}\left(\frac{dH_c}{dT}\right)^2,$$

per unit volume; at $T = T_c$, $H_c = 0$, and we have the Rutgers formula,

$$(11.15) \qquad \Delta C = \frac{T_c}{4\pi}\left(\frac{dH_c}{dT}\right)^2.$$

This relation is in satisfactory agreement with these experimental measurements:[14]

Substance	$T_c(°K)$	$(dH_c/dT)_{T=T_c}$ (oersteds/deg)	ΔC(calc) (cal/deg/mole)	ΔC(observed) (cal/deg/mole)
Tin	3.69	151.2	0.00229	0.0024
Thallium	2.38	137.4	0.00144	0.00148

We note from (11.13) that at the critical temperature there is no latent heat of transition ($\Delta S = 0$), but there is according to (11.15) a discontinuity in the heat capacity, so that the phase transition is of the second kind.

THE BLOCH THEOREM

Before the discovery of the Meissner effect, discussions of the electrodynamics of superconductors were predicated on the assumption of free electrons moving with zero resistance, as this assumption accounts

[14] The first work was by W. H. Keesom and J. A. Kok, Physica **1**, 503, 595 (1934).

directly for the persistent currents and the zero resistivity. Attempts were made to set up quantum-mechanical models which would have the property that the lowest state of the system (or the state of lowest free energy) would exhibit a spontaneous current. Bloch, however, has proved the very important theorem that in general *the lowest state of a quantum-mechanical system in the absence of a magnetic field can carry no current.* The proof of the theorem is given in Appendix K. Bohm[15] has extended the result to show that states of finite current cannot be thermodynamically the most stable even if the temperature is different from zero. In a magnetic field, however, the most stable state *can* carry current.

THE LONDON EQUATIONS

We have explained the Meissner effect by taking $\chi = -1/4\pi$. This is a drastic assumption. An alternative approach is to modify the electrodynamic equations while leaving ϵ and μ unchanged. The assumption of zero resistivity leads to the acceleration equation

$$(11.16) \qquad e\mathbf{E} = m\dot{\mathbf{v}}$$

or, as $\mathbf{j} = ne\mathbf{v}$,

$$(11.17) \qquad \mathbf{E} = \Lambda \, d\mathbf{j}/dt; \qquad \Lambda = m/ne^2;$$

where n is the number of electrons per unit volume. Taking the curl of both sides, we have, as curl $\mathbf{E} = -\dot{\mathbf{H}}/c$,

$$(11.18) \qquad \operatorname{curl} \Lambda \, \frac{d\mathbf{j}}{dt} = -\frac{1}{c}\dot{\mathbf{H}},$$

or, since $4\pi\mathbf{j}/c = \operatorname{curl} \mathbf{H}$,

$$(11.19) \qquad \frac{c}{4\pi}\operatorname{curl}\operatorname{curl}\Lambda\dot{\mathbf{H}} = \operatorname{curl}\Lambda\frac{d\mathbf{j}}{dt} = -\frac{1}{c}\dot{\mathbf{H}}.$$

We have, further, as div $\mathbf{H} = 0$,

$$(11.20) \qquad \frac{\Lambda c^2}{4\pi}\nabla^2\dot{\mathbf{H}} = \dot{\mathbf{H}}.$$

Integrating with respect to time, we have

$$(11.21) \qquad \frac{\Lambda c^2}{4\pi}\nabla^2(\mathbf{H} - \mathbf{H}_0) = \mathbf{H} - \mathbf{H}_0.$$

[15] D. Bohm, Phys. Rev. **75**, 502 (1949).

The result (11.21) admits the particular solution $H = H_0$, where H_0 is an arbitrary field existing at $t = 0$; but we know from the Meissner effect that we cannot have frozen-in fields. It is apparent that (11.21) has more general solutions than allowed by nature. We note that here the currents are considered the only internal source of field; no magnetization as such has been introduced. F. and H. London[16] therefore suggested that the acceleration equation be abandoned, and that we should take instead as the fundamental equation

$$(11.22) \qquad c \text{ curl } \Lambda \mathbf{j} = -\mathbf{H},$$

which is postulated to replace Ohm's law in superconductors. We note that, if $\mathbf{H} = \text{curl } \mathbf{A}$, $\mathbf{j} = -\mathbf{A}/\Lambda c$. On taking curls in $4\pi \mathbf{j}/c = \text{curl } H$, we are led directly, using (11.22), to

$$(11.23) \qquad \frac{\Lambda c^2}{4\pi} \nabla^2 \mathbf{H} = \mathbf{H},$$

which does not necessarily admit the former solution $H = H_0$. If we include the displacement current we have

$$(11.24) \qquad \frac{\Lambda c^2}{4\pi} \left[\nabla^2 \mathbf{H} - \frac{1}{c^2} \ddot{\mathbf{H}} \right] = \mathbf{H}.$$

Equations (11.17) and (11.22), when applied to the superconducting electrons, are known as the London equations and are widely used, with considerable success, in macroscopic descriptions of the electrodynamic behavior of superconductors. London has shown that the usual thermodynamic treatment is consistent with his equations.

SUPERCONDUCTIVITY AT HIGH FREQUENCIES

We suppose that high frequency effects can be described by considering the current

$$(11.25) \qquad \mathbf{j} = \mathbf{j}_n + \mathbf{j}_s$$

as the superposition of a normal (resistive) current given by

$$(11.26) \qquad \mathbf{j}_n = \sigma \mathbf{E}$$

and a superconductive current $\mathbf{j}_s$. Then

$$(11.27) \qquad c \text{ curl } \mathbf{H} = 4\pi(\sigma \mathbf{E} + \mathbf{j}_s) + \dot{\mathbf{E}},$$

[16] F. London and H. London, Proc. Roy. Soc. (London) A149, 72 (1935); Physica 2, 341 (1935); for earlier work leading to (11.21), see Becker, Sauter, and Heller, Z. Physik 85, 772 (1933).

so that

$$c \text{ curl curl } \mathbf{H} = -c \, \nabla^2 \mathbf{H} = 4\pi(\sigma \text{ curl } \mathbf{E} + \text{curl } \mathbf{j}_s) + \text{curl } \dot{\mathbf{E}},$$

or, using (11.22) for curl $\mathbf{j}_s$,

(11.28) $$\nabla^2 \mathbf{H} = \frac{4\pi\sigma}{c^2} \, \dot{\mathbf{H}} + \frac{4\pi}{\Lambda c^2} \mathbf{H} + \frac{\ddot{\mathbf{H}}}{c^2}.$$

We take $H \sim \exp\left[-i(\omega t - \mathbf{k} \cdot \mathbf{r})\right]$, so that (11.28) gives

(11.29) $$k^2 c^2 = -(4\pi/\Lambda) + 4\pi\sigma\omega i + \omega^2,$$

the successive terms on the right representing the effects of the super-conducting penetration depth, the ordinary eddy current skin depth, and the displacement current. This relation determines the propagation characteristics of the medium.

In the limit of low frequencies,

(11.30) $$k \cong i(4\pi/\Lambda c^2)^{1/2},$$

which represents a rapidly decreasing field penetration with H reduced by e^{-1} at the depth

(11.31) $$d = (\Lambda c^2/4\pi)^{1/2}.$$

Using the definition (11.17) of Λ,

(11.32) $$d = (mc^2/4\pi n e^2)^{1/2}.$$

If we taken $n \sim 10^{23}$ electrons/cm^3 as for a metal,

(11.33) $$\Lambda \sim 10^{-31} \text{ sec}^{-2},$$

and

(11.34) $$d \sim 10^{-5} \text{ cm.}$$

Thus at low frequencies the penetration of a magnetic field into a superconductor is severely limited by the superconducting properties of the substance as expressed by the constant Λ.

At frequencies in the infrared, taking $\sigma \approx 10^{20}$ esu (as for normal metals at low temperatures) and $\omega \approx 10^{13}$ sec^{-1}, we have from (11.29)

$$c^2 k^2 \approx 10^{26} + 10^{34}i - 10^{32}.$$

We see that the eddy current term is dominant, so in this range we may take

(11.35) $$k \cong (i)^{1/2}(4\pi\sigma\omega/c^2)^{1/2}.$$

This is just the usual eddy current result. The superconducting properties of the material may be involved only through a change in the number of normal conduction electrons, which enters into σ. At these frequencies $\hbar\omega \gg kT_c$, and electrons are probably raised out of superconducting states by radiation, thus explaining the "normal" behavior of superconductors with respect to reflection of infrared radiation.[17]

The transition between superconducting and normal behavior occurs when the second and third terms on the right in (11.29) become equal to each other, the first term being negligible in the region of validity of ordinary conductivity theory. We see then that the transition in behavior occurs when the skin depth for eddy currents is equal to the London penetration depth (11.31). The transition takes place when $\omega \approx 10^{11}$ sec^{-1}, or $f \approx 10^{10}$ cps, which is in the microwave region, in agreement with experiment. The critical frequency is in fact given by, according to our definition,

$$(11.36) \qquad \omega_c = \frac{1}{\sigma\Lambda} = \frac{m}{n_n e^2 \tau}\frac{n_s e^2}{m} = \frac{1}{\tau}\frac{n_s}{n_n},$$

where n_s = density of superconducting electrons, n_n = density of effective normal electrons, and τ is the time of relaxation of the normal electrons as calculated in the ordinary theory of conductivity, entering by way of the relation

$$(11.37) \qquad \sigma = ne^2\tau/m$$

according to (12.73).

Extensive microwave investigations[18] have been carried out to test the above theory. It appears that the theory describes in a rough way the observed results, but closer examination reveals, according to Pippard, that the London equations must be generalized. He has also shown that the dependence of Λ on magnetic field intensity is very weak, so that (11.23) is in fact approximately linear in H.

SUSCEPTIBILITY OF A SPHERE AND THE PARTICLE SIZE EFFECT

The magnetic field H_i within a sphere is

$$(11.38) \qquad H_i = H - \frac{4\pi}{3}M,$$

---

[17] See, for example, Daunt, Keeley, and Mendlessohn, Phil. Mag. **23**, 264 (1937).
[18] H. London, Proc. Roy. Soc., (London) **A176**, 522 (1940); A. B. Pippard, Proc. Roy. Soc. (London) **A191**, 370, 385, 399 (1947); **A203**, 98, 195, 210 (1950); Maxwell, Marcus, and Slater, Phys. Rev. **76**, 1332 (1949).

as the demagnetizing field is $4\pi M/3$. If the sphere is very large in comparison with the penetration depth, we may write

$$(11.39) \qquad M = \frac{\mu - 1}{4\pi} H_i,$$

or, as $\mu = 0$ for a bulk superconductor,

$$M = -\frac{1}{4\pi} H_i,$$

whence, using (11.38),

$$(11.40) \qquad -\frac{8\pi}{3} M = H,$$

so that the effective susceptibility of a sphere is

$$(11.41) \qquad \chi_0 = -\frac{3}{8\pi}.$$

We now give a more detailed theory of the magnetic moment of a sphere of arbitrary radius a (not necessarily large) in a uniform applied field H_0. We suppose that the sphere obeys the London equation (11.23), which, expressed in terms of the vector potential $\mathbf{A}$, is

$$(11.42) \qquad \frac{\Lambda c^2}{4\pi} \nabla^2 \mathbf{A} = \mathbf{A}.$$

This is a standard boundary value problem.[19]

The vector potential of the uniform applied field is

$$(11.43) \qquad \mathbf{A}_0 = \tfrac{1}{2} H_0 r \sin \theta \; \mathbf{\phi}$$

in spherical coordinates, where $\mathbf{\phi}$ is the unit longitude vector. The total potential external to the sphere is

$$\mathbf{A}_e = \left(\frac{1}{2} H_0 r \sin \theta + \frac{C}{r^2} \sin \theta \right) \mathbf{\phi},$$

while the solution within the sphere, from (11.42), is

$$\mathbf{A}_i = \frac{D}{r^{1/2}} I_{3/2} \{ r[(4\pi/\Lambda C^2)^{1/2}] \} \sin \theta \; \mathbf{\phi},$$

where $I_{3/2}$ is a modified Bessel function. The boundary conditions which determine C and D are

$$\mathbf{A}_e = \mathbf{A}_i$$

[19] The problem is quite similar to that discussed on pp. 397–399 of W. R. Smythe, *Static and dynamic electricity*, McGraw-Hill Book Co., New York, 2nd ed., 1950.

and

$$\frac{\partial}{\partial r} (r \sin \theta \, \mathbf{A}_i) = \frac{\partial}{\partial r} (r \sin \theta \, \mathbf{A}_e),$$

at $r = a$ in both cases.

On solving for C, it is easy to show that the sphere produces an external field as if it possessed a magnetic moment [writing $d = (\Lambda_c^2/4\pi)^{1/2}$] of

$$\mathfrak{M} = - H_0 \frac{a^3}{2} \frac{I_{3/2}(a/d)}{I_{1/2}(a/d)} = - H_0 \frac{a^3}{2} \left[1 + 3 \frac{d^2}{a^2} - 3 \frac{d}{a} \coth \frac{a}{d} \right],$$

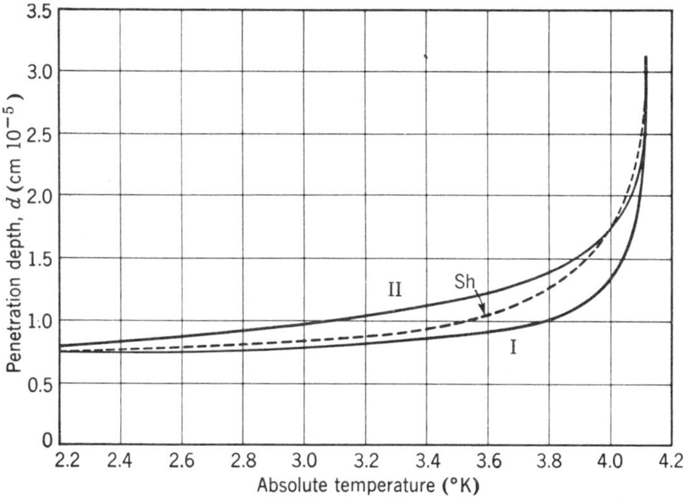

Fig. 11.9. Penetration depth in mercury. Curve Sh from magnetic susceptibility measurements on colloidal mercury [from D. Shoenberg, Nature **143**, 434 (1939)]; curves I and II from high frequency resistance measurements [from A. B. Pippard, Proc. Roy. Soc. (London) **A191**, 370, 385, 399 (1947); Nature **162**, 68 (1948).]

so that, writing $\chi_0 = -3/8\pi$,

$$(11.44) \qquad \frac{\chi}{\chi_0} = \left[1 + 3 \frac{d^2}{a^2} - 3 \frac{d}{a} \coth \frac{a}{d} \right],$$

as given by F. London.[20] For $d/a \ll 1$, $\chi = \chi_0$; for $d/a \gg 1$,

$$\frac{\chi}{\chi_0} \cong \frac{1}{15} \frac{a^2}{d^2}.$$

Equation (11.44) has been widely used to determine d experimentally,[21] and consistent values of d at a given temperature are obtained for colloidal particles of various sizes. Results for mercury are shown in

[20] F. London, Physica **3**, 450 (1936).
[21] D. Shoenberg, Nature **143**, 434 (1939).

Fig. 11.9, where the penetration depths are compared with those obtained by Pippard from high frequency resistance measurements. Other values are given in Table 11.3.

TABLE 11.3. VALUES OF THE PENETRATION DEPTH EXTRAPOLATED TO 0°K
[Except for Hg, the values are from J. M. Lock, Proc. Roy. Soc. (London) **A208,** 391 (1951).]

Element	$10^6 \times d_0$(cm)
Hg	7
In	6.4 ± 0.3
Pb	3.9 ± 0.3
Sn	5.0 ± 0.1

INTERMEDIATE STATE AND DOMAIN STRUCTURE

At the edge of the equatorial plane of a sphere in an applied field H we apply the condition of continuity of the tangential component of H across the boundary, obtaining

(11.45) $H_i = H_{\text{ext}}$ (equator).

Now

$$H_i = H - \frac{4\pi}{3} M,$$

and for a sphere (11.40) gives us

(11.46) $M = - \frac{3}{8\pi} H,$

so that

(11.47) $H_i = \frac{3}{2} H.$

By consideration of the field pattern of a dipole we see that the maximum value of the tangential component of the external field is in the equatorial plane and has a value, by (11.47), of $\frac{3}{2}$ times the value of the uniform applied field. The field H_i will exceed the critical field H_c (as determined from measurements on a long wire in an axial field) when

(11.48) $H > \frac{2}{3} H_c.$

When this situation occurs we can avoid having the whole sphere become normal by having the material around the equator of the sphere become normal; the effective shape of the superconducting material will then become something like a prolate spheroid, thereby reducing the field in the interior. The material at the boundary between normal and superconducting regions will naturally be in the field H_c, but now the material outside the boundary, such as the material on the surface of the sphere, will see a field less than H_c and will become superconducting again. A stable state can only be attained by dividing the sphere up into many fine regions or domains, alternately normal and superconducting.

The effect of domain structure on the magnetic susceptibility of a sphere in the region of field intensities $\frac{2}{3}H_c < H < H_c$ may be discussed; the device of a fictitious "intermediate state" introduced by Peierls[22] and by London to describe the bulk properties of the mixture of superconducting and normal domains will assist in the discussion. The medium as a whole may be characterized by the average values

$$(11.49) \qquad H_i = H_c; \qquad B_i \neq 0.$$

The magnetization adjusts itself so that

$$H_c = H - \frac{4\pi}{3} M;$$

thus, for $\frac{2}{3}H_c < H < H_c$,

$$(11.50) \qquad \chi = \frac{3}{4\pi} \left(1 - \frac{H_c}{H} \right).$$

This is equal to $-(3/8\pi)$ for $H = \frac{2}{3}H_c$ and to 0 for $H = H_c$. The magnetization is a linear function of H:

$$(11.51) \qquad M = \frac{3}{4\pi} (H - H_c); \qquad \left(\frac{2}{3} H_c < H < H_c \right)$$

in agreement with measurements on spheres,[23] as sketched in Fig. 11.4.

The nature and dimensions of the domain structure in superconductors has been discussed theoretically by Landau,[24] who finds that it is necessary to have a rather complicated branching structure in order to satisfy the boundary conditions within the material. A state

[22] R. Peierls, Proc. Roy. Soc. (London) **A155**, 613 (1936).
[23] See, for example, D. Shoenberg, Proc. Roy. Soc. (London) **A152**, 10 (1935).
[24] L. Landau, J. Phys. (U.S.S.R.) **7**, 99 (1943).

with many thin domains is favorable from the standpoint of demag-netizing energy, but has a large area of boundary surface between normal and superconducting phases. The boundary surface energy density is of the order of

$$(11.52) \qquad \sigma \sim \frac{1}{8\pi} H_c^2 d,$$

where d is the penetration depth.

The supposed existence of a domain structure has several indirect consequences which have been confirmed experimentally. Direct experimental observation of domains has been reported by Meshkovsky and Shalnikov,[25] who explored with a fine bismuth strip probe the air

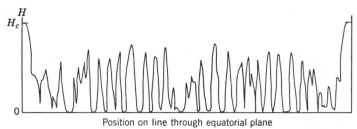

Position on line through equatorial plane

Fig. 11.10. Magnetic field distribution in the equatorial plane of a tin sphere in the intermediate state at 3.05°K, showing the domain structure. Regions of $H \sim H_c$ are associated with slabs of normal material. (After Meshkovsky and Shalnikov.)

gap between two hemispheres of superconductor spaced close together. The magnetoresistive effect of bismuth was used to measure magnetic field intensity as a function of the position of the probe in the plane of the gap; large irregular peaks of field intensity were found which are suggestive of a laminar domain structure (Fig. 11.10).

In a superconducting wire of circular cross section in a transverse magnetic field H, the critical condition for the formation of domains is reached, by an analysis similar to that given for the sphere but using a demagnetizing factor of 2π, when

$$(11.53) \qquad H > \tfrac{1}{2} H_c.$$

The presence of layers of normal material suggests that the electrical resistance of the wire should begin to return when H exceeds $\tfrac{1}{2} H_c$;

[25] A. Shalnikov, J. Phys. (U.S.S.R.) **9**, 202 (1945); A Meshkovsky and A. Shalnikov, J. Phys. (U.S.S.R.) **11**, 1 (1947). A major revision of the London theory in order to include the boundary energy directly in the theory has been attempted by Landau and Ginsburg; a review is given by W L. Ginsburg, Abhandl. sowjetischen Physik **2**, 135 (1951).

such an effect has in fact been observed. Detailed calculations and experiments relating to domain structure in superconducting cylinders in transverse magnetic fields have been made by Desirant and Shoenberg[26] and Andrew.[27]

QUANTUM THEORIES OF SUPERCONDUCTIVITY

Recently there have been a number of attempts to give a quantum-mechanical explanation of superconductivity. We mention work by Heisenberg,[28] Tisza,[29] Slater,[30] Born and Cheng,[31] Fröhlich,[32] and Bardeen.[32] At the present time all these theories are highly controversial, and the difficulties do not lend themselves to analysis in an introductory textbook.

The discovery of the isotope effect, and in particular of the empirical relation (11.3),

$$T_c/\Theta = \text{constant},$$

for the various isotopes of a given element, suggests strongly that superconductivity arises from interactions between electrons and vibrations of the crystal lattice. This interaction enjoys a central role in the theories proposed by Fröhlich and Bardeen. The serious mathematical difficulties in discussing the electronic states in the presence of strong electron lattice interactions are pointed out in a review paper by Bardeen.[32] It is also not yet clear how the typical superconducting properties—infinite conductivity and perfect diamagnetism—follow from the models. In every theory the apparent contradiction between the Bloch theorem and the observed persistence of currents in a superconducting ring is explained by the presumed metastable nature of the current distribution.

The Fröhlich and Bardeen theories have the common feature that the superconducting state is realized when the interaction between electrons and the zero point lattice vibrations exceeds a certain value, which is nearly the same in the two theories. The condition can be

[26] M. Desirant and D. Shoenberg, Proc. Roy. Soc. (London) **A194**, 63 (1948).

[27] E. R. Andrew, Proc. Roy. Soc. (London) **A194**, 80, 98 (1948).

[28] For a review of the Heisenberg theory, see H. Koppe, Ergeb. exak. Naturw. **23**, 283 (1950).

[29] L. Tisza, Phys. Rev. **80**, 717 (1950).

[30] J. C. Slater, Phys. Rev. **51**, 195 (1937); **52**, 214 (1937).

[31] M. Born and K. C. Cheng, J. phys. radium **9**, 249 (1948).

[32] For references and a review of the Fröhlich and Bardeen theories, see J. Bardeen, Revs. Modern Phys. **23**, 261 (1951). The principal papers are H. Fröhlich, Phys. Rev. **79**, 845 (1950); J. Bardeen, Phys. Rev. **80**, 567 (1950).

expresssed in terms of the electrical resistivity ρ at room temperature. In the Bardeen theory the criterion is, approximately,

(11.54) $n\rho > 10^6$,

where ρ is the resistivity at $20°C$ in esu, and n is the number of valence electrons per cubic centimeter. The comparison with experimental results shows that the agreement is quite fair; for example, for sodium (which is not superconducting) $n\rho = 0.14 \times 10^6$, while for lead (which is superconducting) $n\rho = 3.1 \times 10^6$. In fact, the theory is probably not as good as the extent of the agreement with the above criterion.

PROBLEMS

11.1. Often the threshold field curve is represented quite well by a parabola:

$$H_c(T) = H_0[1 - (T/T_c)^2].$$

Show that this relation leads to

$$S_n - S_s = \frac{H_0{}^2}{2\pi T_c}\left[\frac{T}{T_c} - \left(\frac{T}{T_c}\right)^3\right]$$

and

$$C_n - C_s = \frac{H_0{}^2}{2\pi T_c}\left[\frac{T}{T_c} - 3\left(\frac{T}{T_c}\right)^3\right]$$

for the entropy and heat capacity differences, per unit volume.

11.2. Obtain an expression (using the London equation) for the magnetic field H inside a superconducting plate of thickness D and infinite extent in a static field H_0 parallel to the plate.

11.3. Make a quantitative plot of effective susceptibility vs. the applied magnetic field for a long circular cylinder of a superconductor. The applied field is perpendicular to the cylinder axis.

11.4. The results of Problem 1.1 lead to a definite prediction in terms of H_0 and T_c for the coefficient of the linear term in C_n, supposing that the corresponding coefficient in C_s is zero (as seems to be true experimentally). Check this prediction approximately for two metals, using the results in Fig. 11.2 and Table 12.1.

REFERENCES

F. London, *Superfluids*, John Wiley & Sons, New York, 1950, Vol. I.

W. Meissner, Handbuch der Experimentalphysik, **11/2** (1935), pp. 204–262.

K. Mendlessohn, Repts. Prog. Phys. **10**, 358 (1946); **12**, 270 (1949).

D. Shoenberg, *Superconductivity*, Cambridge University Press, Cambridge, 2nd ed., 1952.

F. E. Simon *et al.*, *Low temperature physics*, Academic Press, New York, 1952.

M. von Laue, *Theory of superconductivity*, Academic Press, New York, 1952.

12

Free Electron Theory
of Metals

The electronic structures of metals may differ considerably from one metal to another, from sodium, which we may think of as a sea of negative charge in which are embedded the positive ion cores, to tin and bismuth, which may have binding forces like those of chemical valence bonds. In this chapter we discuss the properties of the free electron model of a metal. On this model, which is approximately applicable in some respects to the alkali metals, the electrons are considered to move freely within the boundaries of the specimen, the only potential energy the electrons see being a potential barrier at the boundaries. We can calculate on this model a number of physical properties, including the electronic heat capacity, the magnetic susceptibility, the Hall coefficient, and some of the optical properties. The model gives us no basis for calculating absolute values of electrical and thermal conductivities because it is not possible to calculate electronic mean free paths without elaborating the model; the ratio of electrical and thermal conductivities may, however, be calculated. Some of the defects of the free electron theory are rectified in the following chapter on the band theory of metals. We now treat the free electron model, first developing as background the elementary quantum mechanics of the free particle problem and the Fermi-Dirac distribution law.

QUANTUM THEORY OF FREE PARTICLES IN A BOX

We consider a particle of mass m confined in a cubical box of side L. It is somewhat more convenient for our later purposes to require as boundary conditions that the wave functions be periodic on the boundaries of the cube; this device allows us to work with running waves instead of standing waves. The wave equation for a free particle is

(12.1) $$-\frac{\hbar^2}{2m} \nabla^2 \psi = W\psi,$$

223

where ψ is the wave function, and W is the kinetic energy of the particle. Solutions of (12.1) are of the form of plane waves

$$(12.2) \qquad\qquad \psi \sim e^{i\mathbf{k}\cdot\mathbf{r}}.$$

We must do two things to (12.2) before it can be an acceptable solution: we must normalize it so that

$$(12.3) \qquad\qquad \int \psi^*\psi\, dV = 1,$$

where the integral is taken over the cube of volume $V = L^3$, and we must arrange that ψ be periodic with period L along each Cartesian axis. A satisfactory solution is

$$(12.4) \qquad\qquad \psi = \frac{1}{(V)^{1/2}}\, e^{i\mathbf{k}\cdot\mathbf{r}},$$

where the allowed values of k_x, k_y, k_z are

$$(12.5) \qquad\qquad k_i = 0,\ \pm\frac{2\pi}{L},\ \pm\frac{4\pi}{L},\ \pm\frac{6\pi}{L},\ \cdots$$

With the k's determined in this way, the wave function is periodic as required; for example,

$$\psi_\mathbf{n}(x+L,\ y,\ z) = V^{-1/2} e^{i\frac{2\pi}{L}[n_x(x+L)+n_y y+n_z z]}$$

$$= \psi_\mathbf{n}(x,y,z);$$

here $\mathbf{n}$ represents the triplet of integer quantum numbers (n_x, n_y, n_z).

The allowed values of the energy W are determined by substituting the allowed ψ's into the wave equation (12.1). We find

$$(12.6) \qquad W = \frac{\hbar^2}{2m}\, k^2 = \frac{\hbar^2}{2m}\left(\frac{2\pi}{L}\right)^2 (n_x^2 + n_y^2 + n_z^2)$$

$$= \frac{\hbar^2 n^2}{2m V^{2/3}}.$$

FERMI-DIRAC DISTRIBUTION LAW[1]

From the elementary kinetic theory of gases we are familiar with the Maxwell-Boltzmann distribution law. This law is a result of classical theory and is valid under the ordinary conditions of molecules in a gas. Electrons are much lighter than molecules; also, in a metal the con-

[1] For a clear elementary exposition of quantum statistics, see M. Born, *Atomic physics*, Hafner, New York, 5th ed., 1951. A short alternative derivation is given by F. Bloch in the reference cited at the end of the chapter.

centration of valence electrons is 10^4 higher than the concentration of molecules in a gas at S.T.P. Under these conditions classical statistics is no longer a valid approximation to the correct quantum statistics.

As applied to electrons, quantum statistics requires that we treat all electrons as *indistinguishable* and that each state of the system may be occupied by at most one electron. A one-particle state of the free particle system is determined by a specification of the values of the quantum numbers n_x, n_y, n_z, and the spin quantum number $m_z = \pm\frac{1}{2}$ of the electron. If we can have only one electron in a state, it follows, when we are dealing with large numbers of electrons, that even in the ground state of the total system many high quantum number states of the individual electrons will be occupied. This is very different from the Maxwell-Boltzmann case where any number of particles can have the identical energy and momentum.

We define a cell by the set of numbers n_x, n_y, n_z, m_z. The occupation number of a cell is either 0 or 1. We consider now a set of g_s cells having approximately the same energy W as given by (12.6), and we let the number of electrons in the set be n_s, so that of the g_s cells n_s are (singly) occupied (1) and $g_s - n_s$ are empty (0). The distribution is characterized uniquely by assigning to each cell its occupation number:

Cell	z_1	z_2	z_3	z_4	z_5	z_6	z_7 · · ·
Occupation number	0	1	0	0	1	1	1 · · ·

We may also give a complete characterization by specifying the cells which are vacant and those occupied by one particle, as in the following sequence:

$$0 \qquad\qquad 1$$
$$z_2\, z_5\, z_6\, z_7\; \cdot\; \cdot\; \cdot \qquad z_1\, z_3\, z_4\; \cdot\; \cdot\; \cdot$$

We now enumerate the *distinguishable distributions*. There are $g_s!$ sequences in which we can write down the names (the z_i) of the g_s cells on a line, as the first spot may be chosen in g_s ways, the second in $g_s - 1$ ways, etc. But many of these sequences are indistinguishable if the electrons are indistinguishable; for example, interchanging the order $z_2\, z_5$ to $z_5\, z_2$ is not a distinguishable change.

We must not count as distinguishable distributions those which differ from one another only by permutation of the n_s occupied cells or the $g_s - n_s$ vacant cells. The number of distinguishable sequences w_s is given by

$$(12.7) \qquad w_s(g_s - n_s)!n_s! = g_s!,$$

because the total number of sequences must be given by the number of distinguishable sequences times the number of indistinguishable sequences contained within each distinguishable sequence. We have then

(12.8)
$$w_s = \frac{g_s!}{(g_s - n_s)!n_s!}.$$

If now we cover the whole energy range by considering also the other sets g_i, we have for the total number of distinguishable arrangements in the entire system

(12.9)
$$w = \prod_p w_p = \prod_p \frac{g_p!}{(g_p - n_p)!n_p!}.$$

It is a fundamental result of statistical mechanics that the observable average properties of a thermodynamic system in equilibrium are quite accurately given by the properties of the most probable distribution. To obtain the most probable distribution we make w a maximum as a function of the n_p, subject to the conditions that the total number of particles should be constant:

(12.10)
$$\Sigma n_p = N,$$

and that the total energy should be constant:

(12.11)
$$\Sigma n_p W_p = W,$$

where W_p is the energy of a particle in the set g_p, and W is the total energy of the system.

The calculation proceeds most conveniently by working with log w:

(12.12)
$$\log w = \sum_p [\log g_p! - \log(g_p - n_p)! - \log n_p!].$$

We expand the logarithms, using Stirling's approximation, valid for large numbers:

(12.13)
$$\log n! \cong n \log n - n.$$

Thus

(12.14) log w
$$= \sum_p [g_p \log g_p - (g_p - n_p) \log (g_p - n_p) - n_p \log n_p].$$

We apply the method of Lagrangian multipliers to find the maximum of log w, subject to the conditions (12.10) and (12.11):

(12.15) $\dfrac{\partial}{\partial n_i} [\log w + \alpha(N - \Sigma n_p) + \beta(W - \Sigma n_p W_p)]$
$$= \log (g_i - n_i) - \log n_i - \alpha - \beta W_i = 0.$$

This gives

$$\frac{g_i - n_i}{n_i} = e^{\alpha + \beta W_i},$$

or

(12.16) $$n_i = \frac{g_i}{e^{\alpha + \beta W_i} + 1}.$$

The Lagrangian multiplier α is determined by the condition $\Sigma n_i = N$. We may determine the constant β by the observation that at very high temperatures n_i/g_i must be $\ll 1$, as very many states are then

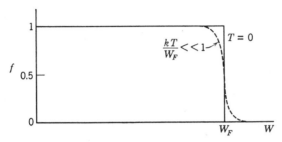

Fig. 12.1. Sketch of the Fermi-Dirac distribution function, for absolute zero and for a low temperature. The region over which the distribution is affected by temperature is of the order of kT in width.

energetically accessible, and we therefore have in the high temperature limit

(12.17) $$n_i \approx g_i e^{-\beta W_i}.$$

By comparison with the Boltzmann distribution law valid in this limit we see that

(12.18) $$\beta = 1/kT.$$

It is convenient to work with the distribution function

(12.19) $$f = \frac{n}{g} = \frac{1}{e^{\alpha} e^{W/kT} + 1},$$

which gives the probability that a given state is occupied. This is called the Fermi-Dirac distribution function, and is plotted in Fig. 12.1. To study the behavior of the function, we define an energy W_F such that

(12.20) $$\alpha = -W_F/kT,$$

giving

(12.21)
$$f = \frac{1}{e^{(W - W_F)/kT} + 1};$$

W_F is called the *Fermi energy*. At $T = 0°K$, $f = 1$ for $W < W_F$, and $f = 0$ for $W > W_F$. Thus at absolute zero W_F has the significance of a cut-off energy; all states with energy less than W_F are completely filled and all states with energy greater than W_F are vacant. As T increases, the distribution rounds off as shown in the figure, states within about kT below W_F being partly depopulated and states within about kT above W_F being partly populated. The value of W_F is determined by (12.10) and depends on the temperature, but for $kT/W_F \ll 1$ it can be shown that $W_F(T)$ is closely equal to its value at $0°K$. At any temperature f has the value $\frac{1}{2}$ for $W = W_F$. The distribution is called *degenerate* when $kT \ll W_F$, and *non-degenerate* when $kT \gg W_F$ (classical limit).

STATISTICS OF FREE ELECTRON GAS

In (5.12) we obtained an expression for the number of modes of an elastic system, per unit volume, for which the magnitude of the wave vector lies between k and $k + dk$. The same result describes the number of states of a free electron, except that we no longer have three polarizations, but instead have two spin states, for each allowed wave vector. Thus the number of states per unit volume with wave vector between k and $k + dk$ is[2]

(12.22)
$$G(k)\, dk = \frac{1}{\pi^2}\, k^2\, dk.$$

Now, from (12.6),

$$dW = \frac{\hbar^2}{m}\, k\, dk,$$

whence the number of states with energy between W and $W + dW$ is

(12.23)
$$g(W)\, dW = \frac{1}{2\pi^2} \left(\frac{2m}{\hbar^2} \right)^{3/2} (W)^{1/2}\, dW,$$

per unit volume.

[2] This is equivalent to saying that there are $2/h^3$ states per unit volume of phase space: in the spherical momentum shell in phase space of volume $4\pi p^2\, dp$ there are then $8\pi p^2\, dp/h^3$ states; as $k = 2\pi p/h$, we have $k^2 dk/\pi^2$ states, in agreement with (12.22).

In thermal equilibrium the number of electrons with energy between W and $W + dW$ is given by [using (12.23) and the Fermi-Dirac distribution function (12.21)]

$$(12.24) \qquad dn = fg(W)\, dW = \frac{1}{2\pi^2}\left(\frac{2m}{\hbar^2}\right)^{3/2} \frac{(W)^{1/2}\, dW}{e^{(W-W_F)/kT} + 1},$$

per unit volume. It is often handy to introduce

$$(12.25) \qquad C = \frac{1}{2\pi^2}\left(\frac{2m}{\hbar^2}\right)^{3/2},$$

so that

$$(12.26) \qquad dn = \frac{C(W)^{1/2}\, dW}{e^{(W-W_F)/kT} + 1},$$

and W_F is determined by setting the integral of dn equal to the number of particles per unit volume, N.

We now consider several limiting cases.

ABSOLUTE ZERO

Here f is unity for W less than $W_F{}^0$, the value of W_F at $0°$K, and is zero for greater values. Thus all states are filled up to W_F, and the value of W_F is determined in terms of the number of electrons per unit volume, N, by

$$(12.27) \qquad N = C\int_0^{W_F{}^0} (W)^{1/2}\, dW = \tfrac{2}{3}C(W_F{}^0)^{3/2},$$

so that

$$(12.28) \qquad W_F{}^0 = \frac{\hbar^2}{2m}(3\pi^2 N)^{2/3}.$$

The order of magnitude of $W_F{}^0$ in metals is about 5 ev. Theoretical values, after Mott and Jones, of the Fermi temperature $T_F = W_F{}^0/k$, assuming one free electron per atom, are as follows:

	Li	Na	K	Cu	Ag	Au
$T_F \times 10^{-4}$ (deg)	5.5	3.7	2.4	8.2	6.4	6.4

It is left to Problem 12.1 to show that the kinetic energy at $0°$K is

$$(12.29) \qquad U_0 = \tfrac{3}{5}NW_F{}^0.$$

LOW TEMPERATURES $(kT \ll W_F)$

At low temperatures the change in the distribution function from its form at $0°$K takes place chiefly when close to $W_F{}^0$. We make use of this fact to obtain an important and useful series expansion for W_F. First consider the integral

$$(12.30) \qquad I = \int_0^\infty f(W) \frac{d}{dW} F(W) \, dW,$$

where $f(W)$ is the Fermi-Dirac distribution function, and $F(W)$ is any function which vanishes for $W = 0$. Integrating by parts,

$$(12.31) \qquad I = [f(W)F(W)]_0^\infty - \int_0^\infty F(W)f'(W) \, dW;$$

the first term on the right vanishes at the upper limit because of the form of $f(W)$ and vanishes at the lower limit because we supposed that $F(0)$ was zero.

We now expand $F(W)$ by Taylor's theorem about W_F:

$$(12.32) \quad F(W) = F(W_F) + (W - W_F)F'(W_F)$$
$$+ \tfrac{1}{2}(W - W_F)^2 F''(W_F) + \cdots .$$

On substituting in (12.31) we have

$$(12.33) \quad I = L_0 F(W_F) + L_1 F'(W_F) + L_2 F''(W_F) + \cdots ,$$

where

$$(12.34) \quad L_0 = - \int_0^\infty f'(W) \, dW; L_1 = - \int_0^\infty (W - W_F)f'(W) \, dW;$$

$$L_2 = - \tfrac{1}{2} \int_0^\infty (W - W_F)^2 f'(W) \, dW.$$

At low temperatures we may replace the lower limits on the integrals by $-\infty$. We see then that $L_0 = 1$, and, as it is readily shown that $f'(W)$ is an even power of $W - W_F$, we have $L_1 = 0$. For L_2, we have, writing $x = (W - W_F)/kT$,

$$(12.35) \qquad L_2 = \frac{1}{2} (kT)^2 \int_{-\infty}^\infty \frac{x^2 e^x \, dx}{(1 + e^x)^2} = \frac{\pi^2}{6} (kT)^2,$$

where the definite integral is given in standard tables. Finally,

$$(12.36) \quad I = \int_0^\infty f(W)F'(W) \, dW = F(W_F)$$

$$+ \frac{\pi^2}{6} (kT)^2 F''(W_F) + \cdots .$$

The number of electrons is given by setting [using (12.23)]

$$(12.37) \qquad F(W) = \int_0^W g(W) \, dW,$$

so that

$$(12.38) \quad N = \int_0^\infty f(W)g(W)\, dW$$

$$= \int_0^{W_F} g(W)\, dW + \frac{\pi^2}{6}\, (kT)^2 g'(W_F).$$

If we subtract from this the relation

$$(12.39) \qquad\qquad N = \int_0^{W_F{}^0} g(W)\, dW, \quad \centerdot$$

we obtain

$$(12.40) \qquad \int_{W_F{}^0}^{W_F} g(W)\, dW + \frac{\pi^2}{6}\, (kT)^2 g'(W_F) = 0,$$

or, approximately,

$$(12.41) \qquad (W_F - W_F{}^0)g(W_F) + \frac{\pi^2}{6}\, (kT)^2 g'(W_F) = 0.$$

Inserting (12.23), we obtain

$$(12.42) \qquad\qquad W_F \cong W_F{}^0 \left[1 - \frac{\pi^2}{12} \left(\frac{kT}{W_F{}^0} \right)^2 \right].$$

The second term in the brackets being small, it is of no consequence whether we write $W_F{}^0$ or W_F in the denominator.

HEAT CAPACITY OF ELECTRON GAS

In classical statistics we would expect a contribution to the heat capacity from the conduction electrons in metals of $\frac{3}{2}R$/mole, where R is the gas constant. This is not observed; instead it is found that the electronic contribution at room temperature is only of the order of $10^{-1}R$ to $10^{-2}R$/mole. The explanation of the anomaly is one of the finest accomplishments of quantum statistics.

Looking at Fig. 12.1, we see that the fraction of the electrons which are elevated in energy on going from 0°K to a temperature T is of the order of kT/W_F. The increase in energy of these electrons is of the order of kT, so that the average thermal energy per electron is $\approx kT(kT/W_F)$, or, per mole (for $T \ll T_F$),

$$(12.43) \qquad\qquad U \approx RT(kT/W_F).$$

The molar heat capacity is then

$$(12.44) \qquad\qquad C_v = \frac{\partial U}{\partial T} \approx R \cdot \frac{T}{T_F},$$

where the *Fermi temperature* T_F is defined by the relation

$$(12.45) \qquad kT_F = W_F^0.$$

In metals the values of T_F are of the order of 10^4 to 10^5 °K, so that electronic contributions to the heat capacity at room temperature of the order of $10^{-2}R$ are anticipated. At low temperatures the total heat capacity of a metal consists of the sum of two terms:

$$(12.46) \qquad C_v = \gamma T + BT^3,$$

the γT term arising from the conduction electrons and the BT^3 from the lattice vibrations; at sufficiently low temperatures the linear term is dominant, so that the experimental determination of the coefficient γ is most accurately carried out at very low temperatures. For copper,[3] $\gamma = 0.888 \times 10^{-4}R$, per mole; and, for aluminum, $\gamma = 1.742 \times 10^{-4}R$, per mole.

We proceed now to calculate the electronic heat capacity of a free electron gas. The total energy per unit volume is given by

$$(12.47) \qquad U = \int_0^\infty Wf(W)g(W) \, dW.$$

Setting

$$(12.48) \qquad F(W) = \int_0^W Wg(W) \, dW,$$

we have from (12.36), at low temperatures,

$$(12.49) \quad U = \int_0^{W_F} Wg(W) \, dW + \frac{\pi^2}{6}(kT)^2 \frac{d}{dW}(Wg)$$

$$\cong U_0 + (W_F - W_F^0)W_F^0 g(W_F^0) + \frac{3}{2}\frac{\pi^2}{6}(kT)^2 g(W_F^0),$$

using (12.29) and (12.23). Now, using (12.42), we have

$$(12.50) \qquad U = U_0 + \frac{\pi^2}{6}(kT)^2 g(W_F^0).$$

The heat capacity is, per unit volume,

$$(12.51) \qquad C_v = \frac{\pi^2}{3}g(W_F^0)k^2 T.$$

Now, from (12.23) and (12.27),

$$(12.52) \qquad g(W_F^0) = (3N/2W_F^0) = 3N/2kT_F,$$

[3] J. A. Kok and W. H. Keesom, Physica **3**, 1035 (1936); **4**, 835 (1937).

so that

(12.53) $$C_v = \tfrac{1}{2}\pi^2 NkT/T_F,$$

per unit volume; or, per mole,

(12.54) $$C_v = \tfrac{1}{2}\pi^2 zRT/T_F = \gamma T,$$

where

(12.55) $$\gamma = \tfrac{1}{2}\pi^2 zR/T_F;$$

here z is the number of valence or conduction electrons per atom. This equation is of the form predicted by our qualitative argument leading to (12.44).

For metals for which the free electron model might be applicable we may expect the molar electronic heat capacity to be of the order of $10^{-4}T$ cal/mole/deg. The observed values given in Table 12.1 are

TABLE 12.1. COEFFICIENT γ OF THE LINEAR TERM γT IN THE MOLAR HEAT CAPACITY OF METALS, FROM LOW TEMPERATURE DATA

(For the superconducting metals, γ refers to the normal state.)

Metal	$\gamma \times 10^4$ (cal/mole/deg^2)	Metal	$\gamma \times 10^4$ (cal/mole/deg^2)
Ag	6.45– 7.82	Mo	5.1
Al	2.59– 3.48	Nb	21.
Cd	1.3 – 1.5	Ni	17.4
Co	12.	Pb	7.1
Cr	3.80	Pd	31.
Cu	1.78	Pt	16.1
Fe(α)	12.	Re	4.6
Ga	0.91	Sn	4.
Hf	6.7	Ta	14.1
Hg	3.7.	Ti	8.0
In	4.3	V	14.
Mg	3.25	Zn	1.5
Mn	35.–40.	Zr	6.92

on the whole much larger than this, although it should be noted that values have not been determined[4] for the alkali metals for which the theory should be fairly good. In the next chapter we shall discuss the anomalous values of γ.

PAULI PARAMAGNETISM

In most metals the conduction electrons have a small temperature-independent paramagnetic volume susceptibility, of the order of 10^{-6},

[4] This has not yet been done because interest has been mainly in the superconducting and transition metals.

in striking disagreement with the Langevin formula which predicts a susceptibility of the order of 10^{-4} at room temperature and varying as $1/T$. Pauli[5] showed that the application of Fermi-Dirac statistics would correct the theory as required.

The Langevin formula (9.3) tells us that the probability that an atom will be lined up parallel to the field H exceeds the probability of the antiparallel orientation by a factor $\sim\mu H/kT$. For N atoms, this

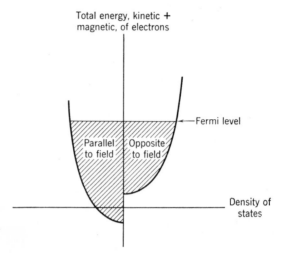

Fig. 12.2. Pauli paramagnetism at $0°K$; the levels in the shaded regions are occupied. At higher temperatures the electrons near the Fermi level will spread out.

gives a net magnetic moment $\sim N H\mu^2/kT$, which is the classical result. For electrons in a metal, however, most of them have zero probability of turning over when a field is applied, because the states with parallel spin are already occupied, at least if they are within the energy $2\mu H$ of the given antiparallel state. As only the electrons within $\sim kT$ of the top of the Fermi distribution have a chance to turn over in the field, only the fraction $\sim T/T_F$ of the total number of electrons should be counted as contributing to the susceptibility. Hence $\chi \sim (N\mu^2/kT)(T/T_F) = N\mu^2/kT_F$, which is independent of temperature and of the correct order of magnitude, as T_F is of the order of 10^4 to 10^5 $°K$. This argument supposes that $\mu H \ll kT$, which is true at room tem-

---

[5] W. Pauli, Z. Physik **41**, 81 (1927); electron spin resonance associated with the Pauli paramagnetism has been observed in sodium by Griswold, Kip, and Kittel, Phys. Rev. **88**, 951 (1952).

perature as the strongest field yet obtained, 5×10^5 oersteds, only corresponds to a temperature of $\sim 50°K$.

We now calculate the expression for the paramagnetic susceptibility of a free electron gas. Following the notation of (12.23) and the method of calculation suggested by Fig. 12.2, we have for the net magnetization

$$(12.56) \quad M = \mu_B \int [\tfrac{1}{2}g(W + \mu_B H) - \tfrac{1}{2}g(W - \mu_B H)]f(W)\,dW,$$

where W is the total energy, kinetic plus magnetic, of an electron. For small H,

$$(12.57) \qquad M \cong \mu_B{}^2 H \int g'(W)f(W)\,dW.$$

We set

$$(12.58) \qquad F(W) = \int_0^W g'(W)\,dW,$$

so that, by (12.36),

$$(12.59) \qquad M \cong \mu_B{}^2 H g(W_F),$$

and at low temperatures we have

$$(12.60) \qquad \chi = M/H = \mu_B{}^2 g(W_F{}^0).$$

Using (12.52),

$$(12.61) \qquad \chi = 3N\mu_B{}^2/2kT_F,$$

the Pauli result. This is of the form suggested by our qualitative argument.

In deriving the paramagnetic susceptibility we have supposed that the spatial motion of the electrons is not affected on applying the magnetic field. Actually the running wave functions (12.4) are modified by the magnetic field, and Landau[6] has shown that there is also a diamagnetic moment which for free electrons is equal to $-\tfrac{1}{3}$ of the paramagnetic moment (12.61), so that the total susceptibility of a free electron gas is

$$(12.62) \qquad \chi_T = N\mu_B{}^2/kT_F.$$

A correction must also be applied for the diamagnetism of the ionic cores. A comparison of theoretical (free electron) and experimental

[6] L. Landau, Z. Physik **64**, 629 (1930).

values of the susceptibility of the alkali metals is given in Table 12.2.

TABLE 12.2. SUSCEPTIBILITY OF THE ALKALI METALS

(After Mott and Jones)

	$\chi \times 10^6$, per gram				
	Li	Na	K	Rb	Cs
Calculated susceptibility, from (12.62)	1.0	0.45	0.40	0.21	0.16
Diamagnetism of ions (observed)	−0.1	−0.26	−0.34	−0.33	−0.29
Total susceptibility (calculated)	0.9	0.2	0.06	−0.12	−0.15
Observed susceptibility	0.5	0.6	0.5	0.2	−0.1—+0.2

THERMIONIC EMISSION EQUATION

We now calculate the Richardson equation for the saturation current density evaporated from a metal, using the free electron model. We

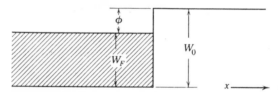

Fig. 12.3.   Model for calculation of thermionic emission.

suppose, following Fig. 12.3, that W_0 is the work necessary to remove to infinity an electron from the lowest free electron state in the metal. If the electron is taken from the Fermi level, the work is

$$(12.63) \qquad \phi = W_0 - W_F;$$

this is the definition of the *work function* ϕ.

The rate at which electrons in the momentum range between $\mathbf{p}$ and $\mathbf{p} + d\mathbf{p}$ strike unit area of the surface is

$$(12.64) \qquad v_x n(\mathbf{p})\, d\mathbf{p} = \frac{\partial W}{\partial p_x}\, n(\mathbf{p})\, d\mathbf{p} = n(\mathbf{p})\, dW\, dp_y\, dp_z,$$

as W is the kinetic energy; here $n(\mathbf{p})$ is the number of electrons per unit volume of phase space and is given by

$$(12.65) \qquad n(\mathbf{p}) = (2/h^3)f.$$

The electronic charge e times the rate at which electrons having

$$p_x{}^2/2m > \phi + W_F$$

strike unit area of the surface will be the emission current density j, apart from a factor representing quantum reflection effects which we neglect. Then

$$(12.66) \qquad j = \frac{2e}{h^3} \int_{-\infty}^{\infty} \int_{-\infty}^{\infty} \int_{\phi}^{\infty} \frac{dp_y \, dp_z \, dW}{e^{(W-W_F)/kT} + 1}$$

$$= \frac{2kTe}{h^3} \int_{-\infty}^{\infty} \int_{-\infty}^{\infty} \log \left[1 + e^{-\theta}\right] dp_y \, dp_z,$$

where

$$\theta = \frac{1}{kT} [\phi + (p_y{}^2 + p_z{}^2)/2m].$$

For ordinary conditions $\theta \gg 1$, so that we may expand the logarithm and retain only the first term:

$$(12.67) \qquad j = \frac{2kTe}{h^3} e^{-\phi/kT} \iint e^{-(p_y{}^2 + p_z{}^2)/2mkT} \, dp_y \, dp_z$$

$$= 4\pi m e (kT)^2 h^{-3} e^{-\phi/kT}.$$

This is the Richardson-Dushman equation. We may write the result as

$$(12.68) \qquad j = AT^2 e^{-\phi/kT},$$

where

$$(12.69) \qquad A = 4\pi m e k^2 h^{-3} = 120 \text{ amp/cm}^2/\text{deg}^2.$$

Experimental values of A and ϕ are given in Table 12.3. The values

TABLE 12.3. REPRESENTATIVE THERMIONIC EMISSION DATA

Metal	A (amp/cm^2/deg^2)	ϕ (ev)
W	~75	4.5
Ta	55	4.2
Ni	30	4.6
Ag	.....	4.8
Cs	160	1.8
Pt	32	5.3
Ba on W	1.5	1.56
Cs on W	3.2	1.36
Cr	48	4.60

are sensitive to surface conditions, particularly to surface films and non-uniform surfaces.[7] Work functions from photoelectric data are

[7] For a careful discussion of the data see C. Herring and M. H. Nichols, Revs. Modern Phys. **21**, 185 (1949).

given in Table 12.4, obtained from the minimum photon energy which will eject a photoelectron.

TABLE 12.4. WORK FUNCTIONS FROM PHOTOELECTRIC DATA

Metal	ϕ (ev)
Na	2.3
K	2.26
Cr	4.37
Zn	4.24
W	4.49
Pt	6.2

ELECTRICAL CONDUCTIVITY

To orient ourselves we consider first the elementary classical treatment of Drude. The current density is given by

$$(12.70) \qquad j = Nev_D,$$

where v_D is the mean drift velocity of the electrons in an electric field; N is the number of electrons per unit volume. The equation of motion of a free electron is

$$(12.71) \qquad m\dot{v} = eE,$$

so that

$$(12.72) \qquad mv = mv(0) + eEt.$$

We suppose that at $t = 0$ each electron suffers a collision of such a nature that immediately·after collision the mean velocity component $\overline{v(0)}$ parallel to the field is zero. If 2τ is the average time between collisions [τ is called the *relaxation time*] the time average drift velocity is $eE\tau/m$. The current density becomes

$$(12.73) \qquad j = Ne^2E\tau/m.$$

We introduce the mean free path Λ by the relation

$$(12.74) \qquad \Lambda = 2\tau u,$$

where u is the root mean square thermal velocity of the electron and is supposed not to be appreciably disturbed by the field E. We have then

$$(12.75) \qquad j = \frac{Ne^2\Lambda}{2m} \overline{\left(\frac{1}{u}\right)} E.$$

The electrical conductivity is given by

$$(12.76) \qquad \sigma = \frac{Ne^2\Lambda}{2m} \overline{\left(\frac{1}{u}\right)}.$$

The more careful averaging carried out by Lorentz replaces the 2 by $\frac{3}{2}$. For a Maxwellian velocity distribution,

$$(12.77) \qquad \overline{\left(\frac{1}{u}\right)} = \left(\frac{\pi k T}{2m}\right)^{\frac{1}{2}},$$

so that, including the Lorentz modification,

$$(12.78) \qquad \sigma = \frac{4}{3} \frac{Ne^2\Lambda}{(2\pi m k T)^{\frac{1}{2}}}.$$

For silver at room temperature, $\sigma = 7 \times 10^5$ mho/cm, or 6×10^{17} esu; $N = 6 \times 10^{22}$ cm^{-3}; $kT = 4 \times 10^{-14}$ ergs; $m = 9 \times 10^{-28}$ grams. We find $\Lambda \approx 10^{-6}$ cm, at room temperature.

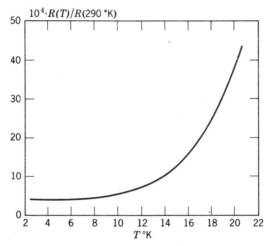

Fig. 12.4. Relative electrical resistance of sodium at low temperatures. The value of the residual resistance at 0°K varies from sample to sample, depending on the purity. [After D. K. C. MacDonald and K. Mendelssohn, Proc. Roy. Soc. (London) **A202**, 103 (1950).]

On using Fermi-Dirac statistics one obtains[8] for the electrical conductivity an expression closely similar to (12.76):

$$(12.79) \qquad \sigma = \frac{Ne^2\Lambda(W_F)}{mu(W_F)},$$

where $\Lambda(W_F)$ is the mean free path of an electron at the Fermi energy and $u(W_F)$ is the velocity $(2W_F/m)^{\frac{1}{2}}$ corresponding to the Fermi

[8] The derivation of this result is given by F. Seitz, *Modern theory of solids*, pp. 168–176. It may be derived in an elementary way by recognizing that, for a Fermi distribution at $T \ll T_F$, $\overline{(1/u)} = \frac{3}{2}(1/u(w_F))$; on making the Lorentz modification we obtain (12.79).

energy. For silver the theoretical Fermi energy is 9×10^{-12} ergs, so that $u(W_F) \cong 1.4 \times 10^8$ cm/sec. In order to fit the observed conductivity at room temperature we must have $\Lambda(W_F) \cong 5 \times 10^{-6}$ cm. Values of Λ for several metals are given in Table 12.5. Resistivity values for a number of metals are given in Table 12.6.

TABLE 12.5. CONDUCTIVITY DATA FOR METALS AT 0°C

One free electron per atom is assumed; Λ is calculated by using Eq. (12.79); values after Mott and Jones, with an error of a factor of 2 in their Λ's corrected.

Metal	Free Electrons per cm³, $N \times 10^{22}$	Observed Conductivity at 0°C, $\sigma \times 10^{-17}$ (esu)	Calculated Fermi Energy, W_F (ev)	Calculated $u(W_F)$ $\times 10^{-8}$ (cm/sec)	Mean Free Path, $\Lambda \times 10^8$ (cm)
Li	4.6	1.06	4.72	1.31	110
Na	2.5	2.09	3.12	1.07	350
K	1.3	1.47	2.14	0.85	370
Rb	1.1	0.78	1.82	0.80	220
Cs	0.85	0.49	1.53	0.75	160
Cu	8.5	5.76	7.04	1.58	420
Ag	5.8	6.12	5.51	1.40	570
Au	5.9	4.37	5.54	1.40	410

TABLE 12.6. RESISTIVITY OF METALS AT 18°C
(Values in parentheses are at 0°C.)

Metal	Ohm-cm $\times 10^6$	Metal	Ohm-cm $\times 10^6$	Metal	Ohm-cm $\times 10^6$
Li	9.1	Zr	45.0	Cu	1.68
Na	4.6	Hf	32.0	Ag	1.58
K	6.9	Ta	14.7	Au	2.21
Rb	12.6	Cr	(2.6)	Zn	5.95
Cs	20.8	Mo	4.72	Cd	7.25
Be	6.3	W	5.32	Hg	95.4
Mg	4.3	Fe	8.7	Ga	43.9
Ca	3.6	Ru	14.5	In	9.1
Sr	32.4	Os	9.45	Tl	17.5
Ba	(57.5)	Co	6.8	Sn	11.3
Al	2.72	Rh	5.0	Pb	20.7
La	59.8	Ir	5.3	As	37.6
Ce	74.0	Ni	7.35	Sb	39.8
Pr	66.8	Pd	10.75	Bi	118.
Ti	89.0	Pt	10.5		

One of the major weaknesses of the free electron theory of conductivity is that it suggests no a priori basis for calculating or estimating the value of the mean free path to be expected; therefore we cannot judge whether or not a value, say of 5×10^{-6} cm as deduced for silver, is reasonable. The resistivity is found empirically to be a strong function of the temperature—varying as T for $T \gg \Theta$ and as T^5 for $T \ll \Theta$. The relative resistivity of sodium at low temperatures is shown in Fig. 12.4. Such results require a mean free path at very low temperatures of the order of 10^3 to 10^4 times the mean free path at room temperature. In the next chapter (on the band model) we shall see how to estimate the temperature dependence of the resistivity.

We should point out that electron-electron collisions do not contribute to the resistivity: the masses of two electrons being equal, the sum of their velocities is the same after collision as before. Collisions of electrons with positive ions would in classical theory lead to mean free paths of the order of the lattice constants, $\approx 10^{-7}$ to 10^{-8} cm; yet the observed resistivities require $\Lambda \sim 10^{-6}$ to 10^{-2} cm, the larger values occurring at low temperatures.

HALL EFFECT

When a conductor is placed in a magnetic field transverse to the direction of current flow, a voltage is developed in the direction perpendicular to the plane of the current and the magnetic field, as in Fig. 12.5. This is called the Hall effect. The voltage is developed

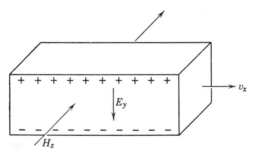

Fig. 12.5. Hall effect. Electrons flowing in the x direction in the presence of the magnetic field H_z are deflected toward the lower face of the specimen, which then charges up until the resulting electric field cancels the effect of the magnetic field.

because the moving charges making up the current are forced to one side by the magnetic field, and they accumulate on a face of the specimen until the electric field associated with the accumulated charge is large enough to cancel the force exerted by the magnetic field. The Hall effect is an important tool in understanding conductivity processes in metals and semiconductors because it gives us the number of conduction electrons.

In the steady state we must have, from the Lorentz force equation

$$\mathbf{F} = e \left[\mathbf{E} + \frac{1}{c} \mathbf{v} \times \mathbf{H} \right],$$

the condition

$N e v_x = j_x =$

(12.80)
$$eE_y = \frac{e}{c} v_x H_z = j_x H_z / Nc,$$

where j_x is the current density. The ratio

(12.81)
$$R_H = \frac{E_y}{j_x H_z} = \frac{1}{Nce}$$

is called the *Hall coefficient* and is negative for free electrons. In esu the Hall coefficient for metals is of the magnitude 10^{-24}. The result obtained for metals, using Fermi-Dirac statistics and taking care to distinguish between instantaneous and drift velocities, is identical with (12.81).

Observed values of the Hall coefficient are compared with calculated values in Table 12.7. The calculated values for the monovalent

TABLE 12.7. COMPARISON OF OBSERVED HALL CONSTANTS WITH THOSE COMPUTED ON FREE ELECTRON THEORY

(After F. Seitz, *Modern theory of solids*, p. 183.)

$R_H \times 10^{12}$ (v-cm/abamp-gauss) at room temperature

Metal	Observed	Calculated
Li	−17.0	−13.1
Na	−25.0	−24.4
Cu	− 5.5	− 7.4
Ag	− 8.4	−10.4
Au	− 7.2	−10.5
Be	+24.4	− 2.5
Zn	+ 3.3	− 4.6
Cd	+ 6.0	− 6.5
Bi	∼−1000	− 4.1

metals are in reasonably good agreement with observation with respect to both sign and magnitude. However, the sign of the effect in beryllium, zinc, and cadmium is opposite to that predicted and suggests that the conductivity is effectively carried by positive charges; this is explained on the band theory as conductivity by positive holes. The anomalously large coefficient for bismuth may also be understood on the band theory.

see p 267

OPTICAL PROPERTIES

We mention here only one feature of the optical properties of the alkali metals, their transparency in the ultraviolet; the effect was discovered by Wood[9] and explained by Zener.[10] The reflection of light in the infrared is the basis of Problem 12.5.

[9] R. W. Wood, Phys. Rev. **44**, 353 (1933).
[10] C. Zener, Nature **132**, 968 (1933).

For good conductors the relaxation time τ is long in comparison with the period $1/\omega$ of light in the visible part of the spectrum, so that to a fair approximation we may omit the resistance term in the equation of motion and write simply

(12.82) $m\ddot{x} = eE,$ $\ddot{x} = a = -\omega^2 x$

which reduces for a periodic field to

(12.83) $x = -eE/m\omega^2.$

As the polarization is $P = Nex$, the complex refractive index $\underset{\sim}{n}$ is given by

(12.84) $\epsilon = \underset{\sim}{n}^2 = 1 + 4\pi(P/E) = 1 - \dfrac{4\pi Ne^2}{m\omega^2}.$

If $4\pi Ne^2/m\omega^2$ is less than unity (short wavelengths), the refractive index is real and the metal is transparent to light at normal incidence; if $4\pi Ne^2/m\omega^2$ is greater than unity, $\underset{\sim}{n}$ is imaginary, and total reflection may be shown to occur.

The critical wavelength is then, setting $\epsilon = 0$,

(12.85) $\lambda_0 = 2\pi(mc^2/4\pi Ne^2)^{\frac{1}{2}}.$

The agreement with observation is quite good:

	Li	Na	K
λ_0 (calculated) (A)	1500	2100	2900
λ_0 (observed) (A)	1550	2100	3150

THERMAL CONDUCTIVITY OF METALS

The first point to decide in discussing the thermal conductivity of metals is whether the electrons or the phonons carry the greater part of the heat current. We shall find that in normal pure metals the electrons usually carry almost all of the heat current, whereas in very impure metals or in disordered alloys the phonon contribution may be comparable with the electron contribution.

At room temperature the relaxation time of phonon-phonon collisions is of the order of, from Table 5.5,

$$\tau_{pp} = \Lambda_p/v \approx 10^{-6}/10^5 \approx 10^{-11} \text{ sec,}$$

while from Table 12.5 we see that the relaxation time of electrons τ_{ep} in electron-phonon collisions is of the order of

$$\tau_{ep} = \Lambda_e/u \approx 10^{-5}/10^8 \approx 10^{-13} \text{ sec.}$$

Given equal numbers of electrons and phonons, as is roughly true at room temperature in a normal metal, the relaxation time τ_{pe} of phonons in electron-phonon collisions will be equal to τ_{ep} as just estimated. Comparing τ_{ep} with τ_{pp}, we see that under the conditions specified phonons in a metal may have considerably shorter relaxation times than phonons in a dielectric solid. Using (5.37), we see that electron and phonon contributions to the thermal conductivity of a metal will stand approximately in the ratio, for $T \approx 300°\text{K} > \Theta$,

$$\frac{K_e}{K_p} = \frac{C_e u \Lambda_e}{C_p v \Lambda_p} \approx \frac{C_e' u^2 \tau_{ep}}{C_p v^2 \tau_{pe}} \approx \frac{10^{-1} R (10^8)^2 10^{-13}}{3R(3 \times 10^5)^2 10^{-13}} \approx 3 \times 10^3,$$

so that in pure metals the electronic contribution is dominant; here the subscripts e and p refer to electron and phonon respectively. It is seen from Table 5.6 that at room temperature metals tend to have values of the thermal conductivity one or two orders of magnitude higher than those of dielectric solids. This is about as expected from the estimate

$$\frac{K_m}{K_d} \approx \frac{C_e u^2 \tau_{ep}}{C_p v^2 \tau_{pp}} \approx 30,$$

using the relaxation times given above.

In disordered alloys we might expect to have $\Lambda_e \approx \Lambda_p$, as both are limited by the scale of the disorder. Then

$$\frac{K_e}{K_p} \approx \frac{C_e u}{C_p v} \approx 3,$$

so that the electron and phonon contributions are of the same order of magnitude. Makinson[11] has given a careful treatment of the relative magnitudes of the electron and phonon heat currents for various metals over a wide temperature range, with results generally in agreement with the above estimates. Berman[12] has measured the thermal conductivity of three alloys (German silver, stainless steel, and constantan) between 2° and 90°K and found electron and phonon contributions of equal orders of magnitude.

CLASSICAL CALCULATION OF CONDUCTIVITY

We give now the kinetic theory calculation of the thermal conductivity with application to a classical electron gas. We consider the transfer of energy by electrons crossing the xy plane. An electron traveling a distance equal to the mean free path Λ and striking the plane at a polar angle θ has a mean energy

[11] R. E. B. Makinson, Proc. Cambridge Phil. Soc. **34**, 474 (1938).
[12] R. Berman, Phil. Mag. **42**, 642 (1951).

$$W(0) + (\Lambda \cos \theta) \frac{\partial W}{\partial z},$$

where $W(0)$ is the mean energy at the plane $z = 0$. By a well-known kinetic theory result the number of molecules which cross unit area of the plane in a direction making an angle between θ and $\theta + d\theta$ with the z axis per second is

$$\tfrac{1}{2} N u \cos \theta \sin \theta \, d\theta,$$

where N is the concentration and u is the average velocity. The net energy flux is

$$(12.86) \qquad \tfrac{1}{2} N u \frac{\partial W}{\partial z} \int_0^\pi \Lambda \cos^2 \theta \sin \theta \, d\theta = \tfrac{1}{3} N u \Lambda \frac{\partial W}{\partial z},$$

which, by the definition of the thermal conductivity K, must be equal to $K(\partial T/\partial z)$. Now

$$(12.87) \qquad N(\partial W/\partial z) = N(\partial W/\partial T)(\partial T/\partial z) = C(\partial T/\partial z),$$

where C is the heat capacity of the electron gas per unit volume. Thus, from (12.86) and (12.87),

$$(12.88) \qquad\qquad K = \tfrac{1}{3} C u \Lambda.$$

The corresponding result[8] using the method of Lorentz and for Fermi-Dirac statistics is

$$(12.89) \qquad\qquad K = \frac{\pi^2}{3} \frac{N k^2 \Lambda (W_F) T}{m u(W_F)},$$

where the heat capacity is expressed explicitly in terms of the Fermi-Dirac result (12.53).

WIEDEMANN-FRANZ RATIO

We note from (12.79) and (12.89) that

$$(12.90) \qquad\qquad \frac{K}{\sigma} = \frac{\pi^2}{3} \left(\frac{k}{e}\right)^2 T.$$

A relationship of this type was first observed by Wiedemann and Franz, and the ratio is named after them. The Lorenz number L is defined by

$$(12.91) \qquad\qquad L = K/\sigma T,$$

and according to (12.90) should be given on the free electron model by

$$(12.92) \quad L = \frac{\pi^2}{3} \left(\frac{k}{e}\right)^2 = 2.7 \times 10^{-13} \text{ esu/deg}^2$$

$$= 2.45 \times 10^{-8} \text{ watt-ohms/deg}^2,$$

for electronic conduction only. A more detailed study of the quantum theory of transport processes in metals shows that the Lorenz number is expected to be independent of temperature only above the Debye temperatures,[13] as the differences between the types of averages involved in electrical and thermal conductivity become important when at low temperatures small angle electron-phonon collisions are dominant. At room temperature the values observed are in fair

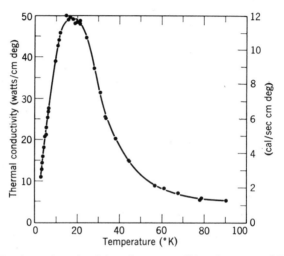

Fig. 12.6. The thermal conductivity of copper. (After Berman and MacDonald.)

agreement with the theoretical value given in (12.92), as shown in Table 12.8. The Lorenz number of pure copper at liquid hydrogen temperatures ($\sim 15°K$) is an order of magnitude smaller than at room temperature. The thermal conductivity of copper vs. temperature is shown in Fig. 12.6.

TABLE 12.8. EXPERIMENTAL LORENZ NUMBERS

$L \times 10^8$ watt-ohms/deg^2			$L \times 10^8$ watt-ohms/deg^2		
Metal	0°C	100°C	Metal	0°C	100°C
Ag	2.31	2.37	Pb	2.47	2.56
Au	2.35	2.40	Pt	2.51	2.60
Cd	2.42	2.43	Sn	2.52	2.49
Cu	2.23	2.33	W	3.04	3.20
Ir	2.49	2.49	Zn	2.31	2.33
Mo	2.61	2.79			

[13] Experimental studies of the temperature dependence of L at low temperatures in sodium and copper have been carried out by R. Berman and D. K. C. Mac-Donald, Proc. Roy. Soc. (London) **A209**, 368 (1951); **A211**, 122 (1952).

PROBLEMS

12.1. Show that the kinetic energy of a free electron gas at $0°K$ is

$$U_0 = \frac{3}{5} N W_F{}^0.$$

12.2. Using conventional valencies, show that for sodium, potassium, and aluminum the values of $W_F{}^0$ are 3.12, 2.14, and 11.7 ev, respectively.

12.3. By qualitative reasoning show that on the free electron model the electronic paramagnetic susceptibility of a metal at low temperatures under the conditions

$$kT \ll \mu H \ll kT_F$$

is

$$\chi \sim N\mu^2/kT_F,$$

of the same form as under the usual conditions $\mu H \ll kT \ll kT_F$.

12.4*. Apply the Boltzmann transport equation to the free electron theory of thermoelectric effects, following the treatment in the book by Seitz listed in the references.

12.5. Show that the complex refractive index $\underset{\sim}{n}$ of a metal at long wavelengths is

$$\underset{\sim}{n}^2 = (n + ik)^2 = 1 + 4\pi i\sigma_0/\omega,$$

where σ_0 is the conductivity for static fields. Using the relation

$$R = \frac{(n - 1)^2 + k^2}{(n + 1)^2 + k^2}$$

for the reflection coefficient at normal incidence, show that

$$R \cong 1 - (2\omega/\pi\sigma_0)^{\frac{1}{2}}.$$

This is the Hagen-Rubens relation. Show that the condition for the validity of the derivation of the results is that $\omega \ll 1/\tau$, where τ is the relaxation time of the electrons. Estimate τ for sodium at room temperature.

12.6. An infinite plane metal surface with the normal in the z direction has a work function ϕ and temperature T. The electrons inside the metal obey Fermi-Dirac statistics with Fermi energy W_F.

(a) Write down the integral expression for the number of electrons per unit volume with an x component of velocity between v_x and $v_x + dv_x$ inside the metal.

(b) Write down the integral expression for the flux of electrons escaping with an x component of velocity between v_x and $v_x + dv_x$ after escape.

(c) Similarly for those with a z component of velocity between v_z and $v_z + dv_z$ after escape.

(d) Neglecting the one in the denominator of the distribution function with respect to the exponential function, calculate the average square of the velocity in the x direction and the average square of the velocity in the z direction of the escaping electrons after escape.

12.7.* Discuss the diamagnetic susceptibility of the conduction electrons and the de Haas-van Alphen effect. This subject is treated in the standard textbooks on the electron theory of metals. See also D. Shoenberg, Trans. Roy. Soc. (London) **A245**, 1 (1952).

12.8.* Discuss magneto-resistance effects in metals according to the free electron theory.

12.9. Derive an equation connecting the pressure and volume of a Fermi electron gas at 0°K.

REFERENCES

R. Becker, *Theorie der Elektrizität*, B. Teubner, Leipzig, 1933, Vol. II.

F. Bloch, *Elektronentheorie der Metalle*, Handbuch der Radiologie, **6.1**, 226–278 (1933).

G. Borelius, *Physikalische Eigenschaften der Metalle*, Handbuch der Metallphysik Akademische Verlagsgesellschaft, Leipzig, **1**, 181–520 (1935).

L. Brillouin, *Die Quantenstatistik*, Springer, Berlin, 1933.

H. Fröhlich, *Elektronentheorie der Metalle*, Springer, Berlin, 1936.

W. Hume-Rothery, *Electrons, atoms, metals and alloys*, Iliffe, London, 1948.

N. F. Mott and H. Jones, *Theory of the properties of metals and alloys*, Clarendon Press, Oxford, 1936.

F. O. Rice and E. Teller, *Structure of matter*, John Wiley & Sons, New York, 1949.

F. Seitz, *Modern theory of solids*, McGraw-Hill Book Co., New York, 1940.

J. C. Slater, "Electronic structure of metals," Revs. Modern Phys. **6**, 209 (1934).

J. C. Slater, *Quantum theory of matter*, McGraw Hill Book Co., New York, 1951.

A. Sommerfeld and H. Bethe, *Elektronentheorie der Metalle*, Handbuch der Physik, Springer, Berlin, **24/2**, 333–622 (1933).

A. H. Wilson, *Theory of metals*, Cambridge University Press, Cambridge, 1953, 2nd ed.

13

Band Theory of Metals

The free electron theory of metals developed in the preceding chapter gives us a good deal of insight into certain of the physical properties of metals, yet there are other properties for which the free electron theory is quite unproductive. A good example is the distinction between a metal and an insulator: the free electron model cannot help us understand this difference, but the band theory which we are about to discuss makes quite useful statements about the difference. Another example is the occurrence of positive Hall coefficients. We shall develop first several general aspects of the band theory, and then apply the theory to the problem of electrical conductivity.

MOTION OF ELECTRONS IN A PERIODIC POTENTIAL

An electron passing through a crystal structure experiences a periodic variation in potential energy, caused in a metal by the positive cores of the metal ions. In sodium, for example, the ion cores are singly charged, with 10 electrons in the configuration $1s^2 2s^2 2p^6$, while the outer electron, which in the free atom is the 3s valence electron, becomes in the metal a conduction electron. The periodic nature of the potential has far-reaching consequences for the behavior of the conduction electrons:

Nature of the wave functions. The plane wave solutions $e^{i\mathbf{k}\cdot\mathbf{r}}$ for the wave functions of the free electron model go over for the periodic potential to solutions of the form

$$\psi = u_k(\mathbf{r})e^{i\mathbf{k}\cdot\mathbf{r}}$$

where $u_k(\mathbf{r})$ has the periodicity of the lattice. Wave functions of this form are called *Bloch functions* and are basic to the theory of metals.

Allowed and forbidden bands. On the free electron model all values of the energy were allowed, but in a periodic potential there are forbidden ranges of energy (Figs. 13.1 and 13.2) where solutions representing an electron moving through the crystal do not exist. It should not be a surprise to us to encounter the concept of allowed

249

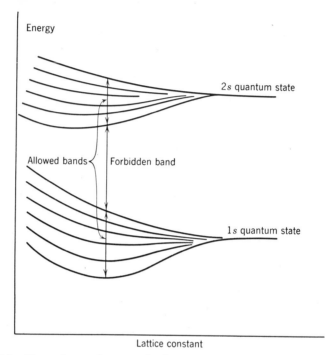

Fig. 13.1. Dependence of energy levels upon lattice constant, for a line of 6 hydrogen atoms, showing the incipient formation of allowed and forbidden energy bands. As the atoms are moved closer together the coupling between atoms increases, splitting the energy levels as shown here. The problem is similar to that of a line of coupled electrical or mechanical oscillators.

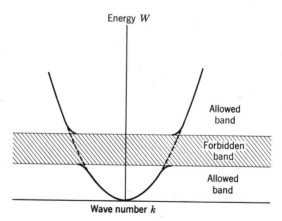

Fig. 13.2. Allowed and forbidden energy bands. The energy is plotted as a function of the wave number k; the dashed line shows the connection with the case of entirely free electrons.

and forbidden bands in periodic structures: lines of electrical filters display similar pass-band and cut-off properties, while the effect is illustrated very well by Fig. 4.3, which shows the allowed and forbidden vibrational frequencies of a diatomic crystal in one dimension. We know also that x-rays do not propagate through crystals at certain frequencies and orientations, but instead are reflected. In fact, the Bragg equation determines the occurrence of the forbidden electronic bands, as waves satisfying the Bragg condition are so strongly reflected that they cannot propagate in the crystal.

Effective mass. Near the top or bottom of a band the energy is generally a quadratic function of the wave numbers, so that by analogy with the expression $W = (\hbar^2/2m)k^2$ for free electrons we may define an effective mass m^* such that $\partial^2 W/\partial k^2 = \hbar^2/m^*$. It may be shown that the motion of a wave packet in applied electric or magnetic fields is characterized by using m^* as the mass. Near the top of a band m^* is negative, so that here the motion corresponds to that of a positive charge.

The effective mass concept does not imply that Newton's second law $F = ma$ fails for metals. The effective mass applies to the acceleration of electrons relative to the crystal lattice. Newton's law holds when applied to the entire system of electrons plus lattice, thereby allowing for momentum transfer between the accelerated electron and the lattice.

BLOCH FUNCTIONS

Bloch[1] has proved the important theorem that the solutions of the Schrödinger equation with a periodic potential are of the form

$$(13.1) \qquad \psi = u_k(\mathbf{r})e^{i\mathbf{k}\cdot\mathbf{r}},$$

where u is a function, depending in general on $\mathbf{k}$, which is periodic in x, y, z with the periodicity of the potential; that is, with the period of the lattice. We see that the plane wave $e^{i\mathbf{k}\cdot\mathbf{r}}$ is modulated with the period of the lattice.

A standard proof of the Bloch result is given in the book by Mott and Jones, pp. 57–59. Bloch[1] gives a rather more satisfying proof based on elementary group theory. We give here an abbreviated and somewhat incomplete indication of the argument. We consider N lattice points on a ring of length Na, and suppose that the potential is periodic in a, so that

$$(13.2) \qquad V(x) = V(x + ga),$$

[1] F. Bloch, Z. Physik **52**, 555 (1928); the result was known earlier to mathematicians as Floquet's theorem.

where g is an integer. Because of the symmetry of the ring we look for eigenfunctions ψ such that

(13.3) $$\psi(x + a) = C\psi(x),$$

where C is a constant. Then

(13.4) $$\psi(x + ga) = C^g\psi(x);$$

and, if the eigenfunction is to be single-valued,

(13.5) $$\psi(x + Na) = \psi(x) = C^N\psi(x),$$

so that C is one of the N roots of unity, or

(13.6) $$C = e^{i2\pi g/N}; \quad g = 0, 1, 2, \cdots, N - 1.$$

We have then

(13.7) $$\psi(x) = e^{i2\pi xg/Na}u_g(x)$$

as a satisfactory solution, where $u_g(x)$ has periodicity a. Letting

(13.8) $$k = 2\pi g/Na,$$

we have

(13.9) $$\psi = e^{ikx}u_k(x),$$

which is the Bloch result.

KRONIG-PENNEY MODEL

We demonstrate some of the characteristic features of electron propagation in crystals by considering the periodic square-well struc-

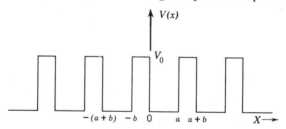

Fig. 13.3. Kronig and Penney one-dimensional periodic potential.

ture[2] in one dimension (Fig. 13.3). The wave equation of the problem is

(13.10) $$\frac{d^2\psi}{dx^2} + \frac{2m}{\hbar^2}(W - V)\psi = 0.$$

[2] R. de L. Kronig and W. G. Penney, Proc. Roy. Soc., (London) **A130**, 499 (1930); see also D. S. Saxon and R. A. Hutner, Philips Research Repts. **4**, 81 (1949); J. M. Luttinger, Philips Research Repts. **6**, 303 (1951).

The running wave solutions will be of the form of a plane wave modulated with the periodicity of the lattice. Using (12.4) and (12.5) for plane waves, we obtain solutions of the form

$$(13.11) \qquad \psi = u_k(x)e^{ikx},$$

where $u(x)$ is a periodic function in x with the period $(a + b)$ and is determined by substituting (13.11) into (13.10):

$$(13.12) \qquad \frac{d^2u}{dx^2} + 2ik\frac{du}{dx} + \frac{2m}{\hbar^2}(W - W_k - V)u = 0,$$

where $W_k = \hbar^2k^2/2m$.

In the region $0 < x < a$ the equation has the solution

$$(13.13) \qquad u = Ae^{i(\alpha-k)x} + Be^{-i(\alpha+k)x},$$

provided that

$$(13.14) \qquad \alpha = (2mW/\hbar^2)^{\frac{1}{2}}.$$

In the region $a < x < a + b$ the solution is

$$(13.15) \qquad u = Ce^{(\beta-ik)x} + De^{-(\beta+ik)x},$$

provided that

$$(13.16) \qquad \beta = [2m(V_0 - W)/\hbar^2]^{\frac{1}{2}}.$$

The constants A, B, C, D are to be chosen so that u and du/dx are continuous at $x = 0$ and $x = a$, and by the periodicity required of $u(x)$ the values at $x = a$ must equal those at $x = -b$. Thus we have the four linear homogeneous equations:

$$A + B = C + D;$$

$$i(\alpha - k)A - i(\alpha + k)B = (\beta - ik)C - (\beta + ik)D;$$

$$Ae^{i(\alpha-k)a} + Be^{-i(\alpha+k)a} = Ce^{-(\beta-ik)b} + De^{(\beta+ik)b};$$

$$i(\alpha - k)Ae^{i(\alpha-k)a} - i(\alpha + k)Be^{-i(\alpha+k)a} = (\beta - ik)Ce^{-(\beta-ik)b}$$
$$- (\beta + ik)De^{(\beta+ik)b}.$$

These have a solution only if the determinant of the coefficients vanishes, or[3]

$$(13.17) \qquad \frac{\beta^2 - \alpha^2}{2\alpha\beta}\sinh\beta b\sin\alpha a + \cosh\beta b\cos\alpha a = \cos k(a + b).$$

[3] Before verifying this for himself the reader should refer to the alternative derivation in the following section.

In order to obtain a handier equation we represent the potential by a periodic delta function, passing to the limit where $b = 0$ and $V_0 = \infty$ in such a way that $\beta^2 b$ stays finite. We set

(13.18) $$\lim_{\substack{b \to 0 \\ \beta \to \infty}} \frac{\beta^2 a b}{2} = P,$$

so that the condition (13.17) becomes

(13.19) $$P\,\frac{\sin \alpha a}{\alpha a} + \cos \alpha a = \cos ka.$$

This transcendental equation must have a solution for α in order that wave functions of the form (13.11) should exist.

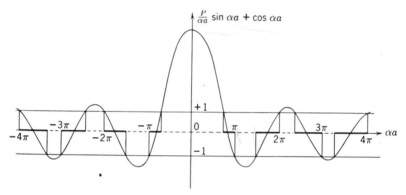

Fig. 13.4. Plot of the function $P\,\dfrac{\sin \alpha a}{\alpha a} + \cos \alpha a$, for $P = 3\pi/2$. The allowed values of the energy W are given by those ranges of $\alpha = [2mW/\hbar^2]^{1/2}$ for which the function lies between $+1$ and -1. (After Kronig and Penney.)

In Fig. 13.4 we have plotted the left side of (13.19) as a function of αa, for the arbitrary value $P = 3\pi/2$. As the cosine term on the right side can have values only between $+1$ and -1, only those values of αa are allowed for which the left side falls in this range. The allowed ranges of αa are drawn heavily in the figure, and through the relation $\alpha = [2mW/\hbar^2]^{1/2}$ they correspond to allowed ranges of the energy W. The boundaries of the allowed ranges of αa correspond to the values $n\pi/a$ for k. In Fig. 13.5 W vs. k is plotted.

If P is small, the forbidden ranges disappear. If $P \to \infty$, the allowed ranges of αa reduce to the points $n\pi$ ($n = \pm 1, \pm 2, \cdots$). The energy spectrum becomes discrete, and the eigenvalues

$$W = n^2 h^2/8ma^2$$

are those of an electron in a box of length a.

In the above example we have carried out an exact calculation of the allowed and forbidden bands for a very special model. It is of value to examine more general and realistic potentials, and we may do this by approximate methods utilizing elementary perturbation theory, as in Appendices L and M, where we consider the approximations of weak and tight binding, respectively. In one case we start out with

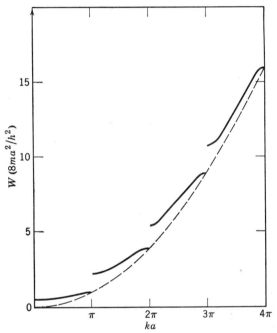

Fig. 13.5. Plot of energy vs. wave number for the Kronig-Penney potential, with $P = 3\pi/2$. (After Sommerfeld and Bethe.)

the wave functions of a free electron, and in the other we start out with wave functions of an electron bound to an atom.

ALTERNATIVE DERIVATION OF THE KRONIG-PENNEY RESULT

We derive here by a direct method the result (13.19) for the delta-function potential array, avoiding the very considerable labor incident to (13.17). We note first that in the region under the delta-function $\beta \gg k$, so that d^2u/dx^2 is much larger than du/dx in this region. Our boundary conditions are then that in the limit of a delta-function potential the value of u is continuous through the potential, or, using the periodicity condition,

$$(13.20) \qquad A + B \cong Ae^{i(\alpha-k)a} + Be^{-i(\alpha+k)a};$$

furthermore, the derivatives are related by

$$(13.21) \quad (du/dx)_a \cong (du/dx)_0 - (d^2u/dx^2)_0 b \cong (du/dx)_0 - b\beta^2 u(0)$$

$$= (du/dx)_0 - (2P/a)u(0),$$

where P is defined by (13.18). Therefore

$$(13.22) \quad [i(\alpha - k) - (2P/a)]A - [i(\alpha + k) + (2P/a)]B$$
$$= i(\alpha - k)Ae^{i(\alpha-k)a} - i(\alpha + k)e^{-i(\alpha+k)a}B.$$

The determinantal equation for the existence of a solution of (13.20) and (13.22) is

$$\begin{vmatrix} 1 - e^{i(\alpha-k)a} & 1 - e^{-i(\alpha+k)a} \\ i(\alpha-k)(1 - e^{i(\alpha-k)a}) - (2P/a) & -i(\alpha+k)(1 - e^{-i(\alpha+k)a}) - (2P/a) \end{vmatrix} = 0.$$

This is readily multiplied out to give (13.19).

MOTION OF ELECTRONS IN AN APPLIED FIELD

We first consider the velocity of an electron in a lattice when the electron is in a state described by the wave vector k. To be more precise, we are concerned with the velocity of a wave packet made up of states close to k, so that what we want is the group velocity:

$$(13.23) \qquad v_g = d\omega/dk = \hbar^{-1}\, dW/dk.$$

$\omega = k\, v_g$

$W = \hbar\vartheta = \hbar\omega = \hbar k$

We now consider the acceleration of a wave packet in an electric field E. The work done on the electron is

$$(13.24) \qquad \delta W = eEv_g\, \delta t;$$

Power: $\dfrac{W}{t} = Fv$

now

$$(13.25) \qquad \delta W = (dW/dk)\, \delta k = \hbar v\, \delta k,$$

from 13.23

using (13.23), so that

$$(13.26) \qquad \delta k = (eE/\hbar)\, \delta t,$$

or

$$(13.27) \qquad dk/dt = eE/\hbar.$$

We have further

$$(13.28) \qquad dv/dt = \hbar^{-1}(d^2W/dk^2)\,(dk/dt),$$

or

$$(13.29) \qquad \frac{dv}{dt} = \frac{d^2W}{dk^2}\frac{eE}{\hbar^2},$$

which may be compared with the classical equation

(13.30)
$$\frac{dv}{dt} = \frac{eE}{m}$$

for free electrons. We see therefore[4] that an electron in a periodic potential is accelerated by an electric field as if endowed with the *effective mass*

(13.31)
$$m^* = \hbar^2 \, (d^2W/dk^2)^{-1}.$$

The identical result for the effective mass is obtained in applied magnetic fields. Expressions for m^* on the weak and strong binding models are given in (L.11) and (M.12), respectively.

THERMAL AND MAGNETIC CONSEQUENCES OF THE EFFECTIVE MASS

We suppose for simplicity that in the portion of a band of interest to us all of the states may be described by the same value of the effective mass m^*. It follows from (12.28) that the Fermi energy W_F and the Fermi temperature T_F of a degenerate electron gas are inversely proportional to m^*; we need then only to introduce m^* consistently in the theory in place of m. We may in this fashion transcribe various results of the free electron theory.

We find for the electronic heat capacity that (12.54) gives us

(13.32)
$$C_v \propto m^*,$$

while for the Pauli spin susceptibility (12.61) gives

(13.33)
$$\chi_s \propto m^*.$$

The proportionality of the heat capacity and spin susceptibility to m^* reflects directly the proportionality of the density of states at the top of the Fermi distribution to the effective mass. The extension[5] of the Landau diamagnetism theory to the effective mass case involves other factors, such as the modification of the Larmor frequency equation, and it turns out that

(13.34)
$$\chi_d \propto 1/m^*.$$

We may draw several qualitative conclusions from this discussion. The metals of the transition groups of the periodic table are known to have unfilled inner shells, and the corresponding bands may be unfilled;

---

[4] For a more complete proof, see H. Jones and C. Zener, Proc. Roy. Soc. (London) **A144**, 101 (1934); J. M. Luttinger, Phys. Rev. **80**, 727 (1950).

[5] R. Peierls, Z. Physik **80**, 763 (1933).

as the overlap of inner shells on adjacent atoms is likely to be relatively small, the bands will be quite narrow in energy, and the density of states will be high. We therefore expect the transition metals to have values of $m^*/m \gg 1$, and to have high electronic heat capacities and high magnetic susceptibilities.

The observed values are in agreement with this idea. Reference to Table 12.1 shows that many of the transition metals, including cobalt, iron, manganese, niobium, nickel, palladium, platinum, and tungsten,

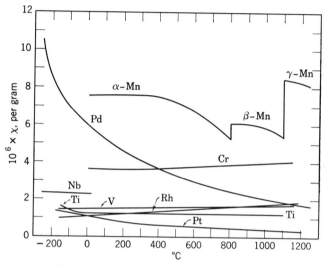

FIG. 13.6. Susceptibility per gram of several transition metals.

have unusually large electronic heat capacities, suggesting that the effective mass ratio m^*/m is of the order of 10 or more. Experimental values of the effective mass ratio are given in Table 13.1. The magnetic susceptibilities are shown in Fig. 13.6; it is seen that some of the transition metals have abnormally high susceptibilities.

TABLE 13.1. EFFECTIVE MASS RATIOS
Experimental Values (from Seitz and from Estermann and co-workers)

	m^*/m		m^*/m
Ni	28.	Mg	1.33
α-Fe	12.	Ti	3.15
Pd	43.	Zr	2.24
Pt	22.	Cr	2.93
Cu	1.47		

Theoretical Values (from Bardeen, Gorin, and Herring and Hill)

	m^*/m		m^*/m
Li	1.53	K	0.58
Na	0.94	Be	1.62

According to (L.11) we may expect values of the effective mass ratio $m^*/m \ll 1$ for states near an energy discontinuity, and H. Jones[6] has explained on this basis the strong diamagnetism of bismuth and gamma-brass, which have diamagnetic susceptibilities $\sim$5 to 10 times larger than normal. In certain directions in the bismuth crystal values of m^*/m of the order of 10^{-2} are required to explain the susceptibility and its anistotropy.

BRILLOUIN ZONES

We have seen, from the Kronig-Penney problem and from Appendix L, that the energy discontinuities in the monatomic one-dimensional lattice occur when the wave number is

(13.35) $$k = n\pi/a,$$

where n is any positive or negative integer. Thus it is the value of k which is important for the energy discontinuities. In three dimensions

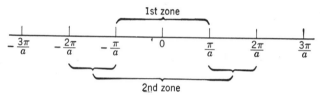

Fig. 13.7. Brillouin zones of a linear monatomic lattice with lattice constant a.

the wave vector $\mathbf{k}$ plays the same role, as we see from (L.15). The equation determining the position of the energy discontinuities which actually occur will depend somewhat on the type of the crystal lattice.

In the one-dimensional monatomic lattice a line representing the value of k is divided up by the energy discontinuities into segments of length π/a, as shown in Fig. 13.7. The line segments are known as *Brillouin zones;* the segment $-\pi/a < k < \pi/a$ is the first Brillouin zone; the two segments $-2\pi/a < k < -\pi/a$ and $\pi/a < k < 2\pi/a$ form the second Brillouin zone, etc. The zone description was introduced by Brillouin, who pointed out that many important and characteristic features of electron propagation in periodic structures could be described by considering the positions in k-space of the boundaries of the zones; these positions are independent of the details of the electron lattice interaction, being determined instead by the crystal structure. The utility of the zone description will emerge when we discuss conductivity.

The Brillouin zones of a simple square lattice in two dimensions are

[6] H. Jones, Proc. Roy. Soc. (London) **A144**, 225 (1934); **A147**, 396 (1934).

shown in Fig. 13.8. The zone boundaries are determined by the solutions of the equation

(13.36) $$k_x n_1 + k_y n_2 = \pi(n_1{}^2 + n_2{}^2)/a,$$

similar to (L.15). Here n_1, n_2 are integers, and a is the lattice constant. The equation essentially expresses the Bragg law for reflection

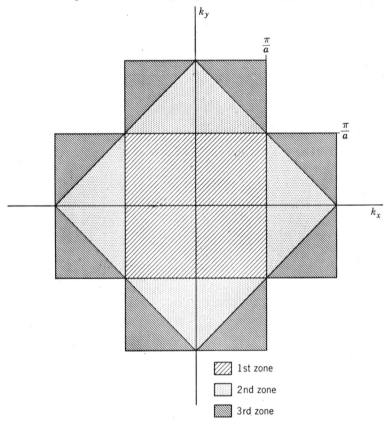

Fig. 13.8. Brillouin zones of a simple square lattice in two dimensions. The first three zones are marked.

of a wave by a periodic lattice. We find the boundaries of the first zone by first setting $n_1 = \pm 1$, $n_2 = 0$, obtaining

(13.37a) $$k_x = \pm \pi/a,$$

and then setting $n_1 = 0$, $n_2 = \pm 1$, obtaining

(13.37b) $$k_y = \pm \pi/a.$$

The four lines (13.37) determine the boundary of the first zone.

The outer boundary of the second zone is determined by setting $n_1 = \pm 1$, $n_2 = \pm 1$, obtaining the equations of the four lines

(13.38) $\pm k_x \pm k_y = 2\pi/a$,

where the signs are independent.

The extension to a simple cubic lattice in three dimensions follows readily and is given as a problem. A method of treating other lattices is given in Appendix N, along with a brief mention of the zone theory explanation of the Hume-Rothery rules for the effect of electron concentration on the crystal structures of alloys.

INSULATORS AND CONDUCTORS

In A. H. Wilson's explanation on the band theory of the difference between insulators and conductors we consider first a linear monatomic lattice containing N atoms. The allowed bands are described by the ranges of the wave number k within the Brillouin zones shown in Fig. 13.7. Each zone or band is readily shown to contain $2N$ electronic states, as may be seen on thinking of the bands as arising from the overlap of atomic states.

If each atom has two valence electrons, there will be a total of $2N$ electrons, completely filling the $2N$ states in a band. If there is an appreciable energy discontinuity separating bands, there will be no way for an applied electric field to accelerate the electrons, as there are no vacant states of higher wave number k into which the electrons may be accelerated. In very intense electric fields the electrons in the filled band may, however, make a transition to a vacant state in a higher empty band,[7] while in the electric fields commonly encountered the specimen will be an insulator. Of course, in the free electron limit the energy gap between the bands will vanish and the specimen will become a conductor.

If there is only one valence electron per atom, the N electrons will only half-fill the conduction band and the specimen will be a conductor. The alkali metals are good examples of this situation. In sodium for example there is one valence electron, the $3s$ electron of the free atom; consequently in the metal the $3s$ band is only half-filled.

On this one-dimensional model the alkaline earth metals would be insulators, contrary to experience, as they possess two valence elec-

---

[7] The theory of excitation by intense electric fields of electrons directly from a filled (valence) band to an empty (conduction) band is discussed by C. Zener, Proc. Roy. Soc. (London) **145**, 523 (1934), and has been observed by McAfee, Ryder, Shockley, and Sparks, Phys. Rev. **83**, 650 (1951); see also W. V. Houston, Phys. Rev. **57**, 184 (1940). The resulting current is called the Zener current.

trons per atom, thereby filling a band. But reference to Fig. 13.8 suggests that the electrons might begin to populate states in the second zone or band before filling the corners of the first zone. If we estimate energies on the free electron model, we find that the kinetic energy of an electron at a corner of the first zone is higher than that of an electron at the midpoint of a side face of the zone by a factor 2 in two dimensions and 3 in three dimensions. Provided only that the energy required to surmount the energy gap is less than the excess energy required to populate the corners of the lower zone, we may expect the electrons in the alkaline earth metals to overflow into a higher zone, so that conductivity may occur by transitions within the upper zone and also by transitions in the lower zone into the empty states with **k** values near the corners of the first zone. In substances such as sulfur or diamond the electrons are more tightly bound and do not overflow their zone boundaries; thus the substances are insulators. It is also possible to discuss the properties of ionic crystals on the band model.[8]

CALCULATION OF THE CONDUCTIVITY OF METALS

The calculation of the electrical conductivity of a metal is usually carried out separately for two different temperature regions, $T \gg \Theta$ and $T \ll \Theta$, where Θ is the Debye temperature of the lattice. The first calculations were made by Bloch. In the high temperature region the calculated conductivity is proportional to T^{-1}, and in the low temperature region it is proportional to T^{-5}. The agreement of the calculated temperature dependence with experiment is quite good, as shown in Fig. 13.9, although T^{-5} is seldom actually obtained.

The calculation of the resistivity is simpler at high temperatures than at low temperatures. The high temperature theory developed here follows the elementary approximate presentation by Weisskopf,[9] the low temperature theory is discussed in Appendix O.

If the lattice of a metal is perfect and there are no lattice vibrations, the electron waves pass through the lattice unscattered, without resistance, just as light passes through a perfect crystal without scattering or attenuation. The electric resistance of an actual metal arises

[8] W. Shockley, Phys. Rev. **50**, 754 (1936); D. H. Ewing and F. Seitz, Phys. Rev. **50**, 760 (1936). For an explanation of the insulating properties of nickel oxide, see J. C. Slater, Phys. Rev. **84**, 179 (1951) and E. Katz, Phys. Rev. **85**, 495 (1952); the elementary band theory predicts that this should be a conductor.

[9] V. Weisskopf, Am. J. Phys. **11**, 1 (1943). Complete derivations are given in all the standard texts on the electron theory of metals. The derivation for $T \ll \Theta$ given by Weisskopf is oversimplified.

from deviations from a perfect lattice caused by thermal motion of the atoms and by structural irregularities such as impurity atoms and lattice defects. In disordered (random) alloys the structural irregularities may dominate the resistance even at room temperature, but in very pure metals the thermal motion is dominant above liquid hydrogen temperatures.

We consider first the effective cross section Q of an ion for the scattering of an electron. The cross section is related to the relaxation time

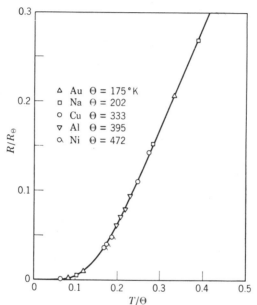

Fig. 13.9.   Theoretical (Grüneisen) temperature variation of electrical resistance, and experimental values for various metals.   (After Bardeen.)

τ by the gas-kinetic relation

$$(13.39) \qquad 2\tau = 1/NvQ,$$

where v is the velocity of the electron and N is the number of ions per unit volume.

We approximate the wave function of an electron incident upon an ion by

$$(13.40) \qquad \psi_i = e^{i\mathbf{k}\cdot\mathbf{r}},$$

neglecting the modulation of the plane wave by the lattice. The wave scattered by an ion at $\mathbf{r}_0$ is written

$$(13.41) \qquad \psi_s = Be^{i\mathbf{k}'\cdot(\mathbf{r}-\mathbf{r}_0)},$$

where B is the amplitude;[10] we suppose that $\mathbf{r}$ is sufficiently far from $\mathbf{r}_0$ so that in the vicinity of $\mathbf{r}$ the scattered wave may be treated as a plane wave in the direction $\mathbf{k}$. The amplitude B will be proportional to the strength of the incident wave at $\mathbf{r}_0$, so that

$$(13.42) \qquad B = B_0 \psi_i(\mathbf{r}_0)$$

and

$$(13.43) \qquad \psi_s(\mathbf{r}_0; \mathbf{r}) = B_0 e^{i(\mathbf{k}-\mathbf{k}') \cdot \mathbf{r}_0} e^{i\mathbf{k}' \cdot \mathbf{r}}.$$

Now in the perfect crystal the totality of scattered waves gives rise to an unscattered but refracted beam. Only if one or more of the ions is displaced from its regular position do we get scattering. We must therefore calculate the effective scattered wave ψ_d as the difference between the scattered wave from the regular position of the ion at $\mathbf{r}_0$ and the displaced position $\mathbf{r}_0 + \mathbf{d}$:

$$(13.44) \qquad \psi_d = \psi_s(\mathbf{r}_0 + \mathbf{d}; \mathbf{r}) - \psi_s(\mathbf{r}_0; \mathbf{r}).$$

If we suppose $d \ll \lambda$, we may expand ψ_d as

$$(13.45) \qquad \psi_d = \mathbf{d} \cdot \mathrm{grad}\ \psi_s,$$

where the gradient is taken with respect to $\mathbf{r}_0$. Then, from (13.43),

$$(13.46) \qquad \psi_d(\mathbf{r}_0; \mathbf{r}) = i(\mathbf{k} - \mathbf{k}') \cdot \mathbf{d}\ \psi_s(\mathbf{r}_0; \mathbf{r}).$$

The amplitude of the effective scattered wave from a displaced ion in a periodic lattice is then different from the scattering from an isolated ion by the factor $i(\mathbf{k} - \mathbf{k}') \cdot \mathbf{d}$.

The cross sections being proportional to the squares of the amplitudes, we have

$$(13.47) \qquad Q_d = [(\mathbf{k} - \mathbf{k}') \cdot \mathbf{d}]^2 Q_s,$$

where Q_d is the effective cross section for scattering of an electron by a displaced ion in an otherwise perfect lattice, and Q_s is the free space scattering cross section for an isolated ion. We write the average of Q_d over all the directions of the displacement $\mathbf{d}$ and over all values of the angle between $\mathbf{k}$ and $\mathbf{k}'$ as

$$(13.48) \qquad \overline{Q_d} = Ck^2\ \overline{d^2 Q_s},$$

where C is a constant of the order of unity; it may be shown[9] that its value is $\frac{2}{3}$.

----

[10] The scattered wave actually also contains the factor $|\mathbf{r} - \mathbf{r}_0|^{-1}$, but we may for the present discussion neglect this variation without doing serious damage to the result.

The conductivity is then, using (13.39) and (12.73),

(13.49) $\sigma = (\frac{3}{2})(e^2\hbar^2/mvp^2d^2\overline{Q_s})$,

where $p = \hbar k$ is the electronic momentum, and we have assumed one conduction electron per atom. We now calculate the mean square value of the ionic displacement d caused by thermal motion. At high temperatures $(T \gg \Theta)$ we may use the Einstein model of independent harmonic oscillators of angular frequency,

(13.50) $\omega = k\Theta/\hbar$.

The mean square displacement of a harmonic oscillator of mass M is given by $\overline{d^2} = W/M\omega^2$, where the energy W is equal to $3kT$. Thus

(13.51) $\overline{d^2} = 3T\hbar^2/Mk\Theta^2$.

The electrical conductivity is then

(13.52) $\sigma = \dfrac{e^2Mk\Theta^2}{2p^3\overline{Q_s}T}$; $(T \gg \Theta)$.

The elastic properties of the metal enter through the Debye temperature Θ. It must be pointed out that in this expression the momentum p is to be evaluated at the top of the Fermi distribution; because $\Theta \ll T_F$ in metals, only the electrons near the top are able to be scattered by the lattice vibrations into vacant states. We may estimate the magnitude of $\overline{Q_s}$ as of the order of a^2, where a is the nearest neighbor distance in the lattice. The values of the conductivity for $T \gg \Theta$ calculated in this way from (13.52) are of the correct order of magnitude for monovalent metals and have the correct temperature dependence. The extension of the theory to the region $T \ll \Theta$ is indicated in Appendix O.

It has been found by Grüneisen[11] that the observed temperatures dependence of the resistivity is described quite well at all temperatures by the semi-empirical formula

(13.53) $\rho \propto TG(\Theta/T)$,

where

(13.54) $G(x) = x^{-4} \displaystyle\int_0^x \frac{s^2\,ds}{(e^s - 1)(1 - e^{-s})}$.

The formula gives proportionality to T for $T \gg \Theta$ and to T^5 for $T \ll \Theta$, as required by theory. The optimum value of Θ to be used here may

[11] E. Grüneisen, Ann. Physik **16**, 530 (1933).

differ[12] somewhat from the value deduced from heat capacities for several reasons, including the fact that only longitudinal phonons are effective in the resistivity, while both longitudinal and transverse contribute to the heat capacity. Figure 13.9 shows that the Grüneisen relation works quite well for the metals indicated there; at quite low temperatures, however, departures from the T^5 law are usually observed.

Reference to detailed theoretical calculations of the conductivity of metals are given in the review by Bardeen.[13] A comparison of observed and calculated values of the conductivity of a number of monovalent metals is reproduced from this paper in Table 13.2. The

TABLE 13.2. COMPARISON OF OBSERVED AND CALCULATED VALUES OF THE ELECTRICAL CONDUCTIVITY AT 0°C, IN 10^4 OHM^{-1} CM^{-1}
(After Bardeen)

Metal	Observed	Calculated
Li	11.8	28.
Na	23.4	23.
K	16.4	20.
Rb	8.6	33.
Cs	5.3	22.
Cu	64.	174.
Ag	66.	143.
Au	49.	142.

agreement is best for sodium and potassium, the two metals for which the assumptions made in the calculations were expected to be valid.

RESIDUAL RESISTANCE

The resistivity of a metal containing impurity atoms may usually be written in the form

$$(13.55) \qquad \rho = \rho_i + \rho_L,$$

where ρ_L is the resistivity caused by thermal motion of the lattice, and ρ_i is the resistivity caused by scattering of the electron waves by impurity atoms which disturb the periodicity of the lattice. If the concentration of impurity atoms is small, ρ_i is independent of temperature; this statement is known as *Matthiessen's rule.*

The residual resistance is the extrapolated resistivity at 0°K and is equivalent to ρ_i, as ρ_L vanishes as $T \to 0$. Measurements on sodium in

[12] M. Blackman, Proc. Phys. Soc. (London) **A64**, 681 (1951); P. G. Klemens, Proc. Phys. Soc. (London) **A65**, 71 (1952).
[13] J. Bardeen, J. Appl. Phys. **11**, 88 (1940).

Fig. 13.10 show that the residual resistance may vary from specimen to specimen, while the resistivity caused by thermal motion is independent of the specimen.

A clear minimum in the electrical resistivities of gold[14] and magnesium[15] has been observed around 5°K.   The effect has so far received

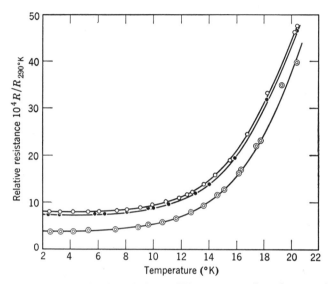

Fig. 13.10.   Resistance of sodium below 20°K, as measured on three specimens by MacDonald and Mendlessohn [Proc. Roy. Soc. (London) **A202**, 103 (1950)].

no satisfactory explanation,[16] although it appears to be associated with impurities.

HALL EFFECT

It was seen in Table 12.7 that beryllium, zinc, and cadmium have positive values of the Hall constant, suggesting that the transport of charge is by positive carriers.   The positive sign is explained on band theory as resulting from the motion of electrons near the top of a nearly filled band.   In this region the value of d^2W/dk^2 is negative; according to (13.31) this may be interpreted as giving a negative mass.   The result may also be interpreted in terms of a positive charge.   It is not surprising that the positive sign should occur in divalent metals, as

[14] de Haas, de Boer, and v. d. Berg, Physica **1**, 1115 (1933).

[15] D. K. C. MacDonald and K. Mendelssohn, Proc. Roy. Soc. (London) **A202**, 523 (1950).

[16] D. K. C. MacDonald and I. M. Templeton, Phil. Mag. **42**, 432 (1951); D. K. C. MacDonald, Phys. Rev. **88**, 148 (1952).

here there may be vacant states near the boundaries of an otherwise full Brillouin zone. We may consider vacant states in a nearly filled band in terms of the motion of positive "holes." This concept is extended in the next chapter.

The *actual* motion is of course that of the electrons in the filled states, and it has been demonstrated experimentally[17] that the sign of e/m for the carriers in conductors with positive Hall coefficients is the same as in conductors with negative Hall coefficients.

QUALITATIVE RESULTS ON BAND STRUCTURE[18]

ALKALI METALS

The alkali atoms have an s valence electron on each atom: $2s$ in lithium, $3s$ in sodium, $4s$ in potassium, $5s$ in rubidium, and $6s$ in cesium. In the metal the s levels are spread out into a very wide band. Slater has shown that in sodium the bands arising from the $3p$ levels overlap the $3s$ band quite strongly. With one valence electron per atom, the $3s$ band is only half-filled so that the zone boundaries have little effect on the conduction electrons. The energy difference between the lowest state of the $3p$ band and the lowest state of the $3s$ band is about 4 ev.

NOBLE METALS

Copper, silver, and gold are monovalent metals, but they differ from the alkali metals by having the d shells in the free atoms filled just at these points in the periodic system. The d band is believed to overlap the s band, as shown in Fig. 13.11. As the d electrons are fairly well shielded in the metal, the d band is not very broad. The effective mass of the d electrons may thus be expected to be rather high, and this is found experimentally (Table 13.1). The color of copper is attributed to the absorption of blue light by transitions between the $3d$ and $4s$-p bands.

DIVALENT METALS

Conditions are more complicated in the divalent metals, beryllium, magnesium, calcium, strontium, and barium, than in the monovalent metals. The first Brillouin zone can hold two electrons per atom; thus the divalent metals would be insulators unless the first and second

---

[17] G. G. Scott, Phys. Rev. **83**, 656 (1951); S. Brown and S. J. Barnett, Phys. Rev. **81**, 657 (1951); for a discussion of these experiments see N. Rostoker, Phys. Rev. **88**, 952 (1952), and W. Shockley, Phys. Rev. **88**, 953 (1952).

[18] A recent review of the band structure of metals and alloys has been given by G. V. Raynor, Repts. Prog. Phys. **15**, 173 (1952).

zones overlapped in energy. The metals do conduct electricity, although it is seen from Table 12.6 that the resistivities of strontium and barium are rather higher than the resistivities of monovalent metals. Various energy band calculations have shown that band overlapping may be expected in the divalent metals, although perhaps to a smaller extent than is suggested by the electrical conductivity.

TRANSITION METALS

The iron transition group is frequently discussed in a qualitative way, a band model as proposed by Mott and Slater being used. On this model a wide $4s$ band ($\sim$10 ev) overlaps a narrower $3d$ band[19]

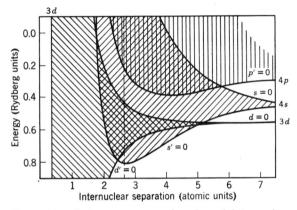

Fig. 13.11. Energy bands in copper as a function of internuclear separation. [After H. M. Krutter, Phys. Rev. **48**, 664 (1935).]

($\sim$5 ev). In the transition metals there are not enough electrons to fill the $3d$ band completely, and the striking thermal and magnetic properties of the transition metals arise largely from the influence of the unfilled $3d$ band. The $3d$ band can hold ten electrons, whereas the $4s$ band can only hold two electrons; this difference in numbers accentuates the difference in band width. Per electron, the $3d$ band is only $\frac{1}{10}$ as wide as the $4s$ band. The narrowness of the $3d$ band means that the effective electronic mass is high, leading to a high heat capacity, high paramagnetic susceptibility, and high electrical resistivity. The electrical current is carried largely by electrons in the $4s$ band, but these have their mean free path shortened by transitions to the $3d$ band, as suggested by Mott.

[19] These estimates of the band widths are due to J. C. Slater, Phys. Rev. **49**, 537 (1936); J. Appl. Phys. **8**, 385 (1937); a recent calculation for nickel suggests that here the width of the $3d$ band is 2.7 ev [G. C. Fletcher, Proc. Phys. Soc. (London) **A65**, 192 (1952)].

It is possible to vary the electron concentration of a metal by alloying with elements of higher or lower valence. A number of interesting effects directly related to band theory have been found in this way. The Hume-Rothery rule relating the crystal structure of certain alloys to their electron concentrations is discussed in Appendix N. The

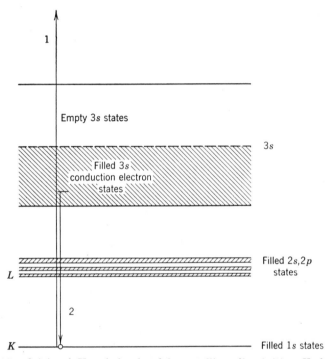

Fig. 13.12. Origin of K emission band in metallic sodium: (1) a K electron is ejected from the metal by electron impact; (2) an electron from the conduction band drops down to fill the vacant K level, emitting an x-ray quantum. The width of the emission line is equal to the width of the filled region of the conduction band, as all conduction electrons may have a chance to emit.

magnetization of ferromagnetic alloys is shown in Fig. 10.26, in connection with Problem 10.1. The review article by Raynor[18] discusses the remarkable sensitivity of the elastic constants of aluminum alloys to electron concentration: $c_{11} - c_{12}$ has a sharp peak at 2.67 valence electrons per atom; the peak is directly associated with the behavior of electrons near Brillouin boundaries.[20] The c/a ratio of hexagonal magnesium alloys is sensitive to electron concentration near 2.0075

[20] R. S. Leigh, Phil. Mag. **42**, 139 (1951).

valence electrons per atom; the band theory[21] of the effect is related to the overlap across a zone face.

SOFT X-RAY EMISSION SPECTRA

The radiation emitted[22] when conduction electrons make transitions into the relatively sharp $K(1s)$ or $L(2s,sp)$ levels which have been ionized by electron impact is a direct source of information about the band structure of metals. The situation is exhibited in Fig. 13.12, which is drawn for the K emission band of sodium. It is important to observe that the width of emission band should be a good measure of the width of the filled portion of the conduction band, although the actual shape of the band will depend on the final state and on the details of the conduction band states ψ_k. The observed band widths for lithium and sodium are 4.2 ± 0.3 ev and 3.0 ± 0.2 ev respectively, while the corresponding Fermi energies calculated for free electrons are 4.8 ev and 3.2 ev. The method may also be applied to non-metals: the observed width of the filled valence band in diamond is 33 ± 3 ev, as compared to 29.5 ev calculated for four free valence electrons per atom.

PROBLEMS

13.1. Make a cut-out paper model of the first and second Brillouin zones of a simple cubic lattice in three dimensions.

13.2. Compare observed electrical conductivity values for five monovalent metals at room temperature with values estimated from (13.52).

13.3. In an anisotropic crystal the energy may be given in terms of the components of the wave vector by

$$W = \alpha_x k_x{}^2 + \alpha_y k_y{}^2 + \alpha_z k_z{}^2.$$

Find the equations of motion which replace $\mathbf{F} = m d^2\mathbf{r}/dt^2$.

13.4. For the first Brillouin zone of the simple cubic lattice, compare the energies of a free electron having wave vectors at the corners and at the face centers of the boundary of the zone.

13.5. Discuss the information on energy bands in metals which may be deduced from the soft x-ray emission spectra; for references to the literature see H. W. B. Skinner, Repts. Prog. Phys. **5**, 257 (1939); Trans. Roy. Soc. (London) **A239**, 95 (1940).

13.6.* Discuss the Wigner-Seitz method of calculation of the cohesive energy of alkali metals. [See E. Wigner and F. Seitz, Phys. Rev. **43**, 804 (1933); **46**, 509 (1934)].

[21] H. Jones, Physica **15**, 13 (1950).

[22] Early work on several light metals in the 50–500 A region is reported by H. M. O'Bryan and H. W. B. Skinner, Phys. Rev. **45**, 370 (1934); review papers by Skinner are cited in Problem 13.5.

13.7. Discuss the principal physical features of the intrinsic dielectric break-down of solids. (See H. Fröhlich and J. H. Simpson, *Advances in electronics*, Academic Press, New York, 1950, Vol. II, pp. 185–217.)

REFERENCES

The references cited at the end of Chapter 12 are all relevant to the present chapter; the following references apply to electrical conductivity:

J. Bardeen "Electrical conductivity of metals," J. Appl. Phys. **11**, 88 (1940).

W. Shockley, *Electrons and holes in semiconductors*, Van Nostrand, New York, 1950.

V. F. Weisskopf, "On the theory of the electric resistance of metals," Am J. Phys. **11**, 1 (1943).

14

Semiconductors

Semiconductors are electronic conductors with values of the electrical resistivity at room temperature generally in the range $\sim 10^{-2}$ to $\sim 10^{9}$ ohm-cm, intermediate between good conductors ($\sim 10^{-5}$ ohm-cm) and insulators ($\sim 10^{14}$ to $\sim 10^{22}$ ohm-cm). At absolute zero a pure and perfect crystal of most semiconductors would behave as an insulator; the characteristic semiconducting properties are usually brought about by thermal agitation, impurities, or lattice defects. A number of devices of wide industrial application are based on the properties of semiconductors: they include rectifiers, modulators, detectors, thermistors, photocells, and crystal triodes or transistors. We discuss in this chapter some aspects of the semiconductor field of marked physical interest, such as the band theory of intrinsic and impurity conductivity, the mechanism of rectification, and the physics of transistor action. We shall be concerned primarily with the properties of silicon and germanium, as their properties are perhaps the best understood in terms of basic theory. Other important semiconducting substances include cuprous oxide, Cu_2O; selenium; lead telluride, $PbTe$; lead sulfide, PbS; and silicon carbide, SiC.

INTRINSIC CONDUCTIVITY

Except at very low temperatures a highly purified semiconductor often exhibits *intrinsic conductivity*, as distinguished from the *impurity conductivity* of less pure specimens. The character of the electronic band scheme leading to intrinsic conductivity is exhibited in Fig. 14.1. At absolute zero we postulate a vacant conduction band, separated by an energy gap W_g from a filled valence band. As the temperature is increased, electrons are thermally excited from the valence band to the conduction band. Both the electrons in the conduction band and the vacant states or holes left behind in the valence band will contribute to the electrical conductivity, as shown in Fig. 14.2. Intrinsic conductivity tends to be dominant at high temperatures, impurity conductivity at low temperatures.

To calculate the intrinsic conductivity at temperature T we must first find the equilibrium concentration n_e of electrons in the conduction band, which is equal to the equilibrium concentration n_h of holes in the valence band, and then we must calculate the mobilities

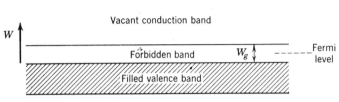

Fig. 14.1. Band scheme for intrinsic conductivity. At 0°K the conductivity is zero, all states in the valence band being filled and all states in the conduction band being vacant. As the temperature is increased, the conductivity increases because electrons are thermally excited up to the conduction band, where they become mobile.

(drift velocity/electric field) μ_e for electrons and μ_h for holes. The conductivity is then given, according to the earlier definitions, by

(14.1) $\sigma = n_e e \mu_e + n_h e \mu_h.$

We may anticipate a temperature dependence of the form $e^{-W/kT}$ for the concentration of electrons in the conduction band, and, as it is unlikely that the mobility will depend on temperature in as strong a fashion, we may expect that the intrinsic conductivity may vary as $e^{-W/kT}$, or the resistivity ρ as $e^{W/kT}$. It will turn out that W should be taken as $W_g/2$, where W_g is the energy gap between bands. If

(14.2) $\rho = A e^{W_g/2kT},$

then

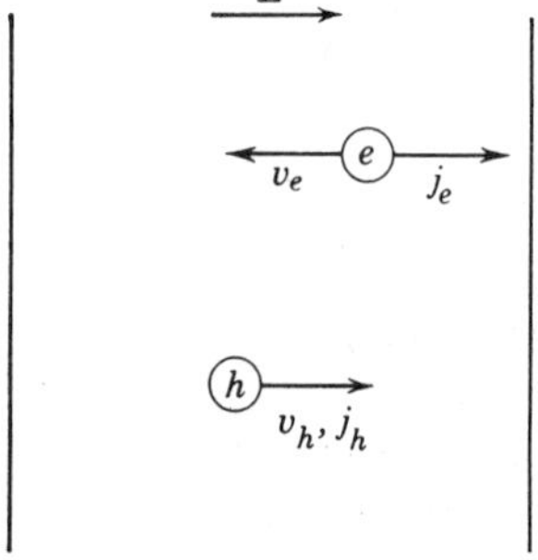

Fig. 14.2. Motion of electrons (e) and holes (h) in an electric field E; the directions of the velocity (v) and current (j) flows are shown.

(14.3) $\log \rho = \log A + (W_g/2kT),$

so that in the intrinsic range $\log \rho$ should be approximately a linear function of $1/T$. This is observed experimentally, as shown in Fig. 14.3.

We now calculate in terms of the Fermi energy W_F the number of electrons excited to the conduction band at temperature T. We measure the energy W from the top of the valence band, as in Fig. 14.1. At low temperatures we may suppose $W - W_F \gg kT$, so that the

Fermi-Dirac distribution function (12.21) reduces to

(14.4) $$f \cong e^{(W_F - W)/kT}.$$

If we suppose that the electrons in the conduction band behave as if they are free, we may take the density of states in the conduction band as equal to that for free electrons, with the energy referred to the bottom of the band. Thus, from (12.23), the number of states with energy between W and $W + dW$ is

(14.5) $$g(W)\, dW = \frac{1}{2\pi^2}\left(\frac{2m_e}{\hbar^2}\right)^{3/2}$$
$$\times (W - W_g)^{1/2}\, dW$$

per unit volume, where m_e is the effective mass of an electron in the conduction band. Combining (14.4) and (14.5), we have for the number of electrons per unit volume in the conduction band

(14.6) $$N_e = \frac{1}{2\pi^2}\left(\frac{2m_e}{\hbar^2}\right)^{3/2} e^{W_F/kT}$$
$$\times \int_{W_g}^{\infty} (W - W_g)^{1/2} e^{-W/kT} dW,$$

which integrates to

(14.7) $$N_e = 2(2\pi m_e kT/h^2)^{3/2}$$
$$\times e^{(W_F - W_g)/kT}.$$

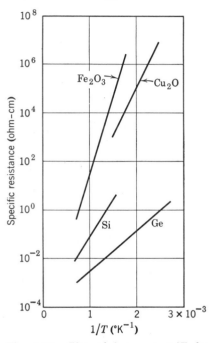

Fig. 14.3. Plot of log ρ vs. $1/T$ for several semiconductors in the intrinsic range. (After J. A. Becker.)

We still have to determine the value of the Fermi energy W_F for the problem. This is accomplished by calculating the concentration of holes N_h in the valence band, and requiring that $N_e = N_h$: every excited electron leaves a hole behind. The distribution function f_h for holes is related to the electron distribution function f_e by

(14.8) $$f_h = 1 - f_e,$$

so that, from (12.21),

(14.9) $$f_h = \frac{1}{e^{(W_F - W)/kT} + 1} \cong e^{(W - W_F)/kT},$$

for $(W_F - W) \gg kT$.   If we suppose that the holes near the top of the valence band behave as free particles with effective mass m_h, the density of hole states is given by

$$(14.10) \qquad g(W) \, dW = \frac{1}{2\pi^2} \left(\frac{2m_h}{\hbar^2} \right)^{3/2} (-W)^{1/2} \, dW.$$

Proceeding as before, we find

$$(14.11) \qquad N_h = 2(2\pi m_h kT/h^2)^{3/2} e^{-W_F/kT}$$

for the number of holes per unit volume in the valence band.
On setting

$$(14.12) \qquad N_e = N_h,$$

we must have

$$(14.13) \qquad W_F = \tfrac{1}{2} W_g + \tfrac{3}{4} kT \log (m_h/m_e).$$

If $m_e = m_h = m$, then

$$(14.14) \qquad W_F = \tfrac{1}{2} W_g,$$

so that at all temperatures for which the assumptions of the calculation are valid the Fermi level is in the center of the forbidden band.   Thus

$$(14.15) \qquad N_e = 2(2\pi mkT/h^2)^{3/2} e^{-W_g/2kT}.$$

Values of W_g deduced from experimental data in the intrinsic range by use of (14.3), which is based on (14.15), are given in Table 14.1.

TABLE 14.1.   VALUES OF THE ENERGY GAP BETWEEN THE VALENCE AND CONDUCTION BANDS IN SEMICONDUCTORS, AT ROOM TEMPERATURE

	Diamond	Si	Ge	Gray Tin	Cu_2O	ZnO	Fe_2O_3	PbTe
W_g(ev)	6–7	1.1	0.7	0.1	1.4–1.8	2.2	2.3	0.63

MOBILITY IN THE INTRINSIC REGION

The mobility μ is defined as the drift velocity per unit electric field and is related to the conductivity by (14.1).   In an ideal intrinsic semiconductor the mobility is determined by lattice scattering; that is, by collisions between lattice waves and electron waves.   In actual intrinsic specimens there are always some impurity atoms which may dominate the scattering of electron waves at low temperatures when the lattice waves are quiescent, but at higher temperatures the lattice scattering is dominant.

The mobility associated with lattice scattering in a non-polar (covalent) crystal such as diamond, silicon, or germanium has been calculated by Seitz and others. Seitz[1] finds

$$(14.16) \qquad \mu = \frac{2^{1/2}6^{1/3}}{4\pi^{5/6}} \cdot \frac{N^{1/3}e\hbar^2 k^2 \Theta^2 M}{m^{*5/2}C^2(kT)^{3/2}},$$

where Θ is the Debye temperature; k is the Boltzmann constant; N is the density of unit cells; m^* is the effective mass; M is the atomic mass; and C is defined using the Bloch function $u(\mathbf{r})e^{i\mathbf{k}\cdot\mathbf{r}}$ by (see Appendix P)

$$(14.17) \qquad C = \frac{\hbar^2}{2m} \int |\text{grad } u|^2 \, d\tau,$$

and is treated as an unknown parameter which has the empirical value ≈ 5 ev in germanium, assuming $m^* = m$. This assumption may not be valid, as it is currently believed that $m^* \cong m/4$ in germanium. Experimental values of the mobilities in silicon, germanium, and lead telluride, in the range in which lattice scattering is dominant are given in Table 14.2. Methods of analyzing the data are discussed later. The mobilities in diamond may be somewhat higher than in silicon.

TABLE 14.2. ELECTRON MOBILITIES IN LATTICE SCATTERING RANGE

	Mobilities (cm²/v-sec)	
	Room temperature	Arbitrary temperature
Si, electrons (polycrystalline)	300	$15 \times 10^5/T^{3/2}$
Si, electrons (single crystal)	1200	....
Si, holes (polycrystalline)	100	$5 \times 10^5/T^{3/2}$
Si, holes (single crystal)	250	....
Ge, electrons	3600	$19 \times 10^6/T^{3/2}$
Ge, holes	1700	$9 \times 10^6/T^{3/2}$
PbTe, electrons (single crystal)	2100	....
PbTe, holes (single crystal)	840	....

IMPURITY CONDUCTIVITY

Certain types of impurities and imperfections may affect drastically the electrical properties of a semiconductor. For example, the addition of boron to silicon in the proportion of 1 boron atom to 10^5 silicon atoms increases the conductivity of the silicon by a factor of 10^3.

We consider in particular the effect of impurities in silicon and germanium. These elements crystallize in the diamond structure as shown in Fig. 14.4, with each atom forming four covalent bonds, one with each of its four nearest neighbors, corresponding to the chemical valence four. If now an impurity atom of valence five, such as phosphorus, arsenic, or antimony, is substituted in the lattice in place of a

[1] F. Seitz, Phys. Rev. **73**, 549 (1948); for the detailed calculation of mobility in nonpolar crystals, see J. Bardeen and W. Shockley, Phys. Rev. **80**, 72 (1950).

normal atom, there will be one valence electron from the impurity atom left over after the four covalent bonds are established with the nearest neighbors, that is, after the impurity atom has been accommodated in the structure with as little disturbance as possible. The situation now is that we have in the structure an excess positive charge from the impurity atom which has lost one electron, and we have also the excess electron. It is verified by lattice constant studies and by determining the density of carriers that the above impurities enter the

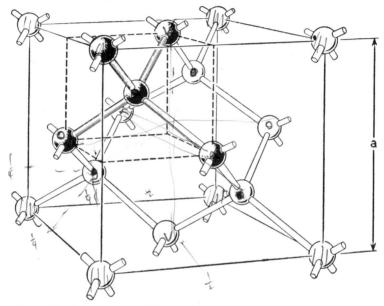

Fig. 14.4. Crystal structure of diamond, showing the tetrahedral bond arrangement. (After W. Shockley, *Electrons and holes in semiconductors.* Copyright 1950. Van Nostrand.)

lattice by substitution for normal atoms, rather than by going into interstitial positions.

The excess electron moves in the Coulomb potential $e/\epsilon r$ of the impurity ion, i.e., reduced by the dielectric constant of the medium. The factor $1/\epsilon$ takes account of the reduction in the Coulomb force between charges caused by the electronic polarization of the medium. This treatment is valid for orbits large in comparison with the distance between atoms, and for slow motions of the electron such that the time required to pass an atom is long in comparison with the period of the motion of the inner bound electrons of the atom. The Bohr theory of the hydrogen atom may readily be modified to take into account both the dielectric constant of the medium and the effective

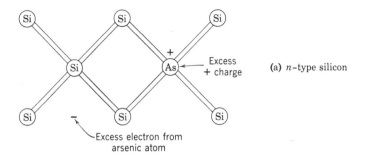

(a) n-type silicon

Excess electron from
arsenic atom

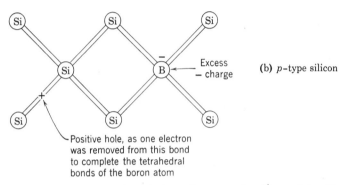

(b) p-type silicon

Positive hole, as one electron
was removed from this bond
to complete the tetrahedral
bonds of the boron atom

Fig. 14.5. Charges associated with impurity atom in silicon; (a) with arsenic impurity an electron is available for conduction; (b) with boron impurity a positive hole is available. The type designation is n for negative carriers and p for positive carriers.

mass of an electron in the periodic lattice potential. We find, on replacing e^2 by e^2/ϵ and m by m^*, the results below, with numerical values calculated for germanium with $\epsilon = 16$, and $m = m^*$:

(14.18)   Bohr radius: $a = \epsilon\hbar^2/m^*e^2 = 8.5\text{A}$;

(14.19)   Angular velocity, first orbit:

$$\omega_0 = m^*e^4/\hbar^3\epsilon^2 = 1.6 \times 10^{14} \text{ sec}^{-1};$$

(14.20)   Ionization energy: $W_i = m^*e^4/2\hbar^2\epsilon^2 = 0.05$ ev.

We expect then that the excess electron at low temperatures will be bound near the impurity atom by the ionization energy $\sim$0.05 ev, but that at room temperature a substantial proportion of the impurity atoms will have lost their excess electron through thermal ionization, the excess electron then being elevated to the conduction band. We

shall shortly calculate the fraction of impurity atoms which are
ionized.

In Figs. 14.5 and 14.6 the physical situation for pentavalent and
trivalent impurities in silicon is illustrated. A pentavalent atom
such as arsenic is called a *donor* atom because it can give up an electron to the conduction band; the conductivity from this cause being
by negative charges, the material is said to be n-type. The intrinsic
conductivity in germanium is also n-type, as the electron mobility is
greater than the hole mobility. A trivalent atom such as boron is
called an *acceptor* atom because it can take on an electron from the
valence band, leaving a positive hole; the resulting conductivity is

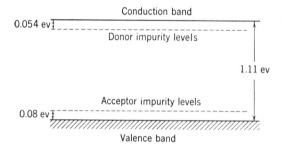

Fig. 14.6. Energy level scheme with donor and acceptor impurity atoms. Values
are for silicon, from work by Pearson and Bardeen. The difference in the energy
required to remove an electron from a donor and to remove a hole from an acceptor
is ascribed to the effective mass ratio $m_e/m_h = 0.67$.

associated with the motion of the positive holes, and the material is
said to be *p-type*. The positive holes may be bound to the acceptor
atoms in hydrogen-like orbits, requiring an ionization energy as calculated from (14.20) to release the hole to move freely in the valence
band. The general description of the physical situation of a donor
atom is equally valid for an acceptor atom, with hole substituted for
electron in the text. The classic analysis by Pearson and Bardeen[2] of
conductivity data for silicon leads to the values 0.054 ev and 0.08 ev for
the ionization energies of donor and acceptor atoms, respectively,
while the theoretical value from (14.20), with $\epsilon = 13$ for silicon and
$m_e = m_h = m$, is 0.08 ev. The remarkable agreement gives strong
support to the theoretical picture. The difference between the values
for donor and acceptor atoms is explained by an effective mass ratio
$m_e/m_h = 0.67$, in close accord with the value 0.65 deduced from the
mobilities in Table 14.2.

² G. L. Pearson and J. Bardeen, Phys. Rev. **75**, 865 (1949).

We calculate now, as a simple example of concentration calculations in the presence of impurity atoms, the equilibrium proportion of ionized donor atoms under the conditions: (a) the temperature is low enough so that thermal excitation from the valence band (intrinsic conductivity) may be neglected; and (b) there are no acceptor atoms. The second assumption is somewhat artificial. In all problems of this type the difficult step is the determination of the Fermi energy W_F.

If there are N_D donor atoms per unit volume, the number n_D of neutral donor atoms is given by, as derived in the book by Mott and Gurney,

$$(14.21) \qquad n_D = \frac{N_D}{\frac{1}{2}e^{(W_D - W_F)/kT} + 1},$$

where the energy W_D of the neutral donor atom and the Fermi energy W_F are measured from the same point, in this case from the top of the valence band. We note further from (14.7) and (14.11) that the population of the conduction band behaves as if the "effective number of states" is equal to $2(2\pi m_e kT/h^2)^{3/2}$. Then in the present problem the number of excess electrons ionized into the conduction band is

$$(14.22) \qquad N_e = 2(2\pi m_e kT/h^2)^{3/2} e^{(W_F - W_g)/kT},$$

where W_g is the width of the gap between bands. Now under the conditions of the problem we must have

$$(14.23) \qquad N_e = N_D - n_D.$$

Setting

$$G = 2(2\pi m_e kT/h^2)^{3/2},$$

we can write (14.21) in the form

$$(14.24) \qquad \frac{N_D}{n_D} = 1 + \frac{\frac{1}{2}Ge^{(W_D - W_g)/kT}}{Ge^{(W_F - W_g)kT}},$$

or, using (14.23) and taking for low temperatures $n_D \cong N_D$,

$$(14.25) \qquad N_e^2 \cong \tfrac{1}{2}N_D Ge^{(W_D - W_g)/kT}.$$

The ionization energy is

$$W_i = W_g - W_D;$$

therefore

$$(14.26) \qquad N_e \cong N_D^{1/2}(2\pi m_e kT/h^2)^{3/4} e^{-W_i/2kT}$$

for the equilibrium number of ionized donors. This expression holds only when the ratio N_e/N_D is $\ll 1$. Exact values of N_e for a typical example are given in Table 14.3. At high temperatures the donors will become completely ionized, so that the concentration of electrons in the conduction band will ultimately, as T is increased, be dominated by excitation from the valence band. At low temperatures the major contribution may be from the donors, provided that $W_i \ll W_g$.

TABLE 14.3. EXAMPLE OF EXACT RESULTS FOR NUMBER OF IONIZED DONORS,
TAKING $N_D = 10^{18}$ DONORS/CM^3; $W_i = 0.2$ EV; $W_g > 3.0$ EV.

$T(°K)$	$N_e(\text{cm}^{-3})$	$W_g - W_F$ (ev)
100	1.8×10^{13}	0.11
400	2.8×10^{17}	0.17
700	8.1×10^{17}	0.28
1000	1.0×10^{18}	0.43
1500	1.0×10^{18}	0.73

MOBILITY IN THE PRESENCE OF IMPURITY ATOMS

When relatively few impurity atoms are present, or at high temperatures, lattice scattering will determine the mobility. At higher impurity concentrations, electron scattering by impurity atoms may be important. The scattering will depend on whether the impurity is neutral or ionized. The neutral atom problem is equivalent to the scattering of an electron by a hydrogen atom, but with the dielectric constant correction. We note that the area of the first Bohr orbit is increased by ϵ^2, or 169 in silicon. An exact solution for the scattering cross section is quite difficult in the energy range of interest in semiconductors.

The scattering by ionized donors or acceptors has been solved by Conwell and Weisskopf,[3] who utilized the Rutherford scattering formula.[4] We give a brief derivation of the expression for the mobility in Appendix Q. Conwell and Weisskopf find

(14.27) $\mu = [2^{7/2} \epsilon^2 (kT)^{3/2} \log (1 + x^2)]/N_e \pi^{3/2} e^3 m^{1/2}$,

where

$$x = 6\epsilon \, dkT/e^2.$$

In these equations N_e is the concentration of ionized donors (or acceptors), and $2d$ is the average distance between near ionized donor neighbors.

[3] E. Conwell and V. F. Weisskopf, Phys. Rev. 77, 388 (1950); see also S. Chapman, Monthly Notices Roy. Astron. Soc. 82, 294 (1922); for scattering by neutral impurities see C. Erginsoy, Phys. Rev. 79, 1013 (1950).

[4] See, for example, M. Born, Atomic physics, Hafner, New York, 5th ed., 1951, App. IX, p. 325.

HALL EFFECT IN SEMICONDUCTORS

If only one type of charge carrier is present, the Hall coefficient is expressed

$$(14.28) \qquad R_H = \pm\, 3\pi/8Nec,$$

where the plus sign applies to n-type and the minus sign to p-type material, under the convention that e is negative; here N is the concentration of carriers. The factor $3\pi/8$ differs from the factor 1, derived in Chapter 12 for metals, because of the different velocity distributions.[5] If both electrons and holes are present in concentrations N_e and N_h, the Hall coefficient is

$$(14.29) \qquad R_H = (3\pi/8ec)[(N_e b^2 - N_h)/(N_e b + N_h)^2],$$

where

$$(14.30) \qquad b = \mu_e/\mu_h$$

is the ratio of the mobilities. The derivation of this result is left to Problem 14.3.

ANALYSIS OF EXPERIMENTAL RESULTS

We discuss now a selection from the measurements and analysis of the electrical properties of pure polycrystalline silicon and silicon alloys carried out by Pearson and Bardeen.[6] The observed values of the Hall coefficient for p-type silicon are shown in Fig. 14.7; the numbers 1, 2, 3, 4 designate specimens with varying amounts of boron added to pure silicon, increasing from "pure" silicon (specimen 1) to 52 atoms in 10^6 (specimen 4). The number of atoms of solute per cubic centimeter of silicon is 0, 6.7×10^{17}, 1.3×10^{18}, and 2.7×10^{18} for specimens 1, 2, 3 and 4, respectively.

The number of charge carriers per unit volume may be calculated directly from the Hall coefficient by using (14.28). The results are given in Fig. 14.8. For specimen 1 the measurements were extended to high temperatures, and we see in the figure the abrupt change of slope as the "impurity region" goes over at high temperatures into the "intrinsic region" with a steeper slope. Estimates of the ionization

[5] See, for example, F. Seitz, *Modern theory of solids*, p. 192.

[6] G. L. Pearson and J. Bardeen, Phys. Rev. **75**, 865 (1949); **77**, 303 (1950). We use the Pearson and Bardeen results for consistency, although later mobility results (footnote 10) on a single crystal are markedly different from the results on polycrystalline specimens.

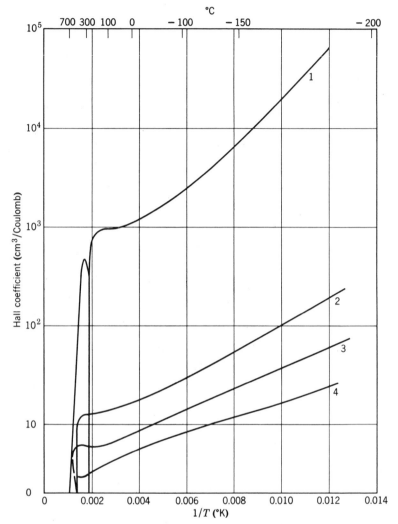

Fig. 14.7. Hall coefficient in silicon-boron alloys as a function of the inverse absolute temperature. Compositions are given in the text. (After Pearson and Bardeen.)

energy W_i and the gap energy W_g may be made from the values of the slopes, and in this way the values $W_g = 1.1$ ev; W_i (donor) $= 0.054$ ev; W_i (acceptor) $= 0.08$ ev were determined.

The conductivity data in Fig. 14.9 may be combined with the concentration data in Fig. 14.8 to yield the values of the hole mobility plotted in Fig. 14.10. At high temperatures the mobilities for the

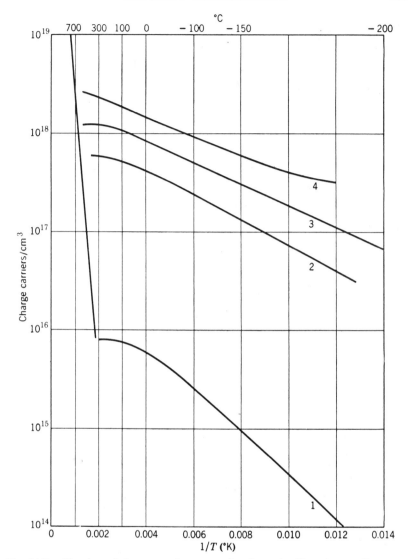

Fig. 14.8.   Number of charge carriers per unit volume in silicon-boron alloys as a function of the inverse absolute temperature.   (After Pearson and Bardeen.)

several specimens coincide with a line of slope $T^{-3/2}$, as expected when the mobility is determined by lattice vibrations.   As impurity scattering is dominant at low temperatures, the mobilities differ from specimen to specimen but generally decrease as the temperature is lowered. The mobilities of specimens 2 and 3 at room temperature correspond to mean free paths of the order of 10^{-6} cm.

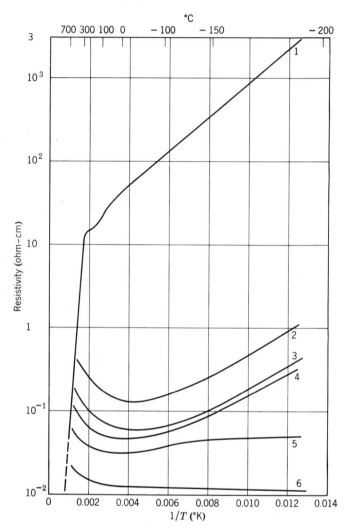

Fig. 14.9. Resistivity of silicon-boron alloys as a function of the inverse absolute
temperature. (After Pearson and Bardeen.)

RECTIFICATION

A rectifier[7] is a device which has a current-voltage characteristic
asymmetrical with respect to voltage, as shown for example in Fig.
14.11. The rectification process requires a low conductivity barrier
layer at the contact between two materials of different conductivity,

---

[7] For details on rectifiers, the book by Torrey and Whitmer listed at the end of
the chapter is recommended. Important early work is due to S. Benzer.

usually a metal and a semiconductor. A rectifier is always of asymmetrical construction, whether by choice of materials, form of the contacts, or surface treatment.

It is easier to understand the physics of rectification by considering first an insulating barrier between two metals that differ in work

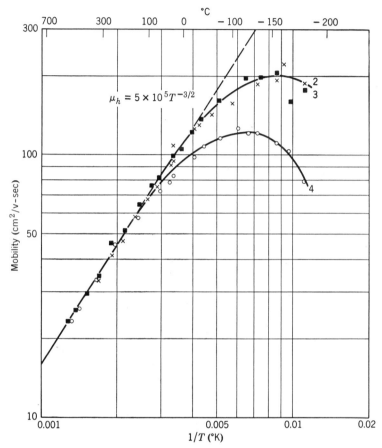

Fig. 14.10.   Hole mobility vs. inverse absolute temperature for silicon-boron alloys.   (After Pearson and Bardeen.)

function. The contact is assembled as shown in Fig. 14.12. The relative positions of the energy bands are determined after equilibrium has been established by the principle that *the Fermi levels must be equal for elements in contact.* This important result is derived in Appendix R.

Immediately after the contact is made in (b) of Fig. 14.12 electrons will flow over the top of the insulating barrier—that is, through the

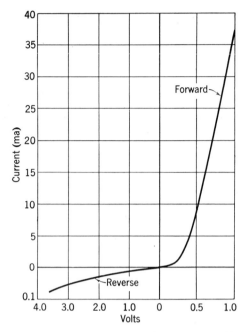

Fig. 14.11.   Current vs. voltage characteristic for a copper oxide rectifier; note the change of scale of the axes about the origin.

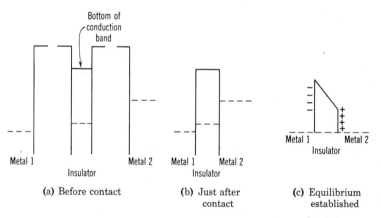

Fig. 14.12.   Formation of a rectifying barrier between two metals of different work function.   The broken line indicates the position of the Fermi level, which must be constant in thermal equilibrium when contact is established.

vacant conduction band of the insulator—preferentially in the direction $2 \rightarrow 1$ because the electrons in the conduction band of metal 2 are closer to the top of the barrier. The flow continues until a double layer of charge as shown in (c) is built up, bringing the Fermi levels of the two metals into coincidence. The positive charge in metal 2 results from the electron deficiency now existing there. When the Fermi levels are equal, there is no longer a net flow of electrons, and equilibrium obtains.

The effect of applying a voltage to the contact is shown in Fig. 14.13. In (a) the conduction band is raised on one side, favoring

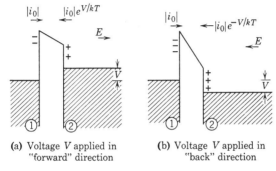

(a) Voltage V applied in "forward" direction

(b) Voltage V applied in "back" direction

Fig. 14.13. Effect of an applied voltage on the current flow through the contact of Fig. 14.12, exhibiting the origin of rectification. In (a) the electrons flow from 2 to 1 with low resistance; in (b) the electrons flow from 2 to 1 with high resistance; the resistance to electrons flowing from 1 to 2 is the same in both (a) and (b).

the "emission" of electrons from the metal of lower work function to the metal of higher work function. In (b) the voltage is reversed and the current flow is greatly reduced. To get significant rectification, $e \times$ the applied voltage must be comparable with kT, which is 0.026 ev at room temperature. It should be noted that the height of the barrier as viewed from metal 1 is independent of the applied voltage.

Many rectifiers are based on the rectifying barrier formed between a metal and a semiconductor, as shown in Fig. 14.14. The Fermi levels here are brought into coincidence in part by electrons flowing from donor impurity levels in the semiconductor to the metal and in part by surface state effects not considered here.[8] The positively

[8] We should note there is evidence that some semiconductors, including germanium and silicon, form a natural barrier layer as a result of surface states, even in the absence of a metallic contact; see J. Bardeen, Phys. Rev. **71**, 717 (1947). The discussion here of the exhaustion layer theory of rectification is due to W. Schottky, Z. Physik **118**, 539 (1942).

ionized impurity levels form an electrical double layer by attracting electrons in the metal toward the contact. The region in the semi-conductor which is practically stripped of conduction electrons is known as the _barrier layer_. The conductivity of the barrier layer will be reduced by the removal of electrons, and it will have all the properties of an insulating barrier, as required for rectification.

Over most of the potential curve of the barrier layer V is $\gg kT$, so that the density of conduction electrons may be supposed to be zero

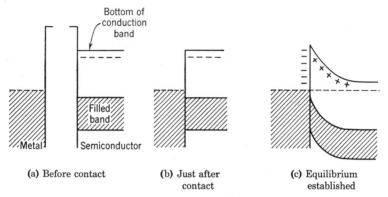

(a) Before contact   (b) Just after contact   (c) Equilibrium established

Fig. 14.14.   Rectifying barrier between a metal and an n-type semiconductor. The Fermi level is shown as a broken line.

in this region for the purpose of estimating the form of the potential variation.   Now

(14.31) $$\operatorname{div} D = 4\pi\rho,$$

or, for the potential ϕ, taking e as positive here,

(14.32) $$\frac{\partial^2\phi}{\partial x^2} = \frac{4\pi Ne}{\epsilon},$$

assuming N ionized donor atoms per unit volume in the barrier layer. As the solution of (14.32) is

(14.33) $$\phi = \frac{2\pi Ne}{\epsilon}x^2,$$

the thickness D of the barrier layer for a potential drop of ϕ_0 is

(14.34) $$D = (\epsilon\phi_0/2\pi eN)^{\frac{1}{2}}.$$

Taking $N = 10^{18}$ cm^{-3}, $\epsilon = 13$ as for silicon, $\phi_0 = 0.5$ volt, we find $D \approx 3 \times 10^{-6}$ cm.

The current-voltage relationship for a rectifying contact is derived in Problem 14.4. The result is that in the "diode" theory the net current density j for applied voltage V is

$$(14.35) \qquad j = \tfrac{1}{4} N e \bar{v} e^{-e\phi_0/kT} (e^{eV/kT} - 1).$$

Here N is the carrier concentration in the bulk semiconductor; $\bar{v}$ is the Maxwellian average velocity of the carriers in the semiconductor; and ϕ_0 is the height of the top of the barrier above the bottom of the conduction band in the semiconductor. It can be shown that this result should be valid as long as the electron mean free path is greater than the distance in which the barrier potential changes by kT. The result (14.35) is of the general form of the experimental results, as in Fig. 14.11.

CRYSTAL TRIODES OR TRANSISTORS

The crystal triode or transistor, discovered by Bardeen and Brattain,[9] is a semiconductor device which performs the functions of a

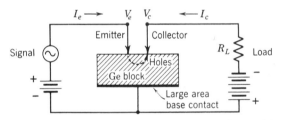

Fig. 14.15. Schematic drawing of a point-contact transistor with a circuit for amplification of an a-c signal. The convention regarding the signs of the currents is shown. The normal bias is I_e, V_e positive; I_c, V_c negative.

vacuum tube triode, such as amplification and modulation. It is now possible to build advanced types of electronic circuits entirely without vacuum tubes, using semiconductor rectifiers and triodes, with benefit from the absence of filament current, reduced size and weight, and increased life. Germanium is generally employed in transistors because the mobilities are higher in germanium than in any other common semiconductor.

There are now a number of different types of transistors. We discuss first the original version of Bardeen and Brattain, known as type A. It consists of a small block of n-type germanium as shown in Fig. 14.15, with a large area base contact and with two closely-spaced point contacts with a separation of the order of 0.01 cm. The emitter

[9] J. Bardeen and W. H. Brattain, Phys. Rev. **75**, 1208 (1949).

point is normally biased in the forward (low resistance) direction of current flow, and the collector point is biased in the back (high resistance) direction.

Transistor action depends on the fact that the current from the emitter is composed largely of positive holes.[10] The holes are attracted to the collector point by the electric field in the germanium arising from the current flowing to the collector which has a strong negative voltage bias, as shown in Fig. 14.16. While the holes are inside the rectifying barrier region next to the collector point they modify the barrier

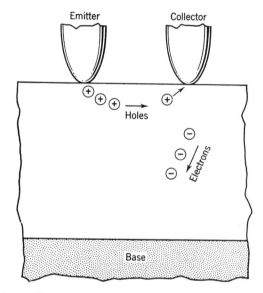

Fig. 14.16. Transistor mechanism. (After Ryder and Kircher.)

rectification properties. Only a little hole current is required before the concentration of holes near the collector becomes substantially greater than the normal concentration of conduction electrons in the germanium. The modification of the collector barrier by the holes injected by the emitter makes possible modulation of the collector

---

[10] A direct experimental demonstration of the injection of holes by the emitter is given by Shockley, Pearson, and Haynes, Bell System Tech. J. **28**, 344 (1949). A somewhat similar arrangement was used to measure drift mobilities in silicon by J. R. Haynes and W. C. Westphal, Phys. Rev. **85**, 680 (1952). The mobility and lifetime against recombination of injected electrons and holes in germanium is discussed by J. R. Haynes and W. Shockley, Phys. Rev. **81**, 835 (1951); it is found that, for small samples, the recombination of holes and electrons takes place principally on the surface of the sample.

current by the emitter current. The current amplification factor α is defined by

(14.36) $\alpha = -(\partial I_c/\partial I_e)_{V_{c=\text{const}}}$

and is found to have values of the order of 2. The power amplification may be quite large, of the order of 20 db or more, because the collector current flows in the high resistance direction. Even without current amplification, it still is possible to have power amplification. Characteristics of a type A transistor are shown in Fig. 14.17.

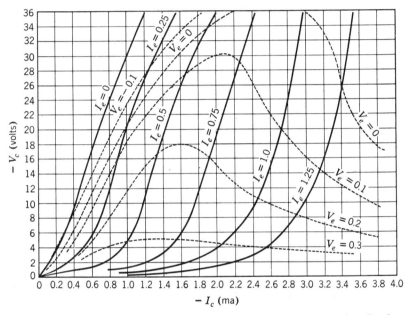

Fig. 14.17.   Characteristics of a type A experimental transistor.   (After Bardeen and Brattain.)

p-n JUNCTIONS

It is possible, by varying the impurity type in the melt during the growth of a single crystal of germanium or silicon, to produce a crystal in which there are both p-type and n-type regions. The boundary between the different regions is called a p-n junction.[11] Such junctions have important electrical properties, including rectification and transistor action.

In such a crystal we expect to find that the conduction electrons contributed by the donors will be found chiefly in the n-region where they

[11] The discussion of p-n junctions follows closely that given by W. Shockley, Proc. I.R.E. **40**, 1289 (1952); the original theory is due to W. Shockley, Bell System Tech. J. **28**, 435 (1949).

neutralize the space charge of the donor ions, while similarly the holes contributed by the acceptor ions will be found chiefly in the p-region. It is not possible for the electrons and holes to remain separated in this way unless an electric field exists in the junction region of the crystal in equilibrium—without an electric field the electrons and holes would intermix by diffusion. If we suppose that initially there is no electric field across the junction, holes will diffuse in one direction leaving behind on one side of the junction negatively charged acceptor ions, while electrons will diffuse in the opposite direction leaving behind positively charged donor ions. This initial diffusion will therefore establish an electrostatic dipole layer at the junction, with an associated electric field in a sense which opposes further diffusion across the junction.

Because of the possibility of recombination of a hole and an electron, with the simultaneous emission of phonons or photons, there will be a small flow of holes from the p-region into the n-region, the holes ending their lives by recombination. This flow will be balanced by holes which are generated in the n-region by thermal fluctuations and which diffuse to the p-region. In equilibrium the recombination and thermal generation hole currents are equal and opposite, as shown in Fig. 14.18a.

We are now in a position to demonstrate the rectification action of a p-n junction. For reverse voltage bias (Fig. 14.18b), negative voltage is applied to the p-region and positive to the n-region, so that the potential difference between the two regions is increased. Now practically no holes can climb the potential hill, and the recombination current I_r drops to a very small value; I_g is not much affected by the reverse bias, as the distance a hole diffuses in its lifetime is large compared with the width of the dipole layer at the junction. When a forward bias V is applied (Fig. 14.18c), I_r increases according to the relation

$$(14.37) \qquad I_r = I_g e^{eV/kT}$$

from the Boltzmann distribution law; we note that for zero bias $I_r = I_g$, as required for equilibrium. The net current of holes from the p-region to the n-region is given by the difference (compare Eq. 14.35)

$$(14.38) \qquad I_r - I_g = I_g(e^{eV/kT} - 1).$$

This current is zero when $V = 0$, increases exponentially to large values for positive eV, and decreases when eV is negative toward a negative saturation value $-I_g$.

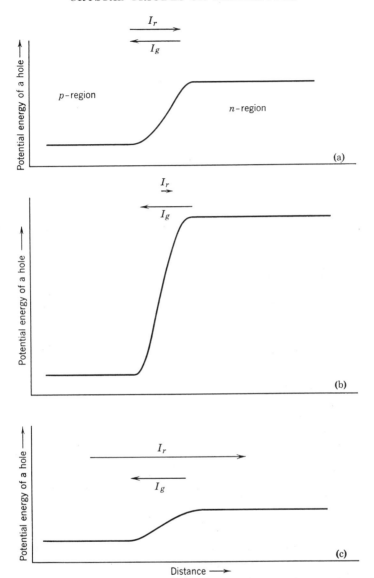

Fig. 14.18. Dependence of recombination I_r and generation I_g hole currents across a p-n junction upon applied voltage bias. (a) Thermal equilibrium, no bias. (b) Reverse bias. (c) Forward bias. (After Shockley.)

The electron current flowing across the junction behaves similarly. The applied voltage which lowers the height of the barrier for holes also lowers it for electrons, so that large numbers of electrons flow from the n- to the p-region under the same voltage conditions that produce large hole currents in the opposite direction. We note that the electrical currents add, so that the total current, including the

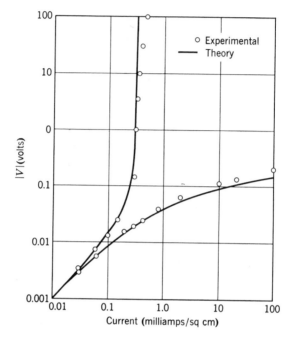

Fig. 14.19. Rectification characteristic for a p-n junction in germanium. (After Shockley.)

effects of both holes and electrons, is given by

$$(14.39) \qquad\qquad I = I_s(e^{eV/kT} - 1),$$

where I_s is the sum of the two generation currents. As shown in Fig. 14.19, this equation is well satisfied for p-n junctions in germanium. The diffusion theory of rectification in p-n junctions developed above has also been checked experimentally by photoelectric experiments by Goucher and co-workers.

Shockley, Sparks, and Teal[12] have described an important type of transistor in which the transistor action takes place within the ger-

[12] Shockley, Sparks, and Teal, Phys. Rev. **83**, 151 (1951); see also R. L. Wallace, **Jr.**, and W. J. Pietenpol, Bell System Tech. J. **30**, 530 (1951).

manium at the junctions between regions of n-type and p-type conductivity. An n-p-n transistor is shown in Fig. 14.20. When the unit is used as an amplifier, the junction J_c is biased in the "reverse" direction as shown in the figure; therefore electrons in the collector region are not encouraged to move to the base region; similarly holes are held in the base region. Electrons in the emitter region may easily enter the base region and then may diffuse to the right p-n

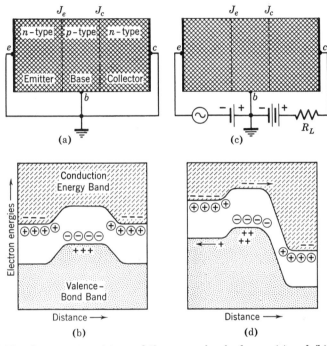

Fig. 14.20. An n-p-n transistor and the energy level scheme: (a) and (b) thermal equilibrium; (c) and (d) biased as an amplifier. (After Shockley, Sparks, and Teal.)

junction. The flow over the potential barrier may be varied by applying a variable potential to the emitter while keeping the base at a constant potential. The emitter region is made more highly conducting than the base region, so that most of the current across the left n-p junction consists of electrons moving to the right, rather than holes moving to the left. Under these conditions the behavior of the device is closely analogous to that of a vacuum tube: the emitter region corresponds to the cathode, the base to the region around the grid, and the collector to the plate.

When the collector electrode is biased positively with respect to the base electrode ("reverse" direction for collector p-n junction), only a small back current of electron and holes will diffuse across the collector barrier. If now the emitter n-p barrier is biased negatively (in the forward direction) with respect to the base, a relatively large forward current of electrons will flow across the reduced emitter barrier into the base region. If the base region is sufficiently thin so that the electrons coming from the emitter do not recombine with holes in the p-type base region, the electrons will diffuse to the collector barrier. From here they are collected with the help of the collector field. Since the electrons were injected through the low forward impedance and collected through the high reverse impedance of bulk p-n junctions, high voltage amplification will result. No current gain is possible in this structure. The detailed theory of the n-p-n transistor is given in reference 12. The theory is simpler than for the type A transistor, as the n-p-n problem is essentially one-dimensional.

PROBLEMS

14.1. Re-derive for dielectric constant ϵ the Bohr theory of the energy levels of hydrogen, using $e^2/\epsilon r$ as the Coulomb interaction energy and m^* as the mass. Take the mass of the nucleus as infinite.

14.2. Find an expression for the Fermi energy under the assumptions leading to expression (14.26) for the equilibrium number of ionized donors.

14.3. Show that, when concentrations N_e of electrons and N_h of holes are present, the Hall coefficient is proportional to

$$(1/ec)[(N_e b^2 - N_h)/(N_e b + N_h)^2],$$

where $b = \mu_e/\mu_h$ is the mobility ratio. Under special assumptions it can be shown that the constant of proportionality is $3\pi/8$.

14.4. If the barrier in a rectifying contact is assumed to be thin in comparison with a mean free path, we may calculate the current-voltage curve for the contact according to what is called the "diode" theory. If ϕ_0 is the height of the top of the barrier above the bottom of the conduction band in the semiconductor, V is the applied voltage across the barrier, and $\bar{v}$ is the Maxwellian average velocity of an electron in the semiconductor, show that the current density j is given by

$$j = \tfrac{1}{4} N e \bar{v} e^{-e\phi_0/kT}(e^{eV/kT} - 1),$$

where N is the number of carriers per unit volume in the bulk semiconductor. *Hint:* Use the fact that $j = 0$ when $V = 0$.

14.5.* Prove that the product of electron and hole concentrations at any temperature is approximately independent of impurity concentration and is given by

$$n_e n_h = 4(2\pi mkT/h^2)^3(m_e m_h/m^2)^{3/2} \exp(-W_g/kT).$$

Note that, if the mobilities of holes and electrons are equal, the electrical conductivity is a minimum at constant temperature when $n_e = n_h$.

14.6. The work function of two metals differs by 2 ev. If these metals are brought into contact, some electrons will flow from one into the other. This phenomenon is entirely limited to the surface of the metal, and it may be assumed that the electrons are displaced over a distance of 3×10^{-8} cm. How many electrons per square centimeter will be transferred?

14.7. The mobility of electrons is 3600 cm^2/v-sec and for holes 1600 cm^2/v-sec in a sample of germanium. This sample shows no Hall effect. What fraction of the current is carried by holes?

14.8. A semiconductor has 10^{18} acceptors per cubic centimeter. The energy level of these acceptors is 0.5 ev above the valence band of the crystal. If the mobility of holes in this band is 100 cm^2/v-sec, calculate the conductivity of the material at room temperature (300°K) and at the temperature of liquid oxygen (90°K).

14.9. Discuss the theory of the Zener current [C. Zener, Proc. Roy. Soc. (London) **A145**, 523 (1934)] and the relevant experiments [K. B. McAfee *et al.*, Phys. Rev. **83**, 650 (1951); G. L. Pearson and B. Sawyer, Proc. I.R.E. **40**, 1348 (1952)].

14.10. Discuss the interpretation of the conductivity of oxides of transition metals. (See the paper by E. J. W. Verwey in the book edited by Henisch cited in the References.)

REFERENCES

R. H. Fowler, *Statistical mechanics*, Cambridge University Press, Cambridge 2nd ed., 1936, Chap. 11.

H. K. Henisch, editor, *Semiconducting materials*, Butterworths Scientific Publications, London, 1951.

J. A. Morton, "Present status of transistor development," Bell System Tech. J. **31**, 411 (1952).

N. F. Mott and R. W. Gurney, *Electronic processes in ionic crystals*, Clarendon Press, Oxford, 2nd ed., 1950.

W. Shockley, *Electrons and holes in semiconductors*, Van Nostrand, New York, 1950.

H. C. Torrey and C. A. Whitmer, *Crystal rectifiers*, McGraw-Hill Book Co., New York, 1948.

Transistor Issue, Proc. I.R.E. **40**, No. 11 (November, 1952).

A. H. Wilson, *Semiconductors and metals; an introduction to the electron theory of metals*, Cambridge University Press, Cambridge, 1939.

15

Imperfections in Solids: I

Much recent work with solids is concerned with the role of structural imperfections, where we interpret the term imperfection to mean any deviation from a perfect homogeneous crystal lattice. Imperfections are essential to many physical processes in solids, including luminescence, atomic diffusion, color center absorption, crystal growth, and mechanical deformation. We shall treat in this and the next chapter a number of the major topics of predominantly physical interest. We discuss first the order-disorder transformation in which the imperfection lies in the irregular arrangement on the lattice sites of the different types of atoms in an alloy.

ORDER-DISORDER TRANSFORMATION[1]

Let us consider a binary alloy AB composed of equal numbers of two types of metal atoms, A and B. The alloy is said to be *ordered* if the A and B atoms stand in a regular periodic arrangement with respect to one another, as in Fig. 15.1a. The alloy is *disordered* if the A and B atoms are randomly arranged, as in Fig. 15.1b. Many of the properties of an alloy are sensitive to the degree of order. A common ordered arrangement is one in which all the nearest neighbor atoms of a B atom are A atoms, and vice versa; this results when the dominant interaction among the atoms is a strong attraction between AB pairs. If dissimilar atoms avoid each other, a two-phase system is formed.

The system is considered completely ordered at absolute zero; it becomes less ordered as the temperature is increased, until a transition temperature is reached above which the disorder is complete. To be more precise, the transition temperature marks the disappearance of *long range order* over many interatomic distances, but some *short range order* or correlation among near neighbors may persist above the transition. A qualitative plot of the equilibrium order is given in Fig. 15.2; long and short range order are defined below. If an

[1] For reviews see F. C. Nix and W. Shockley, Revs. Modern Phys. **10**, 1 (1938); H. Lipson, Prog. Metal Physics **2**, 1–52 (1950).

alloy is cooled rapidly (quenched) from high temperatures to below the transition temperature, a metastable state may be produced in which a non-equilibrium disorder is "frozen" in the structure. An ordered specimen may be disordered at constant temperature by heavy irradiation with nuclear particles.

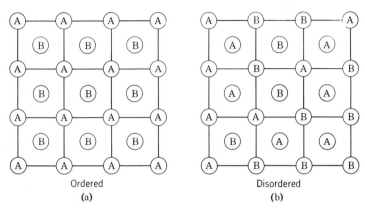

Fig. 15.1.   Ordered (a) and disordered (b) arrangements of AB ions in the alloy AB.

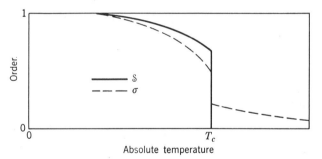

Fig. 15.2.   Long range (S) and short range (σ) order vs. temperature, for an AB₃ alloy.   (After Nix and Shockley.)

The degree of order may be investigated experimentally by several methods, the most powerful being x-ray diffraction. The disordered structure in Fig. 15.1b will have diffraction lines at the same positions as if the lattice points were all occupied by only one type of atom, because the effective scattering power of each plane is equal to the average of the A and B scattering powers. The ordered structure in Fig. 15.1a has extra diffraction lines not possessed by the disordered structure. The extra lines are called *superstructure lines*, and they characterize the diffraction by the A or B lattices separately. Thus in the ordered CuZn alloy the structure is the cesium chloride structure with atoms on a body-centered cubic lattice. This may be thought of as arising from the superposition of two interpenetrating simple cubic lattices, one of copper atoms alone and the other of zinc atoms alone. For example, a bcc lattice of one atom type alone does not have a (100) diffraction line, as the reflection from the atoms at the body centers is 180° out of phase and cancels the reflection from the cube

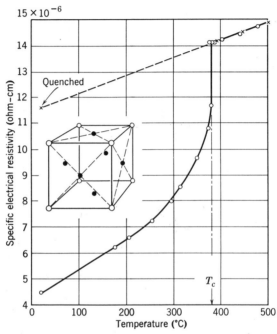

Fig. 15.3.   Electrical resistivity vs. temperature for Cu₃Au.   The alloy was in equilibrium at temperatures above 350°C.   (After Nix and Shockley.)

face.   This tells us that the form factor $S\{100\} = 0$, as discussed in Chapter 1.   The same result holds in a disordered bcc structure, but in the ordered bcc structure the amplitude of the reflection from the body center will in general differ from the amplitude of the reflection from the cube face; the cancellation will now not be complete, ·so that we have a (100) superstructure reflection.

The electrical resistivity (Fig. 15.3) is lower in the ordered state than in the disordered state, as expected in the theory of lattice scattering developed in Chapter 13.   The heat capacity has an anomaly in the neighborhood of the transition temperature, as shown in Fig. 15.4. The anomaly is associated with the extra internal energy required to disorder the structure. The ferromagnetic properties of alloys may be sensitive to the degree of order; in some cases, as in Ni_3Mn, the disordered alloy is weakly ferromagnetic and the ordered alloy is strongly ferromagnetic.[2]

ELEMENTARY THEORY OF ORDER

We give now a simple statistical treatment of the dependence of order on temperature for the case of an AB alloy with a bcc structure.

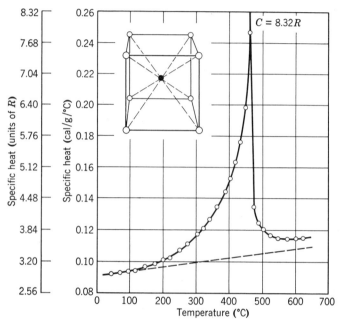

Fig. 15.4. Specific heat vs. temperature of CuZn (β-brass) alloy. (After Nix and Shockley.)

We may mention that the case A_3B differs from AB, the former having a first order transition marked by a latent heat and the latter having a second order transition[3] marked by a discontinuity in the heat capacity. We first introduce the long range order parameter $\S$. We call one simple cubic lattice a and the other b: the bcc structure is composed of the two interpenetrating sc lattices, and the nearest neighbors of an

[2] For a discussion of the influence of order on magnetic properties, see R. Smoluchowski, J. phys. radium **12**, 389 (1951); J. E. Goldman J. Appl. Phys. **20**, 1131 (1949).

[3] For an excellent treatment of second order phase changes, see Chap. 18 of J. C. Slater, *Introduction to chemical physics*, McGraw-Hill Book Co., New York, 1939.

atom on one lattice lie on the other lattice.   If there are N atoms A and N atoms B in the alloy, the *long range order parameter* S is defined so that the number of A's on lattice a is equal to

$$\tfrac{1}{2}(1 + \mathrm{S})N.$$

When $\mathrm{S} = \pm 1$, the order is perfect and each lattice contains only one type of atom.   When $\mathrm{S} = 0$, each lattice contains equal numbers of A and B atoms and there is no long range order.

We consider now that part of the internal energy associated with AA, AB, and BB nearest neighbor bond energies, with the ultimate object of discussing equilibrium conditions.   The energy is

(15.1) $U = N_{AA}V_{AA} + N_{BB}V_{BB} + N_{AB}V_{AB},$

where N_{ij} is the number of nearest neighbor ij bonds, and V_{ij} is the energy of an ij bond.   We have approximately that the number of AA bonds is equal to the number of A's on lattice a times $8/N$ times the number of A's on lattice b.   This approximation is similar to the molecular field assumption in the Weiss theory of ferromagnetism. Thus, by the definition of S,

$$N_{AA} = [\tfrac{1}{2}(1 + \mathrm{S})N][\tfrac{1}{2}(1 - \mathrm{S})N](8/N) = 2(1 - \mathrm{S}^2)N;$$

(15.2) $N_{BB} = [\tfrac{1}{2}(1 + \mathrm{S})N][\tfrac{1}{2}(1 - \mathrm{S})N](8/N) = 2(1 - \mathrm{S}^2)N;$

$$N_{AB} = [\tfrac{1}{2}(1 + \mathrm{S})N]^2(8/N) + [\tfrac{1}{2}(1 - \mathrm{S})N]^2(8/N)$$
$$= 4(1 + \mathrm{S}^2)N.$$

The energy (15.1) becomes

(15.3) $U = U_0 + 2N\mathrm{S}^2 V,$

where

$$U_0 = 2N(V_{AA} + V_{BB} + 2V_{AB});$$

(15.4)

$$V = 2V_{AB} - V_{AA} - V_{BB}.$$

We now calculate the entropy S.   There are $\tfrac{1}{2}(1 + \mathrm{S})N$ atoms A and $\tfrac{1}{2}(1 - \mathrm{S})N$ atoms B on lattice a; there are $\tfrac{1}{2}(1 - \mathrm{S})N$ atoms A and $\tfrac{1}{2}(1 + \mathrm{S})N$ atoms B on lattice b.   The number of arrangements of these numbers of atoms is

(15.5) $w = \left[\dfrac{N!}{[\tfrac{1}{2}(1 + \mathrm{S})N]![\tfrac{1}{2}(1 - \mathrm{S})N]!} \right]^2.$

Recalling the Boltzmann definition of the entropy,

(15.6) $S = k \log w,$

we have, using Stirling's approximation log $x! \cong x(\log x - 1)$,

$$(15.7) \quad S = 2Nk \log 2 - Nk[(1 + \text{S}) \log (1 + \text{S})$$
$$+ (1 - \text{S}) \log (1 - \text{S})].$$

We see that the entropy has the proper limiting behavior: for $\text{S} = \pm1$, $S = 0$; for $\text{S} = 0$, $S = 2Nk \log 2$. This result may be illuminated by the discussion of (9.20).

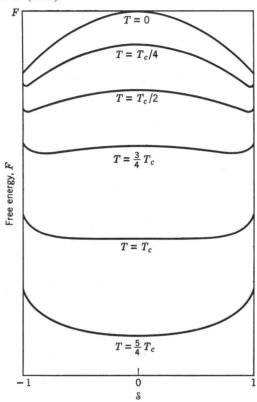

Fig. 15.5. Free energy of an AB alloy as a function of the degree of order S, for various temperatures. (By permission from *Introduction to chemical physics*, by J. C. Slater. Copyright, 1939. McGraw-Hill Book Co.)

The order is determined as a function of temperature by the requirement that the free energy $F = U - TS$ be a minimum with respect to the order parameter S, where U and S are given as functions of S by (15.3) and (15.7). In Fig. 15.5 we have plotted F as a function of temperature. At low temperatures the position of the minimum, giving the stable condition, comes at values of S different from zero, approaching ±1 as the temperature approaches zero. Above the transition temperature T_c the minimum occurs at $\mathcal{S} = 0$, so that the equilibrium state for $T > T_c$ is disordered. On differentiating F with respect to $\mathcal{S}$, we have as the condition for the minimum

(15.8) $$4N\mathcal{S}V + NkT \log \frac{1 + \mathcal{S}}{1 - \mathcal{S}} = 0.$$

This transcendental equation for $\mathcal{S}$ may be solved graphically, and it gives the smoothly decreasing curve shown in Fig. 15.6. Near the transition we may expand (15.8), finding

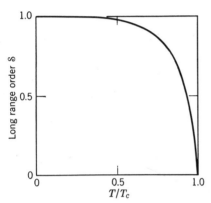

Fig. 15.6. Long range order $\mathcal{S}$ vs. temperature for an AB alloy.

$$4N\mathcal{S}V + 2NkT\mathcal{S} = 0,$$

so that the transition temperature is

(15.9) $\quad T_c = -2V/k.$

LONG AND SHORT RANGE ORDER

We have defined the long range order parameter $\mathcal{S}$ so that the number of A's on lattice a is equal to $\frac{1}{2}(1 + \mathcal{S})N$. If we call a right or r atom an A on a, and a wrong or w atom a B on a, then

(15.10) $$\mathcal{S} = \frac{r - w}{r + w};$$

this may be considered an alternative but equivalent definition of $\mathcal{S}$.

The *short range order parameter* σ is defined as

(15.11) $$\sigma = \frac{q - q(\text{rand.})}{q(\text{max}) - q(\text{rand.})},$$

where q is the fraction of the total number of nearest neighbor bonds in the solid which are between unlike atoms; σ has the limits zero and unity. For the AB structure, q (rand.) $= \frac{1}{2}$ and q (max) $= 1$, so that

(15.12) $$\sigma = 2(q - \frac{1}{2}).$$

We may estimate the short range order in an AB alloy at a temperature $T > T_c$, so that there is no long range order. Consider a particular A atom: the probability[4] that a particular nearest neighbor is a B

---

[4] This estimate assumes that the probability is independent of the other neighbors of the central ion. For a careful discussion of long and short range order, see H. A. Bethe, Proc. Roy. Soc. (London) **A150**, 552 (1935).

atom is q, while the probability that it is an A atom is $(1 - q)$. The ratio of the probabilities is equal to the Boltzmann factor $e^{(V_{AA}-V_{AB})/kT}$; thus

(15.13)
$$\frac{1 - q}{q} = \frac{1 - \sigma}{1 + \sigma} = e^{(V_{AA}-V_{AB})/kT} = x,$$

so that

(15.14)
$$\sigma = \frac{1 - x}{1 + x}.$$

There is no sign of a transition temperature here, and even at high temperatures there are more than the random number of AB pairs;

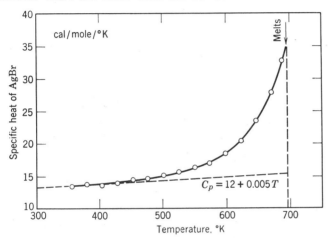

Fig. 15.7. Heat capacity of silver bromide at constant pressure, exhibiting an excess heat capacity from the formation of lattice defects. [After R. W. Christy and A. W. Lawson, J. Chem. Phys. **19**, 517 (1951).]

although they are unable to link up together into regions of long distance order, they are able to form very small domains within which there is order. At T_c the domains begin to join together and cohere into long range order, and as the temperature is lowered the long range order approaches perfection. Many of the details of the theory have been confirmed by recent x-ray work.[5]

LATTICE DEFECTS IN IONIC CRYSTALS[6]

We now consider the occurrence of lattice vacancies and interstitial atoms in ionic crystals, a matter of considerable importance for the

[5] Lipson, ref. 1.; J. M. Cowley, J. Appl. Phys. **21**, 24 (1950).

[6] A detailed account is given by N. F. Mott and R. W. Gurney, *Electronic processes in ionic crystals*, Clarendon Press, Oxford, 2nd ed., 1950, and by K. Hauffe, Ergeb. exakt. Naturwiss. **25**, 193 (1951).

electrical and optical properties of the crystals. There exist in a crystal in thermal equilibrium a number of vacant lattice points. In some crystals the number of vacancies may be of the order of 2 % near the melting point. The excess heat capacity of silver bromide in Fig. 15.7 is, for example, attributed to the formation of lattice defects. We are concerned first with the calculation of the equilibrium number of vacant points. If the ion removed from the vacancy is placed in an interstitial position in the lattice, being squeezed in between normal ions, we have a *Frenkel defect*. If instead the ion removed from the

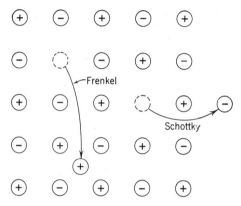

Fig. 15.8.   Schottky and Frenkel defects in an ionic crystal.   The arrows indicate the direction of displacement of the ions.

vacancy is placed on the surface, we have a *Schottky defect*. The two types of defects are illustrated in Fig. 15.8. There is evidence for the existence of many other types of defects in ionic crystals; some of the others are mentioned later in connection with color centers. We calculate now the equilibrium number of Frenkel defects; the result for Schottky defects is derived in Problem 15.3.

CALCULATION OF EQUILIBRIUM CONCENTRATION OF FRENKEL DEFECTS

Let W be the work necessary to remove an atom from a lattice point to an interstitial position. To get the free energy we have next to calculate the entropy, which we obtain from the number of possible arrangements. It is possible to take n atoms from N lattice points in

$$(15.15) \qquad w = \frac{N!}{(N - n)!\,n!}$$

distinct ways, and the n atoms may be distributed among N' interstitial positions in

(15.16)
$$w' = \frac{N'!}{(N' - n)!n!}$$

distinct ways. The increase in entropy of the crystal through the creation of n Frenkel defects is then

(15.17) $S = k \log ww' = k \left[\log \frac{N!}{(N - n)!n!} + \log \frac{N'!}{(N' - n)!n!} \right].$

Using Stirling's formula, we have for the free energy

(15.18) $F = U - TS$
$= nW - kT[N \log N - (N - n) \log (N - n)$
$+ N' \log N' - (N' - n) \log (N' - n) - 2n \log n].$

This is a minimum with respect to n when $(\partial F/\partial n) = 0$, or

(15.19) $W = kT \log [(N - n)(N' - n)/n^2],$

whence, for $n \ll N, N'$,

(15.20) $n = (NN')^{1/2}e^{-W/2kT}.$

In arriving at this result we have neglected other changes in the energy and entropy of the solid: the volume was taken as constant, so that W is independent of T, and the change in lattice frequencies caused by vacancy formation was neglected. Mott and Gurney estimate that, when corrections are made for these approximations, the number of Frenkel defects is increased by a factor $C_F \sim 100$ and the number of Schottky defects is increased by a factor $C_s \sim 10^3$ to 10^4. Electrical neutrality requires that the number of cation Schottky defects should be equal to the number of anion Schottky defects.

EINSTEIN RELATION

The ionic conductivity, mobility, and self-diffusion coefficients are closely related. We recall that the mobility is defined as the drift velocity per unit electric field. If only one ion type, for example the interstitial cations, is mobile, the Einstein relation obtains between the diffusion coefficient D and the mobility μ:

(15.21) $\mu kT = eD.$

This relation is easily proved. Suppose that the particles of charge e are in a constant electric field E. According to the Boltzmann distribution law the concentration of particles $n(x)$ at x is proportional to

$\exp\ (-eEx/kT)$. The condition that in equilibrium no net current should flow is

(15.22) $\mu nE - D(dn/dx) = 0,$

the definition of the diffusivity D being used as the net flux of particles per unit concentration gradient. From (15.22) we see that $n(x)$ is also proportional to $\exp\ (-\mu Ex/D)$; (15.21) follows on equating the exponents.

DIFFUSION OF LATTICE DEFECTS

Interstitial atoms will have a certain rate of diffusion from one interstitial position to another; also, an atom in a normal position may move into a hole, thus effectively changing the position of the hole. Other mechanisms of diffusion are considered in the next chapter.

Usually the diffusion process requires that an atom surmount a potential energy barrier in changing position. If the barrier is of height U, the atom will have sufficient energy to pass over the barrier only a fraction $\exp\ (-U/kT)$ of the time.[7] If ω is the vibrational frequency of the interstitial atom, the probability r per unit time that the atom will get over the barrier is of the order

(15.23) $r \sim \omega e^{-U/kT}.$

We now consider two parallel planes of atoms, the planes separated by the lattice constant a. We suppose that a concentration gradient of interstitial atoms exists, with concentration n at one plane and $(n + a\ dn/dx)$ at the other, the numbers of atoms associated with the planes being na and $(n + a\ dn/dx)a$, respectively. The net number crossing unit area per second is of the order of

$$ra^2\ dn/dx,$$

so that the diffusion coefficient D_i of the interstitial ions may be taken as

(15.24) $D_i = ra^2 = \omega a^2 e^{-U/kT}.$

The gross diffusion coefficient D for the crystal is given by multiplying D_i by the fraction of ions in interstitial positions and thus able to move:

(15.25) $D = nD_i/N = (n\omega^2 a^2/N)e^{-U/kT},$

[7] This argument is rather difficult to justify rigorously, but it may be taken as qualitatively reasonable.

where N is the total number of ions per unit volume. Using (15.21),

$$(15.26) \qquad D = \omega^2 a^2 (N'/N)^{\frac{1}{2}} e^{-(\frac{1}{2}W+U)/kT},$$

apart from a numerical factor containing C_F as discussed above. The factor may be quite large, so that D_0 in the relation

$$(15.27) \qquad D = D_0 e^{-(\frac{1}{2}W+U)/kT}$$

may be of the order of 0.1 to 100 cm^2/sec; Zener and Nowick[8] have suggested that in the more accurate measurements D_0 is very close to 1 cm^2/sec.

IONIC MOBILITY AND CONDUCTIVITY

On combining the Einstein relation (15.21) with the result (15.27) we have for the ionic mobility

$$(15.28) \qquad \mu = (eD_0/kT) e^{-(\frac{1}{2}W+U)/kT},$$

so that the ionic conductivity is

$$(15.29) \qquad \sigma = (Ne^2 D_0/kT) e^{-(\frac{1}{2}W+U)/kT}.$$

Ionic conductivities may be determined experimentally by electrolytic methods, as by finding the change of mass of the electrodes. Results of Lehfeldt for silver and thallium halides are given in Fig. 15.9. The curves at low temperatures are structure-sensitive and vary in the same substance from sample to sample, but at high temperatures different samples give consistent results. For sodium chloride

$$\sigma = 3.5 \times 10^6 e^{-23,600/T} \text{ cm}^{-1} \text{ ohm}^{-1},$$

while for silver chloride Koch and Wagner find

$$\sigma = 3 \times 10^4 e^{-9250/T} \text{ cm}^{-1} \text{ ohm}^{-1};$$

the relative values of the numbers in front of the exponentials suggest that the conduction is caused by Schottky defects in sodium chloride and by Frenkel defects in silver chloride.

COLOR CENTERS

It is observed that, when an alkali halide crystal is heated in an atmosphere of the vapor of the alkali metal, the crystal acquires a stoichiometric excess (that is, an excess over the quantity called for by the chemical formula) of alkali metal and takes on a deep color— magenta in potassium chloride and yellow in sodium chloride, for

[8] A. S. Nowick, J. Appl. Phys. **22**, 1182 (1951).

example.   The coloration is ascribed to *F-centers* or *Farbzentren*, and
the experimental properties of these centers have been investigated in
detail particularly by Pohl and his co-workers.   In recent years many
other types of centers have been found and to some extent their origin

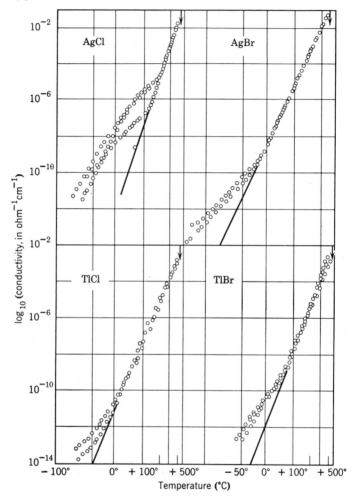

Fig. 15.9.   Ionic conductivity vs. temperature in silver and thallium halides.
[After W. Lehfeldt, Z. Physik **85**, 717 (1933).]

explained theoretically.   Table 15.1 summarizes several types of
centers;[9] we note that vacancies can combine to form clusters of vacancies.   We shall discuss only the *F*- and *V*-centers.   Color centers may

⁹ For a review of color center work see F. Seitz, Revs. Modern Phys. **18**, 384
(1946); N. F. Mott and R. W. Gurney, *Electronic processes in ionic crystals*, Clarendon Press, Oxford, 2nd ed., 1950.

TABLE 15.1. TYPES OF COLOR CENTERS IN ALKALI HALIDE CRYSTALS

Name of Center or Band	Presumed Origin
F	Excess electron near negative ion vacancy
F'	Two excess electrons near negative ion vacancy
V_1	Electron hole near positive ion vacancy†
U	Added H^- ions in negative ion vacancy
$F_2(R$ band)	Pair of bound F-centers
$F_2^+(R$ band)	One excess electron near two negative ion vacancies
M	F-center combined with a pair of vacancies
D	Excess electron near combined positive-negative ion vacancy

† The V-bands are complex, and there are other V-centers which probably are counterparts of the F_2, F_2^+, etc., centers.

also be produced by x-ray irradiation, neutron irradiation, electrolysis, electron bombardment, and in other ways.

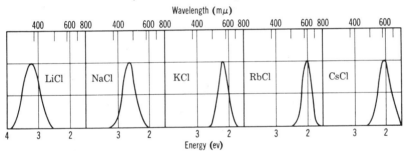

Fig. 15.10. The F-bands for several alkali halides: optical absorption vs. wavelength.

Breckenridge[10] has noted that an associated pair of vacancies of opposite sign should exhibit an electric dipole moment. He has observed contributions to the dielectric constant and dielectric loss in alkali halides which he attributes to pairs of vacancies. The dielectric relaxation time should be a measure of the time required for one of the vacant sites to jump by one atomic position about the other. In sodium chloride the relaxation frequency occurs at 1000 cps at 85°C, with perhaps a 10-percent increase in the dielectric constant at lower frequencies.

F-CENTERS

The F-center absorption band for several alkali halides are shown in Fig. 15.10; associated energies are given in Table 15.2. The F-centers producing the bands may be created in the alkali halides by heating them in the presence of alkali metal vapor and then cooling the

10 R. G. Breckenridge, J. Chem. Phys, **16**, 959 (1948); see also his paper in the book edited by Shockley *et al.* cited at the end of the chapter.

crystals rapidly to room temperature. It is found by chemical analysis that the crystals colored by this process contain a stoichiometric excess of alkali metal atoms, the excess commonly being of the order of 10^{16} to 10^{19} per cubic centimeter.

TABLE 15.2. EXPERIMENTAL F-CENTER ENERGIES (EV)

LiCl	3.1	LiBr	2.7	LiF	5.
NaCl	2.7	NaBr	2.3	NaF	3.6
KCl	2.2	KBr	2.0	KF	2.7
RbCl	2.0	RbBr	1.8		
CsCl	2.0				

As it is believed that the excess alkali atoms fit into the alkali halide crystal in normal alkali ion lattice positions, a corresponding number of negative ion vacancies must be created in the process. A negative ion vacancy in an otherwise periodic lattice behaves like a positive charge, so an electron moving about a negative ion vacancy resembles qualitatively a hydrogen atom. We identify an F-center with an electron bound to a negative ion vacancy, the electron being provided by the ionization of an alkali atom on entering the lattice.

A number of facts support this identification, among them:

(a) The F-band absorption is characteristic of the crystal and not of the alkali metal used in the vapor; that is, the band in potassium chloride is the same whether the crystal is heated in potassium or sodium vapor.

(b) Crystals with F-centers can be bleached by illumination with light absorbed in the F-band, and illumination in any part of the band bleaches the whole band. This proves that the F-centers in any crystal are all similar. The bleaching is attributed to the ionization of the F-center and is accompanied by photoconductivity; that is, the crystal becomes conducting during irradiation. The width of the band may be accounted for by the thermal motion of the ions.

(c) The paramagnetic susceptibility of an F-center corresponds closely to the spin contribution of one electron, and the g-values observed in spin resonance experiments are close to 2.00.

How are we to think of the distribution of the F-center electron around the anion vacancy? In early work the electron was treated as moving in a spherically symmetric potential well centered on the vacancy, with a wave function spreading out over many neighboring ions. This viewpoint has recently been shown[11] to be inconsistent with the g-value observed by Hutchison and Noble in a microwave

[11] A. H. Kahn and C. Kittel, Phys. Rev. **89**, 315 (1953); the measurements are by C. A. Hutchison, Jr., and G. A. Noble, Phys. Rev. **87**, 1125 (1952).

resonance experiment on a colored potassium chloride crystal. It appears to be better to think of the electron as attached in turn as a $4s$ valence electron to each of the six K^+ ions surrounding the anion vacancy. This viewpoint appears to be consistent with the g-value. It does not appear to be difficult to account on this model for the F-center energies in Table 15.2, as the s-p energies observed for optical transitions from the ground states of alkali atoms in free space are of the same general magnitude as the F-center energies. From atomic

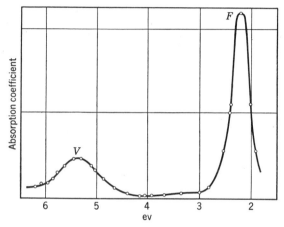

Fig. 15.11. V- and F- bands in a potassium chloride crystal irradiated with 30-kev x-rays at 20°C. [After H. Dorendorf and H. Pick, Z. Physik **128**, 106 (1950).]

spectra we find for the s-p energies: lithium, 1.8 ev; sodium 2.1 ev; potassium, 1.6 ev; rubidium, 1.6 ev; cesium, 1.45 ev.

V-CENTERS

The V-bands have been observed in several alkali halide crystals after bombardment with high energy radiation, such as 3-Mev electrons. In Fig. 15.11 we show the V- and F-bands found by Dorendorf and Pick in a potassium chloride crystal after irradiation with 30-kev x-rays; Fig. 15.12 shows the interpretation of the V-band as arising from the ionization of a positive hole near an alkali metal vacancy.

LUMINESCENCE

This is a large field, at present imperfectly understood. Luminescence is a general term denoting the absorption of energy by a substance and its re-emission as visible or near visible radiation. The initial excitation may be by light, electron or positive ion bombardment, mechanical strain, chemical reaction, or heating. If the emission occurs during excitation, or within 10^{-8} sec of excitation, the process is commonly called *fluorescence*. The interval 10^{-8} sec is chosen as of the order of the lifetime of an atomic state for an allowed (electric dipole) transition. If the emission occurs after excitation has ceased, the process is called *phosphorescence* or *after-glow*. The after-glow period may be of the order of microseconds to hours.

Many solids are luminescent with low efficiency for the conversion of other forms of energy into radiation. The ability of a given material

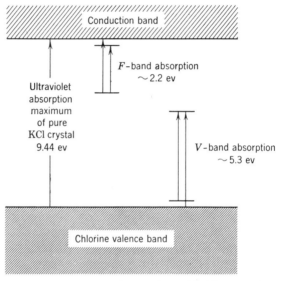

Fig. 15.12. Energy level scheme of potassium chloride crystal, as proposed by Dorendorf and Pick.

to luminesce with high efficiency is frequently related to *activator atoms*, which are "impurity" atoms present in only small proportions; there are also a large number of pure materials which luminesce efficiently.

Our discussion of luminescence is limited to three substances which illustrate different aspects of the phenomenon: (a) a fluorescent crystal, thallium-activated potassium chloride; (b) a phosphorescent organic dye, acid fluorescein; (c) a phosphorescent crystal with electron traps, copper-activated zinc sulfide.

THALLIUM-ACTIVATED POTASSIUM CHLORIDE

The theory has been considered by Seitz and Williams.[12] It is found experimentally that only fluorescence occurs if the concentration

[12] Seitz, J. Chem. Phys. **6**, 150 (1938); F. E. Williams, J. Chem. Phys. **19**, 457 (1951).

of thallous ions is small (less than 0.0015 mole percent).   Phosphorescence occurs for higher concentrations and is believed to be peculiar to
pairs of adjacent thallium ions in the lattice.

We consider here only the fluorescence of single thallium ions substituted for alkali metal ions in the lattice.   Three absorption bands

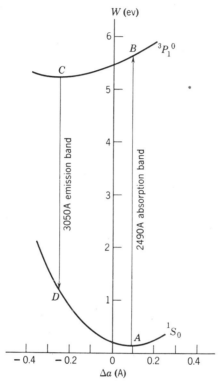

Fig. 15.13.   Two energy levels of thallium ion in a potassium chloride lattice, as a
function of a configurational coordinate representing the symmetric displacement
of the six chlorine ions around a thallium ion from the perfect potassium chloride
lattice positions.   (After F. Williams.)

are found which can be interpreted; the transition giving rise to one of
the absorption bands is shown Fig. 15.13.

The thallium ion in the ground state is close to point A, with some
spread about this point caused by the thermal motion of the lattice.
When irradiated with light near 2490 A, a transition $A \rightarrow B$ to the
upper state may take place.   According to the Franck-Condon principle, which is discussed in books on molecular spectra, the transition
occurs and maintains the atomic configuration characteristic of the

See 520
P60

ground state: thus the absorption occurs from A to B, rather than from A to C. After the transition a rearrangement of the neighboring ions takes place with the system ending up at the equilibrium position C, the energy difference $B - C$ being dissipated in lattice vibrations. From C the system emits light in a band around 3050 A, passing to D, and, after giving energy to the lattice, passes down to the equilibrium position A.

Williams calculated the configurational energy curves shown in Fig. 15.13; he used approximate wave functions and treated in detail the interactions between a thallium ion and the lattice. His calculated absorption and emission bands are in quite good accord with experiment. By measurements on thallium in other alkali halide crystals it is found that the bands are more characteristic of the thallium than of the matrix crystal.

FLUORESCEIN DYE

Lewis and co-workers[13] have studied the phosphorescence of acid fluorescein dye in a rigid borax glass. The results can be understood in terms of the energy level scheme portrayed in Fig. 15.14. An allowed optical absorptive transition takes place between A and B. Both states are supposed to be singlet states (spin zero), and the transition is presumably an allowed electric dipole transition. By some radiationless rearrangement the system passes from B to C, where it is in a triplet state ($S = 1$). The transition $C \rightarrow D$ between the triplet state and the singlet ground state is highly forbidden, but because of spin orbit coupling there is in C a slight singlet mixture which makes the transition possible with a lifetime of the order of 2 sec. It has been confirmed by direct magnetic susceptibility measurements that the excited state C is a triplet state.

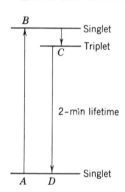

Fig. 15.14. Energy level scheme for phosphorescence of fluorescein.

COPPER-ACTIVATED ZINC SULFIDE

In copper-activated zinc sulfide phosphors a number of processes occur which are not important in the substances previously discussed. In the first place there is an effective mechanism in zinc sulfide for transferring excitation energy from the atoms of the base crystal to

[13] See, for example, Lewis, Calvin, and Kasha, J. Chem. Phys. **17**, 804 (1949).

the activator atoms.   Even if only 1 atom in 10^4 is an activator atom, it is possible for 10% of the energy of fast electrons to be emitted as light from the activator atoms.   It is supposed that the excitation energy is transferred in waves from one atom of the base crystal to the next, until an activator atom breaks the chain.

A second feature is the fact that copper-activated zinc sulfide becomes photoconducting when irradiated with light which stimulates luminescence.   The photocurrent is associated with the excitation of electrons into the conduction band of the phosphor crystal.   A third feature is that the intensity decay law is no longer exponential, as it is for example in fluorescein, but rather follows the relation

$$(15.30) \qquad I(t) \cong \frac{I_0}{(\beta t + 1)^n} \qquad n \approx 2,$$

which is similar to the rate equation for a bimolecular chemical reaction.   The constant β is often dependent on temperature, in the form

$$(15.31) \qquad \beta = Be^{-W/kT}.$$

On the basis of the last two features we form the following picture of the after-glow process in this material: The activator atoms become ionized when excited with ultraviolet light or otherwise.   The freed electrons become trapped at various types of electron traps in the lattice.   The trapped electrons may be freed from the traps thermally, or by further irradiation.[14]   A freed electron has a certain probability of recombination with an ionized activator, and on recombination radiation is emitted, which in the case of copper-activated zinc sulfide is green.

EXCITONS

In the volume edited by Shockley *et al.*, cited at the end of the chapter, Seitz shows that the principal physical effects of imperfections in almost perfect crystals are in large measure the result of six primary types of imperfection and of the interactions between them.   The six *primary imperfections* are: (a) phonons; (b) electrons and holes; (c) excitons; (d) vacant lattice sites and interstitial atoms; (e) foreign atoms; (f) dislocations.

[14] In some cases the traps are shallow and the electrons may be released by infra-red radiation.

We have discussed phonons in Chapters 4 and 5; electrons and holes in Chapter 14; excitons are discussed below; vacant lattice sites and interstitial atoms earlier in the present chapter; foreign atoms in Chapter 14 and the present chapter; and dislocations in Chapter 16.

An *exciton*[15] or excitation wave is produced when an insulator is raised to the first non-conducting excited state of its electronic system. The first electronic transition is called the *first fundamental absorption band* of the crystal. It is centered at 1580 A in sodium chloride, at 1920 A in sodium bromide, and at 2200 A in potassium iodide. In silicon and germanium it lies in the near infrared. The associated absorption of light is very intense. An exciton may be thought of as the excited state of an atom or ion, with the excitation wandering from one cell of the lattice to another. If we excite one atom in a solid, the excitation will in general not remain localized on the original atom, but at later times there is a finite probability that any other identical atom in the solid will happen to be excited. A moving state of excitation is called an exciton.

The transmission of the excitation takes place by means of electrostatic or electromagnetic coupling between the excited atom and its neighbors. It should be noted that an excitation wave will not carry current, as there is no translation of charge. An excitation wave may be compared in some respects with a ferromagnetic spin wave as discussed in Appendix J. The energy of an exciton may be treated in the simplest case as the sum of the internal energy required to excite a single ion and a translational energy related to the velocity with which the excitation state moves from one atom to another.

The simplest way to form an exciton is to irradiate the crystal with light in the region of the first electronic transition. The region in good insulators is usually in the ultraviolet and is termed the first fundamental absorption band of the crystal. Apker and Taft[16] have found direct evidence of the mobility of the excited states thus formed. The excitons produced by irradiation of a number of alkali halides in the first fundamental band have been shown to wander for distances at least of the order of 1000 lattice constants; one way an exciton may end its life is to use the excitation energy to eject electrons from *F*-centers. The ejected electrons have been detected as external

[15] J. Frenkel, Phys. Rev. **37**, 17, 1276 (1931); R. Peierls, Ann. Physik **13**, 905 (1932); J. C. Slater and W. Shockley, Phys. Rev. **50**, 705 (1936); G. H. Wannier, Phys. Rev. **52**, 191 (1937); W. R. Heller and A. Marcus, Phys. Rev. **84**, 809 (1951).

[16] L. Apker and E. Taft, Phys. Rev. **79**, 964 (1950); **81**, 698 (1951); **82**, 814 (1951); M. H. Hebb, Phys. Rev. **81**, 702 (1951); D. L. Dexter and W. R. Heller, Phys. Rev. **84**, 377 (1951).

photoelectrons. The conclusion that excitons are responsible for the ejection of electrons from F-centers rests on the close similarity (Fig. 15.15) between the optical absorption curves obtained in the absence of F-centers and the photoelectric yields obtained when F-centers are present.

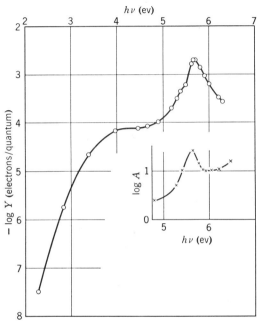

Fig. 15.15. Evidence for the existence of excitons. The photoelectric yield Y for potassium iodide with F-centers is similar in form near 5.6 ev to the optical absorption constant A (arbitrary units) for potassium iodide substantially without F-centers, suggesting that the excitons may ionize the F-centers. [After L. Apker and E. Taft, Phys. Rev. **79**, 964 (1950).]

PROBLEMS

15.1. Cu_3Au alloy (75% Cu, 25% Au) has an ordered state below 400°C, in which the gold atoms occupy the 000 positions and the copper atoms the $\frac{1}{2}\frac{1}{2}0$, $\frac{1}{2}0\frac{1}{2}$, and $0\frac{1}{2}\frac{1}{2}$ positions in a face-centered cubic lattice. Give the indices of the new x-ray reflections which appear when the alloy goes from the disordered to the ordered state. List all new reflections with indices ≤ 3. Can you give a general rule for the indices of the additional reflections?

15.2. Derive an expression for the anomalous or configurational heat capacity of an AB alloy (50%A, 50%B), sketching the form of the heat capacity vs. T, using Fig. 15.6.

15.3. Show that the number n of Schottky defects in equilibrium in a crystal of N lattice points is

$$\frac{n}{N - n} = e^{-W/kT},$$

where W is the work required to remove an atom from a lattice point inside the crystal and then to add the atom to the surface. Show first that the free energy is given as a function of n by

$$F = nW - kT \log [N!/n!(N - n)!],$$

and then set $\partial F/\partial n = 0$ for equilibrium.

15.4. We consider a system of n ionized centers and n free electrons; if β is the probability of recombination, the intensity decay equation is

$$I_t = dn/dt = \beta n^2.$$

Find the solution for I_t as a function of t and of the initial intensity of emission I_0. This is the result of the "bimolecular decay hypothesis" applied to phosphors.

15.5. Suppose that the energy required to remove a sodium atom from the inside of a sodium crystal to the boundary is 1 ev. Calculate the number of Schottky vacancies at room temperature (300°K). If a neighboring sodium atom has to move over a potential hill of 0.5 ev, and the atomic vibration frequency is 10^{12}, estimate the diffusion coefficient at room temperature for radioactive sodium in normal sodium. Repeat the calculation for 373°K.

15.6. Discuss the physical principles governing the response of crystal counters for ionizing radiation. [See, for example, R. Hofstadter, Nucleonics **4**, No. 4, 2 (1949); **4**, No. 5, 29 (1949); A. G. Chynoweth, Am. J. Phys. **20**, 218 (1952)].

15.7. Discuss the physical changes resulting from radiation damage in solids. Radiation damage is caused by the passage of neutrons or fast charged particles through the material. [See F. Seitz, Discussions Faraday Soc. No. 5, 271 (1949); J. C. Slater, J. Appl. Phys. **22**, 237 (1951); K. Lark-Horowitz, in H. K. Henisch, editor, *Semiconducting materials*, Butterworths Scientific Publications, London, 1951.]

15.8. Discuss the present physical picture of the photographic process. [See the books by Mitchell and by Mott and Gurney cited in the References.]

REFERENCES

R. M. Barrer, *Diffusion in and through solids*, Cambridge University Press, Cambridge, 1951.

B. Chalmers, editor, *Progress in metal physics*, Butterworths Scientific Publications, London, 1949, vol. 1; 1950, vol. 2; 1952, vol. 3.

G. Fonda and F. Seitz, editors, *Preparation and characteristics of solid luminescent materials*, John Wiley & Sons, New York, 1948.

G. F. J. Garlick, *Luminescent materials*, Clarendon Press, Oxford, 1949.

H. W. Leverenz, *Introduction to the luminescence of solids*, John Wiley & Sons, New York, 1948.

J. W. Mitchell, editor, *Fundamental mechanisms of photographic sensitivity*, Butterworths Scientific Publications, London, 1951.

N. F. Mott and R. W. Gurney, *Electronic processes in ionic crystals*, Clarendon Press, Oxford, 2nd ed., 1950.

F. C. Nix and W. Shockley, "Order-disorder transformations in alloys," Revs. Modern Phys. **10**, 1 (1938).

P. Pringsheim, *Fluorescence and Phosphorescence*, Interscience Publishers, New York, 1949.

Shockley, Hollomon, Maurer, and Seitz, editors, *Imperfections in nearly perfect crystals*, John Wiley & Sons, New York, 1952.

16

Imperfections in Solids: II

The present chapter is concerned principally with the modern physical interpretation of the mechanical properties of solids. We are rapidly gaining a basic qualitative understanding of many aspects of the mechanical and metallurgical properties of solids. Several of the central physical concepts underlying the recent advances are discussed below, with particular reference to the theory of dislocations.

SHEAR STRENGTH OF SINGLE CRYSTALS

The classical prediction for the strength of crystals is that the critical shear stress σ_c should be of the order of magnitude of the shear modulus G, which in a cubic crystal is equal to c_{44}. If x is the shear displacement of one lattice plane relative to a neighboring plane,

$$(16.1) \qquad \sigma = Gx/d,$$

where d is the interplanar spacing. We may expect the crystal to yield when neighboring planes have been displaced by a distance of the order of $d/4$, as at a displacement of $d/2$ the shear force between planes vanishes by symmetry. Thus we estimate for the critical shear stress

$$(16.2) \qquad \sigma_c \approx G/4.$$

From values of c_{44} given in Table 3.1 we may expect the critical shear stress to be of the order of 10^{10} to 10^{11} dynes/cm^2.

The observed shearing stress required to produce macroscopic plastic flow in single crystals is very small compared with the observed shear modulus. Critical shear stresses as low as 10^5 dynes/cm^2 have been observed in mercury crystals. In rock salt the breaking stress is 5×10^7 dynes/cm^2. Values of the ratio of the shear modulus to the elastic limit are given for single crystal and polycrystalline specimens in Table 16.1. In the hardest technical alloys the theoretical yield point is only about ten times greater than observed, but in pure single crystals the factor is very much higher. We conclude that macroscopic plastic flow can be induced in pure single crystals by strains of the order of 10^{-5} or less.

The great importance of lattice properties for plastic strain is indicated by the highly anisotropic nature of plastic strain. Even in the cubic metals the displacement takes place along well-defined crystallographic planes with a small set of Miller indices, such as the (111) planes in fcc metals and the (110), (112), and (123) planes in bcc metals. Under all conditions the slip direction lies in the line of closest atomic packing, $[10\bar{1}]$ in fcc metals and $[111]$ in bcc metals.

DISLOCATIONS[1]

The low observed values of the critical shear stress can be explained in terms of the motion through the lattice of a particular type of imper-

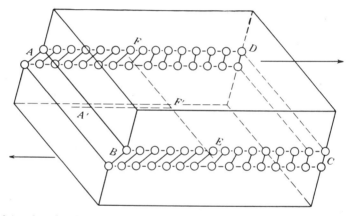

Fig. 16.1. An edge dislocation, showing the glide plane $ABCD$, the slipped region $ABEF$ in which the atoms have been displaced by more than half a lattice constant, and the unslipped region $FECD$ with displacement less than half a lattice constant. The dislocation line is EF and the slip direction is $A'F'$. (After Cottrell, *Progress in metal physics*, No. 1, Butterworths Scientific Publications, London, 1949.)

fection known as a *dislocation*. The idea that slip propagates over glide or slip planes by the motion of dislocations was published in 1934 independently by Taylor, Orowan, and Polanyi; the concept of dislocations was introduced into physics somewhat earlier by Prandtl and Dehlinger.

We first describe a *Taylor-Orowan* or *edge dislocation*, Fig. 16.1. The dislocation may be thought of (Fig. 16.2) as caused by the insertion of an extra partial plane of atoms in the crystal. Near the dislocation

---

[1] An excellent review of dislocation theory is given by A. H. Cottrell, Prog. Metal Phys. **1**, 77 (1949); see also F. Nabarro, Advances in Physics **1**, 271 (1952).

line marking the termination of the extra plane the crystal is highly strained. The simple edge dislocation extends indefinitely in the slip plane in a direction normal to the slip direction. Edge dislocations are called positive or negative according to the position of the extra

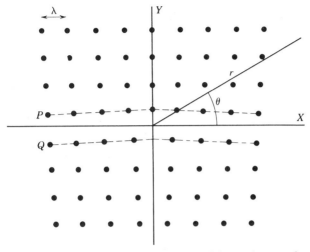

Fig. 16.2. Structure of an edge dislocation. The deformation may be thought of as caused by inserting an extra plane of atoms on the upper half of the y axis. Atoms in the upper half-crystal P are compressed and those in the lower half Q are extended. This is defined as a positive dislocation; if the extra plane is put in from below, the dislocation is negative. (After Cottrell.)

plane of atoms above or below the slip plane. All the dislocation drawings shown are for simple cubic structures.

TABLE 16.1. COMPARISON OF SHEAR MODULUS AND ELASTIC LIMIT

(After Mott)

	Shear Modulus G (dynes/cm^2)	Elastic Limit B (dynes/cm^2)	G/B
Sn, single crystal	1.9×10^{11}	1.3×10^7	15,000
Ag, single crystal	2.8×10^{11}	6×10^6	45,000
Al, single crystal	2.5×10^{11}	4×10^6	60,000
Al, pure, polycrystal	2.5×10^{11}	2.6×10^8	900
Al, commercial drawn	$\sim 2.5 \times 10^{11}$	9.9×10^8	250
Duralumin	$\sim 2.5 \times 10^{11}$	3.6×10^9	70
Fe, soft, polycrystal	7.7×10^{11}	1.5×10^9	500
Heat-treated carbon steel	$\sim 8 \times 10^{11}$	6.5×10^9	120
Nickel-chrome steel	$\sim 8 \times 10^{11}$	1.2×10^{10}	65

The mechanism responsible for the mobility of a dislocation and the attendant slip is shown in Fig. 16.3. When the atoms on one side of the slip plane are moved with respect to those on the other side, part of the atoms at the slip plane will experience repulsive forces and part will experience attractive forces from their neighbors across the slip plane. To a first approximation these forces cancel, so that the external force required to move a dislocation will be quite small. If the dislocation line is not straight, the cancellation will be even more com-

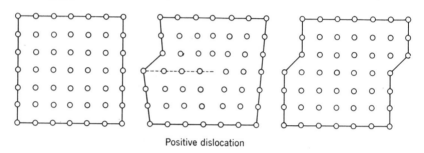

Positive dislocation

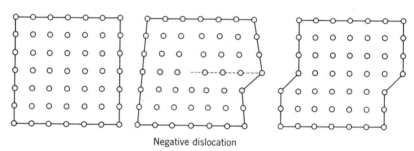

Negative dislocation

Fig. 16.3. Motion of a dislocation under a shear tending to move the upper surface of the specimen to the right. Above, a positive dislocation moves from left to right; below, a negative dislocation moves from right to left. Note that the positive and negative dislocations leave the specimen on opposite sides. (After Taylor.)

plete. Calculations show that dislocations in an otherwise perfect crystal can be made to move by very low stresses, probably below 10^5 dynes/cm^2. Thus dislocations may make a crystal very plastic. In Fig. 16.4 we show a photograph of a dislocation in a two-dimensional soap bubble raft obtained by the method of Bragg and Nye.[2]

[2] W. L. Bragg and J. F. Nye, Proc. Roy. Soc. (London) **A190**, 474 (1947); W. L. Bragg and W. M. Lomer, Proc. Roy. Soc., (London) **A196**, 171 (1949). A film based on this work is distributed by Kodak Ltd., London, as 'Cinegraph' 16-mm film No. 2015.

SCREW DISLOCATIONS AND DISLOCATION RINGS

The second fundamental type of dislocation is the *Burgers or screw dislocation* (Fig. 16.5). Here the slip is parallel to the dislocation line rather than perpendicular as in the edge dislocation.

Compound and ring dislocations may be formed from segments of edge and screw dislocations. Burgers has shown that the most general form of linear dislocation pattern in a continuous medium can be described as shown in Fig. 16.6. We consider any closed curve not

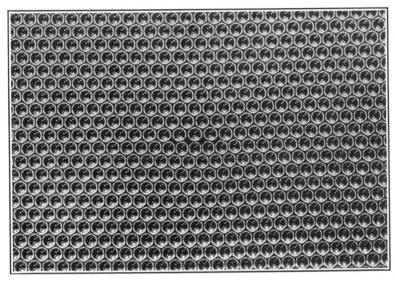

Fig. 16.4. A dislocation in a two-dimensional bubble raft. The dislocation is most easily seen by turning the page by 30° in its plane and sighting at a low angle. (Photograph courtesy of W. M. Lomer, after Bragg and Nye.)

necessarily planar within a solid, or an open curve terminating on the surface at both ends. Make a cut along any simple surface bounded by the line. Displace the material on one side of this surface by **d** relative to the other side; **d** is a fixed vector called the *Burgers vector*. In regions where **d** is not parallel to the surface this relative displacement will either produce a gap or cause the two halves to overlap. In these cases material is either added to fill the gap or is subtracted to prevent overlap. Then rejoin the material on both sides, leaving the strain displacement intact at the time of the rewelding, but afterwards allowing the medium to come to internal equilibrium. The resulting strain pattern is that of a line dislocation and is characterized by the boundary curve and the Burgers vector.

DISLOCATION CONCENTRATIONS

The concentration of dislocations is specified by giving the number of times dislocation lines intersect a unit area in the crystal. This is 10^8 or less per square centimeter in good natural crystals, near $10^9/cm^2$ in good artificial crystals, and may be as large as $10^{12}/cm^2$ in cold-worked specimens. The methods of arriving at these estimates are discussed below.

The detailed investigations which have been made of the arrangement of atoms in the immediate vicinity of the dislocation line show

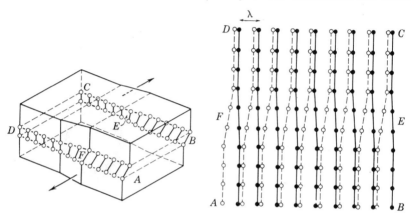

Fig. 16.5. A screw dislocation. A part $ABEF$ of the slip plane has slipped in the direction parallel to the dislocation line EF. A screw dislocation may be visualized as a spiral arrangement of lattice planes, such that we change planes on going completely around the dislocation line. (After Cottrell.)

that the region of appreciable disregistry is of the order of five atom distances in linear dimension. The energy of a dislocation is of the order of 1 ev volt per atomic plane, being of the order of the energy of an interatomic bond.

Using this rough estimate of the energy, we may estimate the density of dislocation lines in a cold-worked specimen from the energy stored in the specimen during cold-work. The maximum energy stored in lattice distortions as a consequence of severe cold-working, as by twisting or compression, has been measured thermally for several metals, with results given in Table 16.2. About 10% of the energy expended

TABLE 16.2. MAXIMUM ENERGY STORED BY COLD-WORK (CAL/G)

Aluminum	1.1
Copper	0.5
Iron	1.2
Nickel	0.8
Brass	0.5

in plastic flow is stored in the lattice. It is found empirically that after continuous work-hardening the stored energy approaches a saturation value.

If the energy of a dislocation is of the order of 1 ev per atom plane, the energy per centimeter length is of the order of 10^{-4} ergs/cm. The observed values of the stored energy correspond to about 10^8 ergs/cc;

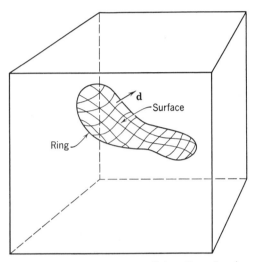

Fig. 16.6. General method of forming a dislocation ring in a medium. The medium is represented by the rectangular block. The ring is represented by the closed curve in the interior in the block. A cut is made alone the surface bounded by the curve and indicated by the contoured area. The material on one side of the cut is displaced relative to that on the other by the vector distance **d**, which may be arbitrarily oriented relative to the surface. Forces will be required to effect the displacement. The medium is filled in or cut away so as to be continuous after the displacement. It is then joined in the displaced state and the applied forces are relaxed. The surface may be chosen arbitrarily in a continuous isotropic medium for àny ring or displacement vector without altering the final stress-strain field. This is also true in a crystalline medium if **d** is a translation vector of the lattice; otherwise the final field depends upon the choice of surface. (After Seitz.)

this energy density is consistent with a density of dislocations[3] equal to 10^{12}/cm^2, or one dislocation per square 100 A on a side. This is also believed on other grounds to be the concentration of dislocations characteristic of severely cold-worked metals.

Analyses by Warren and Averbach[4] of the breadth of x-ray dif-

[3] For more careful estimates, see J. S. Koehler, Phys. Rev. **60**, 397 (1941).

[4] B. L. Averbach and B. E. Warren, J. Appl. Phys. **20**, 1066 (1949); B. E. Warren and B. L. Averbach, J. Appl. Phys. **21**, 595 (1950).

fraction lines from cold-worked brass yield a stored energy of 1.4 cal/g, of the same order as the calorimetric value. From the shape of the lines they conclude that a major fraction of the strains are non-uniform over distances of several cell dimensions, as might be expected on a dislocation model. They find also that the shape of the line is in better agreement with that expected from random local strains than with a "fragmentation" model, on which it is assumed that cold-work breaks the material down into crystals so small that ordinary particle size broadening appears.

We mention now other estimates of the density of dislocations in cold-worked materials. The electrical resistivity of metals increases with cold-working, the increase being 2 percent in heavily cold-worked copper. Dexter[5] has worked out the theory of the resistivity change on a dislocation model, finding that of the order of 4×10^{12} dislocations/cm^2 will account for the observations on copper, while Koehler[3] estimated for copper from energy storage measurements 6×10^{11} dislocations/cm^2; part of the discrepancy may be caused by vacancy scattering of electron waves. From magnetic saturation measurements in nickel Brown[6] estimates 3×10^{11} dislocations/cm^2 for severe cold-working.

As regards the lower limit of dislocation concentration, organic crystals grown under low supersaturation and studied by the electron microscope have been found with about 2×10^6 dislocations/cm^2. It is customary to take 10^8 dislocations/cm^2 as characteristic of good natural inorganic crystals.

In annealed metal crystals there are probably about 10^9 to 10^{10} dislocations/cm^2. Evidence from the extinction and breadth of x-ray lines[7] suggests that an annealed single crystal is usually composed of mosaic blocks perhaps 5000 A on a side and tilted with respect to one another by angles of the order of 10 to 15 min. This tilt corresponds (Fig. 16.7a) to dislocations about 300 atom distances apart in the boundaries of the blocks, giving about 10^{10} dislocations/cm^2.

[5] D. L. Dexter, Phys. Rev. **86**, 770 (1952).

[6] W. F. Brown, Jr., Phys. Rev. **60**, 139 (1941).

[7] The integrated intensity of x-ray reflections is often many times larger than calculated for a perfect crystal, and the lines may also be wider than calculated. For a discussion of intensity relations with reference to the role of mosaic structures in accounting for the observed intensities, the reader is referred to Chap. VI of R. W. James, *Optical principles of the diffraction of x-rays*, G. Bell and Sons, Ltd., London, 1950. The dislocation interpretation of mosaic and grain boundaries is due to J. M. Burgers, Proc. Roy. Acad. Sci. Amsterdam **42**, 393 (1939). Boundary energies are calculated successfully on the dislocation model by W. T. Read and W. Shockley, Phys. Rev. **78**, 293 (1950).

Burgers suggested that small angle grain boundaries in metals consist of arrays of like dislocations. This interpretation is supported by the fact that these boundaries can, under certain conditions, be made to move by the application of a shear stress. The motion has been demonstrated in a beautiful experiment by Washburn and Parker. The nature of their results is exhibited in Fig. 16.7b. The specimen consisted of a bicrystal of zinc having an orientation difference of 2°.

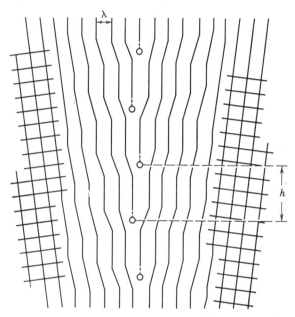

Fig. 16.7a. Transition surface between crystallites formed by a set of parallel edge dislocations. (After Burgers.)

One side of the crystal was clamped, and a force was applied at a point on the opposite side of the boundary. Motion of the boundary apparently took place by a cooperative motion of the dislocations in the array, each dislocation moving an equivalent distance in its own slip plane. Opposite top and bottom intersections of the boundary with the surface moved approximately the same amount. The motion was produced by stresses of the order of magnitude of the yield stress for zinc crystals: this fact may be taken as very strong evidence that ordinary deformation results from the motion of dislocations.

TAYLOR THEORY OF WORK-HARDENING AND PLASTIC SLIP

If a gradually increasing stress is applied to a pure single crystal of a metal, it is sometimes found that the permanent strain is related to

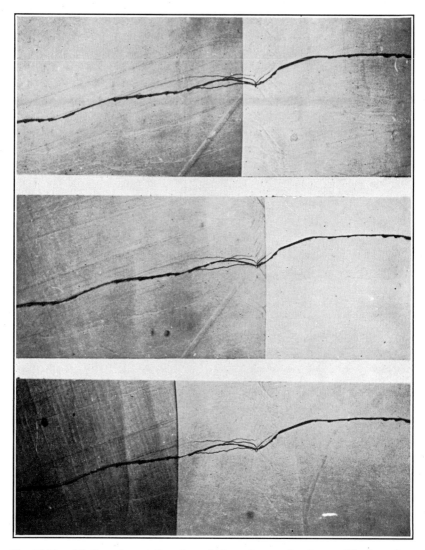

Fig. 16.7b. Motion of a small angle grain boundary under stress. The boundary is the straight vertical line, and it is photographed under vertical illumination, thereby making evident the 2° angular change in the cleavage surface of the zinc crystal at the boundary. The irregular horizontal line is a small step in the cleavage surface which serves as a reference mark. The crystal is clamped at the left; at the right it is subject to a force normal to the plane of the page. Top, original position of boundary; center, moved 0.1 mm to the right; bottom, moved back 0.4 mm. (After J. Washburn and E. R. Parker, J. Metals, October 1952, 1076.) A motion picture showing these and related experiments has been prepared by Professor E. R. Parker, University of California, Berkeley, California.

the stress by a parabolic relation,[8] as shown for aluminum in Fig. 16.8. The phenomenon that even after plastic flow has begun it requires a larger stress to continue the motion than to initiate it is known as *work-hardening.* We present here a simplified version of the original theory of plastic slip due to G. I. Taylor.[9] The theory of plastic slip is currently in a state of flux, and the presentation below is not to be taken too literally.

The stresses around dislocations are discussed in Appendix S. The stresses are somewhat like those between electric charges in that dislocations of like sign repel each other, while dislocations of opposite

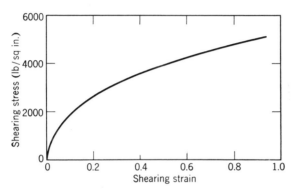

Fig. 16.8.   Cold-work curve of a single crystal of aluminum, where the stress and strain are referred to the plane of easy slip.   (After G. I. Taylor.)

sign attract each other.   It may be shown that a collection of dislocations in a crystal will tend to take on a lattice character.   On a given slip plane all dislocations must be of one sign, as otherwise the positive and negative dislocations would easily annihilate each other.   The force per unit length between two edge dislocations is approximately, from Appendix S,

$$(16.3) \qquad F_x = \pm \frac{Ax}{x^2 + y^2},$$

where A is given in terms of the shear modulus G, Burgers vector d, and Poisson ratio ν by

$$(16.4) \qquad A = Gd^2/2\pi(1 - \nu).$$

[8] Many metals show instead a linear connection.   There is currently a tendency to minimize the significance of the parabolic curve, and we discuss it here largely to illustrate the physical processes causing work-hardening.

[9] G. I. Taylor, Proc. Roy. Soc. (London) **A145**, 362 (1934); for a modern interpretation see N. F. Mott, Phil. Mag. **43**, 1151 (1952).

If the dislocations are at a spacing a, the maximum force between dislocations will be of the order of

(16.5)　　　　　　　　　$F_x \approx A/a.$

The repulsion between dislocations of opposite sign is responsible for work-hardening.　If the force is supplied by an external shear stress σ we have, from Problem 16.1,

(16.6)　　　　　　　　　$F_x = d\sigma,$

where d is the magnitude of the Burgers vector.

As the number of dislocations per unit area is $1/a^2$, the total displacement of a mosaic block of width L_1 in the slip direction and thickness L_2 normal to the slip plane is approximately

$$dL_1L_2/2a^2,$$

supposing that on the average each dislocation will have traveled halfway across the mosaic block.　The shear strain γ is given by

(16.7)　　　　　　　　　$\gamma = dL_1/2a^2.$

Thus, from (16.5) and (16.6),

$$\sigma d = A(2\gamma/L_1d)^{\frac{1}{2}},$$

or

(16.8)　　　　　　　$\sigma = \dfrac{G(2d/L_1)^{\frac{1}{2}}}{2\pi(1 - \nu)}\gamma^{\frac{1}{2}}.$

This gives a parabolic connection between stress and strain, in qualitative agreement with the results in Fig. 16.8.　For aluminum at low temperatures Taylor, using an expression similar to (16.8), finds that $L_1 \approx 5 \times 10^{-4}$ cm fits the experimental curve.　This value of L_1 is of the order of the size of the mosaic blocks deduced from x-ray work. It may seem surprising, since dislocations were introduced to explain easy slip, that slip becomes more difficult as the number of dislocations is increased.　The greater difficulty of slip is believed, on Taylor's theory, to come about from the interference of the strain fields of dislocations.

Taylor's theory of the plastic flow process depends on the three assumptions that the dislocations do not travel through the boundary regions between mosaic blocks, that the spacing between dislocations in the slip direction is the same as in the normal direction, and that new dislocations are generated proportional to the strain.　The process of dislocation generation is not well understood at present.

We do not yet possess a well-integrated theory of plastic flow adequate to describe the details of the slip process. It is known experimentally that a large fraction of the strain displacement is concentrated in regions called *slip bands*, which appear visually or under an optical microscope as lines on the surface of the specimen defining the planes in which the shear displacement has occurred. Electron microscope studies on aluminum by Heidenreich and Shockley show that the region in which the displacement occurs is about 50 A in thickness, with neighboring slip lines, in highly strained material separated by laminae about 2000 A thick. The maximum relative displacement of adjacent laminae is about 2000 A.

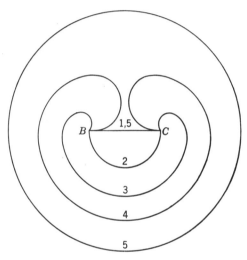

Fig. 16.9. Frank-Read mechanism for multiplication of dislocations, showing successive stages in the generation of a dislocation loop by the segment BC of a dislocation line. The process can be repeated indefinitely.

FRANK-READ MECHANISM FOR THE MULTIPLICATION OF DISLOCATIONS

To produce any appreciable non-recoverable deformation we must assume that some multiplication of dislocations must occur. The slip bands observed in the plastic deformation of crystals show that on an active slip plane there is about 1000 times more slip than would result from the passage of a single dislocation across a plane. It is thus important to find processes by which dislocations can produce a large amount of slip and can multiply. We describe here one of the processes discovered by Frank and Read; further details are given in the Carnegie-ONR conference report cited at the end of the chapter.

The Frank-Read mechanism leading to continued slip and to generation of dislocations is shown in Fig. 16.9. The segment BC of a dislocation line lies in the slip plane; as the other parts of the line lie outside the plane, points B and C are anchored. An applied shear stress causes BC to curve as shown and to generate a succession of dislocation rings.

PRECIPITATION HARDENING

Directly after quenching, an alloy in the form of a supersaturated solid solution is mechanically soft. It becomes harder as precipitation of the excess component proceeds. As aging continues, the particle size of the precipitate becomes large and resoftening takes place; the effect is known as over-aging. We see that the yield strength depends on the state of dispersion of the precipitate. Maximum hardness is found when the average spacing between precipitate particles is of the order of 25 to 50 lattice spacings. An alloy in which the precipitate particles are visible under an optical microscope is generally thoroughly over-aged.

Mott and Nabarro have developed a dislocation theory of precipitation hardening. Their basic idea is that the misfit of precipitate particles in the solvent matrix causes internal stresses in the matrix. These internal stresses offer resistance to the passage of dislocations and thus hinder slip. It is supposed that a dislocation is unable to move through a region which is under internal stress unless the external stress is of the same magnitude as the internal stress. The theory considers the flexibility of dislocation lines and shows that the local radius of curvature of a dislocation line is equal to the ratio of the shear modulus to the local internal stress. When the particle spacing is less than the radius of curvature, the dislocation line is effectively rigid and will not be able to follow the local stresses; these will then average out. The material is soft in this condition. When the radius of curvature is comparable with the particle spacing, each wiggle of the dislocation line must be carried separately through the stress field of each precipitate particle. In this case the different parts of the dislocation line cannot assist one another over the obstacles. The material is hard in this condition. Orowan has discussed the mechanism of resoftening on over-aging. He shows that, as the precipitate particles grow and become farther apart, it becomes possible for a dislocation line to bulge forward around the obstacle, the right and left parts of the line joining together again on the far side of the obstacle. This process reduces the external stress required to move the dislocation.

The classic example of a precipitation-hardened alloy is duralumin, an Al-Cu alloy containing about 4% copper by weight. The yield strength when properly aged is about 10 times that of pure aluminum and about four times that of commercial aluminum (Table 16.1). In Al-Cu alloys Guinier and Preston found by beautiful x-ray work that the beginning of the precipitation process is marked by the precipitation of fine platelets of a transition phase richer in copper than the matrix. The platelets are formed parallel to cube planes of the matrix and, when first detectable, are a few atomic layers in thickness and several hundred angstroms in diameter. The dimensions increase as aging progresses. The crystal structure of the precipitate is coherent with the structure of the matrix; the stresses accompanying the enforced continuity of atomic positions in coherent structures are the internal stresses responsible for hardening through interference with the passage of dislocations.

COTTRELL IMPURITY HARDENING

Cottrell has suggested that impurities present interstitially or substitutionally may diffuse to the neighborhood of dislocations and lock them in position. Solute atoms differing in size from those of the solvent can relieve hydrostatic stresses in a crystal by migrating to dislocations where regions of high and low density of packing exist. The solute atoms will accordingly cluster around dislocations, forming an "atmosphere" of impurity atoms. In very slow creep the dislocations carry their atmospheres along with them, but for rapid slip the atmospheres cannot diffuse in time; thus they act to anchor the dislocations in place and increase the yield stress. The activation energy for strain aging in steel is the same as for the diffusion of carbon; this suggests that carbon atoms cluster around dislocations.

DISLOCATIONS AND CRYSTAL GROWTH

It has been shown by Frank[10] and his collaborators that in some cases dislocations may be the controlling factor in crystal growth. When crystals are grown in conditions of low supersaturation, of the order of 1%, it has been observed that the growth rate is faster than that calculated for an ideal crystal by a factor, in one case, of the order of e^{3000}. The actual growth rate is explained by Frank in terms of the effect of dislocations on growth.

The theory of growth of ideal crystals, due to Gibbs, Volmer, Becker, and others, predicts that in crystal growth from vapor a supersaturation (pressure/equilibrium vapor pressure) of the order of 10 is required

[10] For a full review of this field see F. C. Frank, Advances in Physics **1**, 91 (1952); detailed calculations are given by Burton, Cabrera, and Frank, Trans. Roy. Soc. (London) **A243**, 299 (1951). A motion picture has been prepared by the General Electric Research Laboratory, Schenectady, N.Y.

to nucleate new crystals, of the order of 5 to form liquid drops, and of 1.5 to form a two-dimensional monolayer of molecules on the face of a perfect crystal. Actually Volmer and Schultze observed growth of iodine crystals at vapor supersaturations down to less than 1%, where the growth rate should have been down by e^{-3000} from the rate defined as the minimum observable growth.

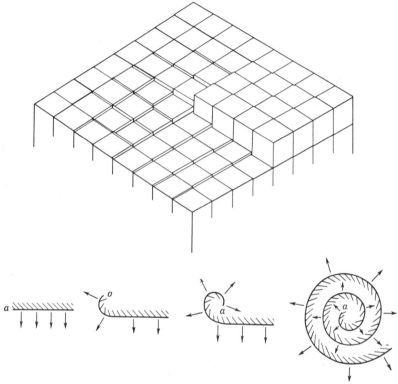

Fig. 16.10.   Development of a spiral step produced by intersection of a screw dislocation with the surface of a crystal.   Each cube represents a molecule.   (After F. C. Frank.)

Frank pointed out that the large factor just mentioned expresses the difficulty of nucleating a new surface on a completed surface of the crystal and that if there is a screw dislocation present as in Fig. 16.10 it is never necessary to nucleate a new surface, as the crystal will grow in spiral fashion at the edge of the discontinuity shown.   The calculated growth rates for this mechanism are in good agreement with observation.   We therefore expect that nearly all crystals in nature grown at low supersaturation will contain dislocations, as otherwise they might not have grown.

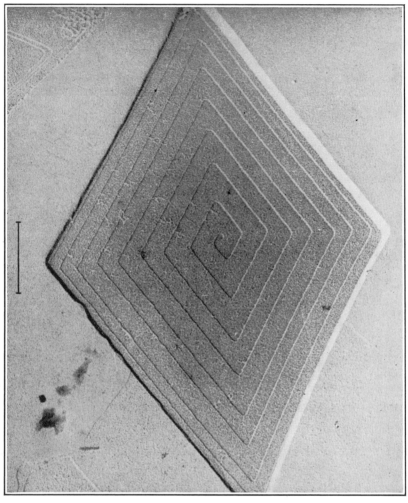

Fig. 16.11. Growth pattern from single dislocation on single crystal of paraffin n-$C_{36}H_{74}$. [Electron micrograph courtesy of H. F. Kay and B. J. Appelbe, after Dawson and Vand, Proc. Roy. Soc. (London) **A206**, 555 (1951).]

Spike-shaped or dendritic crystals sometimes grow in conditions of inhomogeneous supersaturation without the necessity for dislocations. Herring and Galt[11] have observed in this connection that thin whiskers of tin (radius $\sim 10^{-4}$ cm) have elastic and plastic properties near those expected from theoretically perfect crystals. They observed yield strains of the order of 10^{-2}, about 1000 times greater than in bulk tin.

[11] C. Herring and J. K. Galt, Phys. Rev. **85**, 1060 (1952).

Griffin and others, using optical and electron microscopes, have observed spiral growth patterns on a large number of crystals. Their photographs are convincing evidence of the reality of dislocations. A beautiful example of the growth pattern from a single screw dislocation is given in Fig. 16.11. If the growth rate were independent of direction in the plane of the surface, the growth pattern would be an Archimedes spiral,

$$(16.9) \qquad\qquad r = a\theta,$$

where a is a constant, with a limiting minimum radius of curvature near the dislocation determined by the supersaturation. If the radius of curvature is too small, atoms on the curved edge evaporate until the equilibrium curvature is attained. Away from the origin each part of the step acquires new atoms at a constant rate, so that

$$(16.10) \qquad\qquad dr/dt = \text{const.}$$

The spiral appears to rotate with uniform angular velocity during growth, for, if $d\theta/dt$ is constant, dr/dt will appear to be constant, as required for uniform deposition by (16.10).

Dawson and Vand,[12] working with the straight chain hydrocarbon $C_{36}H_{74}$, find a step height of 43 ± 5 A, in suitable agreement with the x-ray cell height 47.5 A. The ledge widths were in the range 1000 to 4000 A. For their crystals the number of dislocations N was correlated empirically with the total area A_{001} of the (001) face of the crystal by the relation

$$(16.11) \qquad\qquad N = 1.6 + (2 \times 10^6)A_{001},$$

suggesting that there are on the average 1.6 dislocations present in the nucleus from which growth takes place, and that there are $\sim 2 \times 10^6$ dislocations/cm^2 in a large crystal grown under their conditions.

DIFFUSION AND THE KIRKENDALL EFFECT[13]

It is possible to describe diffusion in solids in terms of the three basic processes pictured in Fig. 16.12. The relative probability of the several processes depends quite strongly on the values of the appropri-

---

[12] I. M. Dawson and V. Vand, Proc. Roy. Soc. (London) **A206**, 555 (1951).

[13] Our present understanding of diffusion in solids is reviewed by F. Seitz, *Phase transformations in solids;* edited by Smoluchowski, Mayer, and Weyl; John Wiley & Sons, New York, 1951, pp. 77–148. Measurements of internal friction have been of value in elucidating several aspects of diffusion as well as other metallurgical processes in solids; this work is reviewed in the book by Zener cited at the end of the chapter.

ate activation energies.   Calculations by Huntington and Seitz[14] for metallic copper, summarized in Table 16.3, show a marked preference for vacancy diffusion, process (c) in Fig. 16.12.   The observed self-diffusion activation energy of 2.1 ev is in fair agreement with the calculated $1.0 + 1.8 = 2.8$ ev for vacancy diffusion.

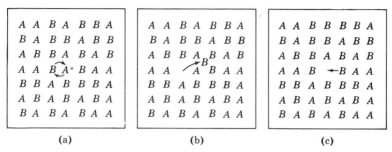

(a)   (b)   (c)

Fig. 16.12.   The three basic mechanisms of diffusion.   (a) Interchange by rotation about a midway point, forcing neighboring atoms apart.   (b) Migration through interstitial sites.   (c) Atoms exchange position with vacant lattice sites.   (From Seitz.)

It is at present believed that vacancy diffusion is preferred in metals such as iron, nickel, copper, zinc, tin, and tungsten, which resemble copper in having large inner shells.   In the alkali metals it is not known whether the interstitial or the vacancy mechanism is preferred.

TABLE 16.3.   ENERGIES OF INTEREST FOR SELF-DIFFUSION IN METALLIC COPPER

(Calculated by Huntington and Seitz)

Process	Event	Energy (ev)
(a) Interchange	Direct interchange	11
(b) Interstitial migration	Atom from surface to interstitial position	9.5
	Migration of interstitial atom	~0.5
(c) Vacancy diffusion	Formation of vacancy	1.8
	Motion of vacancy	~1.0
Observed activation energy		2.1

A distinction between the interchange mechanism on the one hand and interstitial and vacancy mechanisms on the other hand is offered by the Kirkendall effect,[15] Fig. 16.13.   Suppose that it is possible to

[14] H. B. Huntington and F. Seitz, Phys. Rev. **61**, 315 (1942); H. B. Huntington, Phys. Rev. **61**, 325 (1942).

[15] A. D. Smigelskas and E. O. Kirkendall, Trans. Amer. Inst. Mining Met. Engrs. **171**, 130 (1947).   A review is given by J. Bardeen and C. Herring in the volume edited by Shockley *et al.* cited in the References.

regard the lattice framework of a crystal as a rigid frame of cells between which the atoms jump; on the interchange mechanism, pairs of atoms change places simultaneously, and there is no displacement of the assembly of atoms as a whole relative to the framework. However, in the case of vacancy or interstitial diffusion it is possible for the assembly to be displaced relative to the framework if there is a net flow of vacancies from one side to the other. This is possible if the specimen contains a concentration gradient allowing vacancies to enter one side more easily than the other. The vacancies may also be created or absorbed at edge dislocations and grain boundaries.

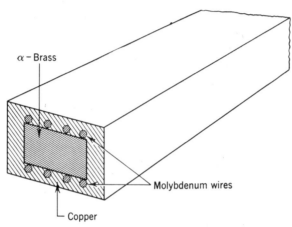

Fig. 16.13. The experiment of Smigelskas and Kirkendall. Molybdenum wires are located at the boundary between the inner CuZn block and the outer copper covering. After prolonged heating the markers are observed to move inward, suggesting that the zinc diffuses more rapidly than the copper. (After LeClaire, Progress in metal physics 1, Butterworths Scientific Publications, London, 1949.)

In the Kirkendall effect markers are placed at the interface between an alloy (CuZn) and a metal (copper). On heating to a temperature at which diffusion is possible, the markers are observed to move inwards, the opposite sets moving together. This is explained by saying that the zinc diffuses more rapidly than the copper and thus diffuses out of the inner block. If diffusion were due to direct exchange of atoms, the diffusion coefficients of the two metal in the alloy would have to be equal. As this is not observed, we are inclined to suppose that the diffusion is due to the movement of vacancies and that a zinc atom changes place with a vacancy more easily than with a copper atom. This picture requires that sources and sinks of vacancies be present within the alloy. It is not unlikely that dislocations act to maintain the equilibrium concentration of vacancies.

PROBLEMS

16.1. Consider a crystal in the form of a cube of side L containing an edge dislocation of Burgers vector d. If the crystal is subjected to a shear stress σ on the upper and lower faces in the direction of slip, show by considering energy balance that the force acting on the dislocation is $F = d\sigma$ per unit length.

16.2. Consider a crystal of width L_1 in the slip direction and thickness L_2 normal to the slip planes. Show that if an edge dislocation moves a distance l the average shear strain γ of the crystal is $\gamma = dl/L_1L_2$, where d is the magnitude of the Burgers vector.

16.3. Suppose that there are ρ dislocation lines crossing perpendicularly a plane of unit area. If the average velocity of the dislocations is v, show that the rate of shear is $d\gamma/dt = \rho vd$, where d is the magnitude of the Burgers vector.

16.4.* Discuss the Volmer-Becker theory of the growth of ideal crystals. References: R. Becker and W. Döring, Ann. Physik **24**, 719 (1935); M. Volmer, *Kinetik der Phasenbildung*, Steinkopff, Dresden and Leipzig, 1939.

16.5.* Discuss the theory of the precipitation hardening of solids. (See the paper by Mott and Nabarro in the report of the Bristol conference on the strength of solids, and references cited there.)

16.6. Discuss the detailed interpretation of the photographs of dislocations obtained by J. W. Mitchell, Phil. Mag. (Feb. 1953).

REFERENCES

C. S. Barrett, *Structure of metals: crystallographic methods, principles, data*, McGraw-Hill Book Company, New York, 2nd ed., 1952.

W. Boas, *An Introduction to the physics of metals and alloys*, John Wiley & Sons, New York, 1947.

Ewald, Pöschl, and Prandtl, *Physics of solids and fluids*, Blackie and Son, Ltd., Glasgow, 2nd ed., 1936.

N. F. Mott, "Mechanical properties of metals," Proc. Phys. Soc. (London) **B64**, 729 (1951).

Plastic deformation of crystalline solids, Carnegie-ONR conference, Office of Technical Services, U.S. Department of Commerce, PB 104 604.

W. T. Read, *Dislocations in crystals*, McGraw-Hill Book Company, New York, 1953.

A. H. Cottrell, *Dislocations and plastic flow in crystals*, Clarendon Press, Oxford, 1953.

Report of a conference on the strength of solids, University of Bristol, Physical Society, London, 1948.

F. Seitz, *Physics of metals*, McGraw-Hill Book Co., New York, 1943.

Shockley, Hollomon, Maurer, and Seitz, editors, *Imperfections in nearly perfect crystals*, John Wiley & Sons, New York, 1952.

Smoluchowski, Mayer, and Weyl, editors, *Phase transformations in solids*, John Wiley & Sons, New York, 1951.

C. Zener, *Elasticity and anelasticity of metals*, University of Chicago Press, Chicago, 1948.

Appendix

A. INTERFERENCE CONDITIONS AND THE RECIPROCAL LATTICE[1]

The conditions for an x-ray beam to be diffracted by a crystal may be expressed in an elegant form with the help of the reciprocal lattice transformation. The reciprocal lattice is very widely used in x-ray crystallography and in the quantum theory of metals. We let $\mathbf{a}$, $\mathbf{b}$, $\mathbf{c}$ be the primitive translations of the crystal lattice. We define the primitive translations $\mathbf{a}^*$, $\mathbf{b}^*$, $\mathbf{c}^*$ of the reciprocal lattice by the relations

(A.1) $\qquad \mathbf{a}^* \cdot \mathbf{a} = \mathbf{b}^* \cdot \mathbf{b} = \mathbf{c}^* \cdot \mathbf{c} = 1;$

(A.2) $\quad \mathbf{a}^* \cdot \mathbf{b} = \mathbf{a}^* \cdot \mathbf{c} = \mathbf{b}^* \cdot \mathbf{c} = \mathbf{b}^* \cdot \mathbf{a} = \mathbf{c}^* \cdot \mathbf{a} = \mathbf{c}^* \cdot \mathbf{b} = 0.$

Equations (A.1) define the magnitude of $\mathbf{a}^*$, $\mathbf{b}^*$, $\mathbf{c}^*$, while (A.2) define their directions, which are such that, for example, $\mathbf{a}^*$ is perpendicular to the plane of $\mathbf{b}$ and $\mathbf{c}$, and is in fact given by

$$\mathbf{a}^* = \frac{\mathbf{b} \times \mathbf{c}}{\mathbf{a} \cdot [\mathbf{b} \times \mathbf{c}]}.$$

Similar expressions obtain for the other vectors.

The properties of the reciprocal lattice that make it of value in diffraction problems are: (i) The vector $\mathbf{r}^*(hkl)$ to the point (h, k, l) of the reciprocal lattice is normal to the (hkl) plane of the crystal lattice. (ii) The length of the vector $\mathbf{r}^*(hkl)$ is equal to the reciprocal of the spacing of the planes (hkl) of the crystal lattice. As proof we note that $(\mathbf{a}/h) - (\mathbf{b}/k)$ is a vector in the (hkl) plane. Then

$$\mathbf{r}^*(hkl) \cdot \left(\frac{\mathbf{a}}{h} - \frac{\mathbf{b}}{k} \right) = (h\mathbf{a}^* + k\mathbf{b}^* + l\mathbf{c}^*) \cdot \left(\frac{\mathbf{a}}{h} - \frac{\mathbf{b}}{k} \right) = 0,$$

proving the first result. Furthermore, if $\mathbf{n}$ is the unit normal to the plane, $\mathbf{a} \cdot \mathbf{n}/h$ is the interplanar spacing, and, as $\mathbf{n} = \mathbf{r}^*/|r^*|$,

$$d(hkl) = \mathbf{n} \cdot \mathbf{a}/h = (\mathbf{r}^* \cdot \mathbf{a})/h|r^*| = 1/|r^*|,$$

using (A.1) and (A.2). This proves the second result.

[1] This appendix follows closely the development given by R. W. James, *Optical principles of the diffraction of x-rays*, G. Bell and Sons, Ltd., London, 1948. For a more elementary discussion see M. J. Buerger, *X-ray crystallography*, John Wiley & Sons, New York, 1942.

It is efficacious to write the Bragg equation in the form $2d(hkl) \sin \theta$ $= \lambda$. If h, k, l have a common factor n, the diffracted ray may be considered either as an nth order reflection from lattice planes with their true spacing, or else as a first order reflection from a set of planes parallel to the true lattice planes but with a spacing $d(hkl)$ equal to $1/n$ of the true spacing. The vector $r^*(hkl)$ in the reciprocal lattice is in the same direction but n times as long as the vector corresponding to the true crystal plane. That is, the nth point from the origin in a given row in the reciprocal lattice corresponds to the nth order reflection from the associated crystal planes. Every point in the reciprocal lattice corresponds to a possible reflection from the crystal lattice.

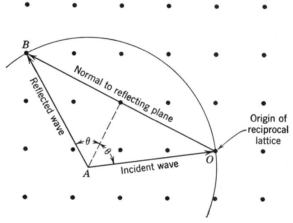

Fig. A.1.   Ewald's construction in the reciprocal lattice.

The Bragg equation has a simple geometrical significance in the reciprocal lattice. In Fig. A.1 we draw AO as a vector of length $1/\lambda$ in the direction of the incident radiation and terminating at the origin of the reciprocal lattice. Following Ewald, we draw a sphere of radius $1/\lambda$ about A as center; then the possible directions of the diffracted rays for this incident ray are determined by the intersections of the sphere with the points of the reciprocal lattice. That is, the direction AB is the direction of a diffraction maximum.

We prove this by noting that OB is normal to one of the lattice planes (hkl) and of length $1/d(hkl)$; it is also equal in length to $(2/\lambda) \sin \theta$, where θ is the glancing angle between the planes (hkl) and the incident and reflected rays. Therefore $2d(hkl) \sin \theta = \lambda$, which is just the Bragg condition.

As a problem the reader may show that a bcc lattice has as its reciprocal a fcc lattice.

B. EWALD METHOD FOR CALCULATING LATTICE SUMS

The Ewald[2] calculation is developed here by a method which is simpler than the original derivation. The present form is due to Ewald and to Shockley, but does not appear to have been published previously. The problem is to calculate the electrostatic potential experienced by one ion in the presence of all the other ions in the crystal. We shall consider a lattice made up of ions with positive or negative charges of the same magnitude and shall assume that the ions are spherical and do not overlap.

We compute the total potential

(B.1) $$\psi = \psi_1 + \psi_2$$

at a lattice point as the sum of two distinct but related potentials. The potential ψ_1 is that of a lattice with a Gaussian distribution of charge situated at each lattice point, with signs the same as those of the real lattice. According to the definition of the Madelung constant, the charge distribution on the reference point is not considered to contribute to the potential ψ_1 or ψ_2 (Fig. B.1a). We therefore calculate the potential ψ_1 as the difference

(B.2) $$\psi_1 = \psi_a - \psi_b$$

of two potentials, ψ_a being the potential of a continuous series of Gaussian distributions and ψ_b is the potential of the single Gaussian distribution on the reference point. The potential ψ_2 is that of a lattice of point charges with an additional Gaussian distribution of opposite sign superposed upon the point charges (Fig. B.1b).

The point of splitting the problem into the two parts ψ_1 and ψ_2 is that by a suitable choice of the parameter determining the width of each Gaussian peak we can get very good convergence of both parts at the same time. The Gaussian distributions drop out completely on taking the sum of the separate charge distributions giving rise to ψ_1 and ψ_2, so that the value of the total potential ψ is independent of the width parameter, but the rapidity of convergence depends on the value chosen for the parameter.

We calculate first the potential ψ_a of a continuous Gaussian distribution. We expand ψ_a and the charge density ρ in Fourier series:

(B.3) $$\psi_a = \sum_k c_k e^{i\mathbf{k}\cdot\mathbf{r}} ;$$

(B.4) $$\rho = \sum_k \rho_k e^{i\mathbf{k}\cdot\mathbf{r}}.$$

[2] P. P. Ewald, Ann. Physik **64**, 253 (1921).

The Poisson equation is

$$\nabla^2 \psi_a = -4\pi\rho,$$

or

$$\Sigma k^2 c_k e^{i\mathbf{k}\cdot\mathbf{r}} = 4\pi \Sigma \rho_k e^{i\mathbf{k}\cdot\mathbf{r}}$$

so that

(B.5) $$c_k = 4\pi\rho_k/k^2.$$

We suppose in finding ρ_k that each lattice point is the center of a charge

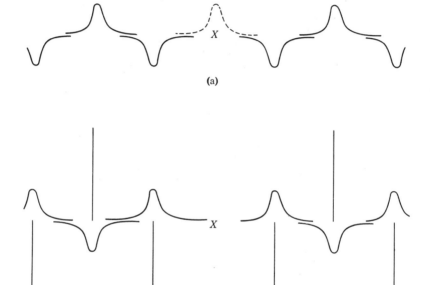

(a)

(b)

Fig. B.1.   (a) Charge distribution used for computing potential ψ_1; the potential ψ_a is computed (it includes the dashed curve at the reference point), while ψ_b is the potential of the dashed curve alone.   (b) Charge distribution for potential ψ_2. The reference point is denoted by an X.

distribution of density

(B.6) $$\rho(x,y,z) = \pm Ce^{-\eta r^2}.$$

where η is the width parameter and is at our disposal.   Normalizing the total charge associated with each lattice point to ± 1, we have

(B.7) $$\rho = \pm (\eta/\pi)^{3/2} e^{-\eta r^2}.$$

We would normally evaluate ρ_k by multiplying both sides of Eq. (B.4) by $e^{-i\mathbf{k}\cdot\mathbf{r}}$ and integrating over the volume Δ of one cell, in which case the charge distribution to be considered is that originating on the lattice point within the cell and also that of the tails of the distributions originating on all the other lattice points. It is easy to show, however, that the integral of the total charge density times $e^{-i\mathbf{k}\cdot\mathbf{r}}$ over a single cell is equal to the integral of the charge density associated with a single lattice point times $e^{-i\mathbf{k}\cdot\mathbf{r}}$ over all space.

We have

$$(\eta/\pi)^{3/2} \int_{\substack{\text{all} \\ \text{space}}} e^{-\eta r^2} e^{-i\mathbf{k}\cdot\mathbf{r}} \, d\mathbf{r} = \rho_k \int_{\substack{\text{one} \\ \text{cell}}} e^{i\mathbf{k}\cdot\mathbf{r}} e^{-i\mathbf{k}\cdot\mathbf{r}} \, d\mathbf{r} = \rho_k \Delta,$$

so that, from Eqs. (B.3) and (B.5),

$$\psi_a = \frac{4\pi}{\Delta} \sum_k k^{-2} e^{i\mathbf{k}\cdot\mathbf{r}} \int e^{-(i\mathbf{k}\cdot\boldsymbol{\xi} + \eta\xi^2)} (\eta/\pi)^{3/2} \, d\boldsymbol{\xi},$$

which integrates to

(B.8) $$\psi_a = \frac{4\pi}{\Delta} \sum_k k^{-2} e^{i\mathbf{k}\cdot\mathbf{r} - (k^2/4\eta)}.$$

At the origin $r = 0$ and

(B.9) $$\psi_a = \frac{4\pi}{\Delta} \sum_k k^{-2} e^{-k^2/4\eta}.$$

The potential ψ_b at the origin due to the central Gaussian distribution is

(B.10) $$\psi_b = \int_0^\infty 4\pi r\rho \, dr = 2(\eta/\pi)^{1/2},$$

so that

(B.11) $$\psi_1 = \frac{4\pi}{\Delta} \sum k^{-2} e^{-k^2/4\eta} - 2(\eta/\pi)^{1/2}.$$

The potential ψ_2 is to be evaluated at the reference point, and it differs from zero as a result of the fact that other lattice points have the tails of their Gaussian distributions overlapping the reference point. The potential is due to three contributions from each lattice point:

$$\pm \left[\frac{1}{r_l} - \frac{1}{r_l} \int_0^{r_l} \rho(r) \, d\tau - \int_{r_l}^\infty \frac{\rho(r)}{r_l} \, d\tau \right],$$

where the terms are from the point charge, the part of the Gaussian distribution lying inside a sphere of radius r_l about the lth lattice point and from that part lying outside the sphere, respectively. On substituting for $\rho(r)$ and carrying out elementary manipulations we have

(B.12)
$$\psi_2 = \sum_l \frac{(\pm)}{r_l} G(\sqrt{\eta} r_l)$$

where
$$G(x) = \frac{2}{\sqrt{\pi}} \int_x^\infty e^{-s^2}\, ds.$$

Finally,

(B.13)
$$\psi = \frac{4\pi}{\Delta} \sum_k \frac{e^{-k^2/4\eta}}{k^2} - 2(\eta/\pi)^{1/2} + \sum_l \frac{(\pm)}{r_l} G(\sqrt{\eta} r_l).$$

We may note that the method is of quite general application to all periodic charge and multipole arrays.

EXAMPLE. *Calculation of the Madelung constant by the Ewald method for the sodium chloride lattice.* We take R_0 as the nearest neighbor distance, so that $\Delta = R_0{}^3$. By consideration of the symmetry of the charge distribution we see that the lowest values of $\mathbf{k}$ are

$$\mathbf{k} = (2\pi/2R_0)(\pm 1, \ \pm 1, \ \pm 1),$$

giving eight combinations. As a trial we may take $\eta = (2/R_0)^2$, so that

$$\psi \cong (4\pi/R_0{}^3)8(R_0{}^2/3\pi^2)e^{-3\pi^2/16} - (2/\sqrt{\pi})(2/R_0)$$
$$- (6/R_0)(2/\sqrt{\pi}) \int_2^\infty e^{-x^2}\, dx,$$

where we include only the lowest k's and the tails from nearest neighbors. The values of the successive terms of $R_0\psi$ are 0.53, -2.26, and -0.03, so that $\alpha \cong 1.76$. The correct value is 1.747558; it is seen that the convergence of the Ewald method is excellent for our choice of η. The reader may verify that for a choice such as $\eta = (4/R_0)^2$ we should have to consider further terms in k to get 1% accuracy, while for $\eta = (1/R_0)^2$ we should have to consider other values of r_l.

EWALD-KORNFELD METHOD FOR LATTICE SUMS FOR DIPOLE ARRAYS

Kornfeld[3] has extended the Ewald method to dipolar and quadrupolar arrays. We discuss here the field of a dipole array at a point which is not a lattice point. According to (B.8) and (B.12) the potential at a point $\mathbf{r}$ in a lattice of positive unit point charges is

(B.14) $\psi = (4\pi/\Delta) \sum\limits_k k^{-2} \exp\left[i\mathbf{k} \cdot \mathbf{r} - (k^2/4\eta)\right] + \sum\limits_l G(\sqrt{\eta} r_l)/r_l,$

[3] H. Kornfeld, Zeits. Physik **22**, 27 (1924).

where r_l is the distance from $\mathbf{r}$ to the lattice point l. The first term on the right gives the potential of the charge distribution $\rho = (\eta/\pi)^{3/2} e^{-\eta r^2}$ about each lattice point. By a well-known relation in electrostatics we obtain the potential of an array of unit dipoles pointing in the z direction by taking $-d/dz$ of the above potential. The term under discussion contributes

(B.15) $\qquad -(4\pi i/\Delta) \sum_{\mathbf{k}} (k_z/k^2) \exp [i\mathbf{k} \cdot \mathbf{r} - k^2/4\eta],$

and the z component of the electric field from this term is $E_z = \partial^2 \psi / \partial z^2$, or

(B.16) $\qquad -(4\pi/\Delta) \sum_{\mathbf{k}} (k_z^2/k^2) \exp [i\mathbf{k} \cdot \mathbf{r} - k^2/4\eta].$

The second term on the right on one differentiation gives

(B.17) $\qquad - \sum_{l} z_l [(G(\sqrt{\eta} r_l)/r_l^3) + (2/r_l^2)(\eta/\pi)^{1/2} \exp (-\eta r_l^2)],$

and the z component of this part of the field is

(B.18) $\qquad - \sum_{l} \{z_l^2[(3G(\sqrt{\eta} r_l)/r_l^5) + (6/r_l^4)(\eta/\pi)^{1/2} \exp (-\eta r_l^2)$
$\qquad\qquad + (4/r_l^2)(\eta^3/\pi)^{1/2} \exp (-\eta r_l^2)] - [(G(\sqrt{\eta} r_l)/r_l^3)$
$\qquad\qquad\qquad\qquad + (2/r_l^2)(\eta/\pi)^{1/2} \exp (-\eta r_l^2)]\}.$

The total E_z is given by the sum of (B.16) and (B.18). The effects of any number of lattices may be added.

C. QUANTUM-MECHANICAL EXPRESSION FOR THE POLARIZABILITY

We compute the energy of interaction of an atomic system with an applied static electric field and set this equal to the macroscopic expression for the energy, which is

(C.1) $\qquad\qquad \Delta W = -\int E \, dP = -\tfrac{1}{2}\alpha E^2.$

The result of second order perturbation theory is

(C.2) $\qquad\qquad \Delta W = - \sum_{j} \frac{e^2 |x_{ij}|^2 E^2}{\hbar \omega_{ij}}$

when the perturbing energy is eEx and $\hbar \omega_{ij} = W_j - W_i$. Therefore

(C.3) $\qquad\qquad \alpha = \sum_{j} 2e^2 |x_{ij}|^2 / \hbar \omega_{ij},$

which is the expression to which (6.16) reduces when $\omega = 0$. The association of the polarizability with the second order perturbation energy of a single atomic level i depends for its validity on the condition $\hbar\omega_{ij} \gg kT$; that is, only the ground state i is significantly populated at the temperature considered.

D. ONSAGER THEORY OF THE DIELECTRIC CONSTANT OF POLAR SUBSTANCES

The Lorentz treatment of the local field assumes explicitly that the dipole moments of all the atoms are parallel, and this is clearly a valid assumption for the induced moments in sufficiently symmetrical structures. The assumption is not valid, however, for permanent dipole moments which are oriented more or less at random. Onsager has carried out an approximate treatment of the latter situation by considering a very small spherical cavity, just large enough to contain one molecule. If we consider this cavity real, we may ask what is the value of the field inside it, when the boundary condition is that the field at large distances from the cavity is uniform and equal to E_0. We consider the potential ϕ such that $\mathbf{E} = -\nabla\phi$. Outside the cavity the potential may be written as

$$(D.1) \qquad \phi = -\left(\frac{A}{r^2} + E_0 r\right)\cos\theta,$$

while inside the cavity

$$(D.2) \qquad \phi = -E_{\text{loc}} r \cos\theta.$$

The boundary conditions at the surface of the sphere $r = a$ are that the normal component of D and the tangential component of E should be continuous across the interface, so that, taking the dielectric constant of the medium as ϵ and of the cavity as unity,

$$\epsilon(-2A + E_0 a^3) = E_{\text{loc}} a^3;$$

$$A + E_0 a^3 = E_{\text{loc}} a^3;$$

whence

$$(D.3) \qquad E_{\text{loc}} = \frac{3\epsilon}{2\epsilon + 1} E_0.$$

The polarization is given by (6.27):

$$P = N p^2 E_{\text{loc}}/3kT = x E_{\text{loc}}/4\pi,$$

where we have written $x = 4\pi N p^2/3kT$. Then

$$(D.4) \qquad \epsilon E_0 = E_0 + \frac{3\epsilon x}{2\epsilon + 1} E_0,$$

which may be solved for ϵ:

(D.5) $\qquad \epsilon = \frac{1}{4}[1 + 3x + 3(1 + \frac{2}{3}x + x^2)^{\frac{1}{2}}],$

which is Onsager's result. This probably overestimates the correction which must be applied to the Lorentz field in dipolar media.

Pirenne[4] has suggested that the Onsager theory will lead to a Curie point when non-linear effects are considered, although the Curie point is at about 0.2 of that predicted by the Lorentz expression.

E. QUANTUM THEORY OF DIAMAGNETISM OF MONONUCLEAR SYSTEMS

The magnetic vector potential $\mathbf{A}$ is defined by the relation $\mathbf{H} = $ curl $\mathbf{A}$. In a magnetic field the generalized momentum $\mathbf{p}$ of a particle of charge e is

(E.1) $\qquad \mathbf{p} = \mathbf{p}_{kin} + \mathbf{p}_{pot} = m\dot{\mathbf{r}} + e\mathbf{A}/c,$

so the kinetic energy is

(E.2) $\qquad T = \frac{1}{2} m\dot{r}^2 = \frac{1}{2m} \left(\mathbf{p} - \frac{e}{c} \mathbf{A} \right)^2$

$$= \frac{1}{2m} p^2 - \frac{e}{mc} \mathbf{p} \cdot \mathbf{A} + \frac{e^2}{2mc^2} A^2.$$

In quantum mechanics in the Schrödinger coordinate representation the momentum $\mathbf{p}$ is the operator $-i\hbar\nabla$; therefore the effect of a magnetic field is to add to the Hamiltonian the terms

(E.3) $\qquad \mathcal{3C}' = \frac{ie\hbar}{2mc} (\nabla \cdot \mathbf{A} + \mathbf{A} \cdot \nabla) + \frac{e^2}{2mc^2} A^2,$

which may usually be treated as a small perturbation. If the magnetic field is uniform and in the z direction, we may write

$$A_x = -\tfrac{1}{2}yH, \qquad A_y = \tfrac{1}{2}xH, \qquad A_z = 0,$$

and (E.3) becomes

(E.4) $\qquad \mathcal{3C}' = \frac{ie\hbar H}{2mc} \left(x \frac{\partial}{\partial y} - y \frac{\partial}{\partial x} \right) + \frac{e^2 H^2}{8mc^2} (x^2 + y^2).$

The first term on the right is proportional to the orbital angular momentum component L_z if $\mathbf{r}$ is measured from the nucleus, and in mononuclear systems gives rise only to paramagnetism. The

[4] J. Pirenne, Helv. Phys. Acta **22**, 479 (1949).

second term gives for a spherically symmetric system a diamagnetic contribution

(E.5) $$W' = \frac{e^2 H^2}{12mc^2} \overline{r^2}$$

to the perturbation energy, and the associated magnetic moment is

(E.6) $$\mu = -\partial W'/\partial H = -(e^2 \overline{r^2}/6mc^2)H,$$

in agreement with the classical result (8.5). For further details of the derivation the book by Van Vleck may be consulted.

F. VAN VLECK TEMPERATURE-INDEPENDENT PARAMAGNETISM

We consider a molecular system which has no magnetic moment in the ground state, by which we mean that the diagonal matrix element of the magnetic moment operator μ_z is zero.

Suppose that there is a non-diagonal matrix element $(n|\mu_z|0)$ of the magnetic moment operator, connecting the ground state 0 with the excited state n of energy $\Delta = W_n - W_0$ above the ground state. Then by standard perturbation theory we see that the wave function of the ground state in a small field ($\mu_z H \ll \Delta$) becomes

(F.1) $$\psi_0' = \psi_0 + \frac{H(n|\mu_z|0)}{\Delta} \psi_n;$$

and the wave function of the excited state becomes

(F.2) $$\psi_n' = \psi_n - \frac{H(0|\mu_z|n)}{\Delta} \psi_0.$$

The ground state now has a moment

(F.3) $$(0'|\mu_z|0') = 2H|(n|\mu_z|0)|^2/\Delta,$$

and the upper state has a moment

(F.4) $$-2H|(n|\mu_z|0)|^2/\Delta.$$

There are now two interesting cases to consider:

Case (a). $\Delta \ll kT$ *(low frequency matrix elements).* The surplus population [see derivation of (9.8)] in the ground state is approximately equal to $N\Delta/2kT$, so that the resultant magnetization is

$$M = (2H|(n|\mu_z|0)|^2/\Delta)(N\Delta/2kT),$$

which gives for the susceptibility

$$(F.5) \qquad \chi = \frac{N \Sigma |(n|\mu_z|0)|^2}{kT}.$$

This contribution is of the usual Curie form, although the mechanism of magnetization here is through polarization of the states of the system, whereas with free spins the mechanism of magnetization is the redistribution of ions among the spin states. We note that the splitting Δ does not enter in (F.5), on the assumption $\Delta \ll kT$.

Case (b). $\Delta \gg kT$ *(high frequency matrix elements).* Now the population is nearly all in the ground state, so that

$$M = 2NH_z |(n|\mu_z|0)|^2/\Delta,$$

and the susceptibility is, summed over all suitable states n,

$$(F.6) \qquad \chi = 2N \sum_n \frac{|(n|\mu_z|0)|^2}{W_n - W_0},$$

independent of temperature. This type of contribution is known as Van Vleck paramagnetism.

G. MAGNETIC AND ELECTROSTATIC ENERGY

We shall consider explicity only magnetic energy, as the corresponding expressions for electric energy are obtained by appropriate transcription. Our treatment is simple and rather naive, but it leads to the correct results.

PERMANENT MOMENT μ IN EXTERNAL FIELD H

If we consider the effects of the moment μ ($=2ma$) as reproduced by N and S poles $\pm m$ separated by a distance $2a$, it is apparent by symmetry that it is reasonable to take the zero point, from which we shall measure changes in energy, as the state with $\mu \perp \mathbf{H}$. If we turn the magnet toward the field by an angle θ, we change the potential of the N pole by $-m(a \sin \theta)H$, and the potential of the S pole by the same amount, so the interaction energy of the magnet with the field may be written

$$(G.1) \qquad W = -2maH \sin \theta = -\mu \cdot \mathbf{H}.$$

If the external field is produced by a coil, the work done in turning the magnet goes into the electrical circuit keeping the value of H constant; if the external field is produced by a permanent magnet, the work done serves to increase the potential energy of the permanent magnet.

INTERACTION ENERGY OF AN ASSEMBLY OF PERMANENT MAGNETS

The energy is

$$(G.2) \quad W = \sum_{i<j} r_{ij}^{-5}[r_{ij}^2 \mathbf{\mu}_i \cdot \mathbf{\mu}_j - 3(\mathbf{\mu}_i \cdot \mathbf{r}_{ij})(\mathbf{\mu}_j \cdot \mathbf{r}_{ij})] = -\tfrac{1}{2} \sum_i \mathbf{\mu}_i \cdot \mathbf{H}_i,$$

where $\mathbf{H}_i$ is the field at magnet i caused by all the other magnets in the assembly. If the assembly is in the form of an ellipsoid magnetized along one of the principal axes, the self-field is given by $H = -NM$, where N is the demagnetization factor as discussed in Chapter 6. Then

$$(G.3) \qquad\qquad W = \tfrac{1}{2}NM^2 V,$$

where M is the magnetization and V the volume.

ENERGY OF INDUCED MAGNETIZATION

From the Maxwell equations,

$$c \text{ curl } \mathbf{H} = 4\pi \mathbf{j};$$
$$c \text{ curl } \mathbf{E} = -d\mathbf{B}/dt;$$

we have on multiplication by appropriate factors

$$4\pi \mathbf{j} \cdot \mathbf{E} \, dV = c \text{ (curl } \mathbf{H}) \cdot \mathbf{E} \, dV;$$
$$(d\mathbf{B}/dt) \cdot \mathbf{H} \, dV = -c \text{ (curl } \mathbf{E}) \cdot \mathbf{H} \, dV;$$

here dV is an element of volume. It follows that

$$\int dV \mathbf{H} \cdot (d\mathbf{B}/dt) + 4\pi \int dV \mathbf{E} \cdot \mathbf{j} = c \int dV (\mathbf{E} \cdot \text{curl } \mathbf{H} - \mathbf{H} \cdot \text{curl } \mathbf{E}).$$

The integral on the right is equal to div $\mathbf{H} \times \mathbf{E}$, by a vector identity. If, as is usually true in our problems, $\mathbf{H} \times \mathbf{E}$ approaches zero for large r faster than r^{-2}, then by the Gauss theorem the integral on the right vanishes. Hence we have

$$-\int dV \mathbf{E} \cdot \mathbf{j} \delta t = \frac{1}{4\pi} \int dV \mathbf{H} \cdot \delta \mathbf{H} + \int dV \mathbf{H} \cdot \delta \mathbf{M}.$$

The term on the left is the work done in the coils of the system during the interval δt, supposing that the coils are resistanceless. The work done in the coils appears in the terms on the right. The first term on the right may be considered the work done in building up the magnetic field, and the second term the work done in building up the magnetization. Thus the energy of magnetization W_m is

$$(G.4) \qquad\qquad W_m = \int dV \int \mathbf{H} \cdot d\mathbf{M};$$

the corresponding result for the energy of dielectric polarization comes out by a similar argument to be

(G.5) $$W_e = \int \cdot dV \int \mathbf{E} \cdot d\mathbf{P}.$$

If $M = \chi H$ and χ is independent of H,

(G.6) $$W_m = \tfrac{1}{2}\chi H^2 V.$$

A good general discussion of magnetic and electrostatic energy is given by E. A. Guggenheim, Proc. Roy. Soc. (London) **A155,** 49 (1936); see also R. Becker and W. Döring, *Ferromagnetismus,* J. Springer, Berlin, 1939, pp. 53–66.

H. QUENCHING OF THE ORBITAL ANGULAR MOMENTUM BY CRYSTALLINE ELECTRIC FIELDS

The easiest way to understand quenching of the orbital moment is to consider the behavior of a simple model. We consider a single electron with orbital quantum number $L = 1$ moving about a nucleus, the whole being placed in an inhomogeneous crystalline electric field. We omit electron spin from the problem, as we are concerned here only with what happens to the orbital motion.

We suppose that the ion is embedded in a crystal of orthorhombic symmetry; then the charges on neighboring ions located along the x, y, z axes will produce an electrostatic potential V about the nucleus of the form

(H.1) $$eV = Ax^2 + By^2 - (A + B)z^2,$$

where A and B are constants. This expression is the lowest degree polynomial in x, y, z which is a solution of the Laplace equation $\nabla^2 V = 0$ and which is compatible with the symmetry of the crystal; that is, invariance under the operations $x \rightarrow -x$; $y \rightarrow -y$; $z \rightarrow -z$. Let us now consider what will be the effect of the crystal field on the energy levels of the model. The ground state has $L = 1$, and in free space this level is three-fold degenerate; that is, it consists of the $2L + 1$ magnetic sublevels which are associated with the magnetic quantum numbers $M_L = 1, 0, -1$. In a magnetic field these levels are split by energies proportional to the field H, and it is this field-proportional splitting which is responsible for the normal paramagnetic susceptibility of the ion. In the crystal field the picture may, however, be quite different. Let us take as the three wave functions associated with the unperturbed ground state of the ion the following:

$$U_x = xf(r);$$

(H.2) $$U_y = yf(r);$$

$$U_z = zf(r).$$

These wave functions are orthogonal, and we suppose that they are normalized. We may confirm that each of the U's has the property

(H.3) $$\mathcal{L}^2 U_i = L(L + 1) U_i = 2 U_i,$$

where $\mathcal{L}^2$ is the operator for the square of the orbital angular momentum, in units of $\hbar$. The result (H.3) confirms that the selected wave functions are in fact p functions, having $L = 1$.

We observe now that the U's are diagonal with respect to the perturbation (H.1), as by symmetry the non-diagonal elements vanish:

(H.4) $$(U_x|eV|U_y) = (U_x|eV|U_z) = (U_y|eV|U_z) = 0.$$

Consider for example

(H.5) $(U_x|eV|U_y) = \int xy|f(r)|^2\{Ax^2 + By^2 - (A + B)z^2\}\ dx\ dy\ dz;$

the integrand is an odd function of x (and also of y) and therefore the integral must be zero. The energy levels are then given by the diagonal matrix elements:

(H.6) $(U_x|eV|U_x) = \int|f(r)|^2\{Ax^4 + By^2x^2 - (A + B)z^2x^2\}\ dx\ dy\ dz$

$$= A(I_1 - I_2),$$

where

(H.7)
$$I_1 = \int|f(r)|^2x^4\ dx\ dy\ dz;$$
$$I_2 = \int|f(r)|^2x^2y^2\ dx\ dy\ dz.$$

In addition,

(H.8)
$$(U_y|eV|U_y) = B(I_1 - I_2);$$
$$(U_z|eV|U_z) = -(A + B)(I_1 - I_2).$$

We note that the three eigenstates in the crystal field are p functions with their angular lobes directed along each of the x, y, z axes, respectively.

The orbital moment of each of the levels is zero, since

$$(U_x|L_z|U_x) = (U_y|L_z|U_y) = (U_z|L_z|U_z) = 0.$$

This is what is known as *quenching*. The level still has a definite total angular momentum, since $\mathcal{L}^2$ is diagonal and gives $L = 1$, but the spatial components of the angular momentum are not constants of the motion and their time average is zero in the first approximation. Therefore the orbital magnetic moment also vanishes in the same approximation. The role of the crystal field in the quenching process is to split the originally degenerate levels into "non-magnetic" levels separated by energies $\gg \mu H$, so that the magnetic field is a small perturbation in comparison with the crystal field.

Bethe[5] has treated thoroughly the splitting of levels in crystalline fields of various symmetries.

I. SPECTROSCOPIC SPLITTING FACTOR g IN PARAMAGNETIC SALTS

We refer to Appendix H and suppose for convenience that the crystal field constants, A, B are such that $U_x = xf(r)$ is the orbital wave function of the ground state of the atom in the crystal. For a spin $S = \frac{1}{2}$ there are two possible spin states $S_z = \pm\frac{1}{2}$ represented by the spin functions α, β, which in the absence of a magnetic field are degenerate in the zeroth approximation. The problem is to take into account the spin-orbit interaction energy $\lambda \mathbf{L} \cdot \mathbf{S}$.

If the ground state function is $\psi_0 = U_x\alpha = xf(r)\alpha$ in the zeroth approximation, then in the first approximation, considering the $\lambda \mathbf{L} \cdot \mathbf{S}$ interaction by standard perturbation theory, we have

(I.1) $$\psi = [U_x - i(\lambda/2\Delta_1)U_y]\alpha + i(\lambda/2\Delta_2)U_z\beta,$$

where Δ_1 is the energy difference between the U_x and U_y states, and Δ_2 is the difference between the U_x and U_z states. The term in $U_z\beta$ actually has only a second order effect on the result and may be discarded. The expectation value of the orbital angular momentum to the first order is given directly by

(I.2) $$(\psi|L_z|\psi) = -\lambda/\Delta_1,$$

and the magnetic moment of the state as measured in the z direction is

(I.3) $$\mu_B(\psi|L_z + 2S_z|\psi) = [-(\lambda/\Delta_1) + 1]\mu_B.$$

As the separation between the levels $S_z = \pm\frac{1}{2}$ in a field H is

(I.4) $$\Delta W = g\mu_B H = 2[1 - (\lambda/\Delta_1)]\mu_B H,$$

the g value or spectroscopic splitting factor in the z direction is

(I.5) $$g = 2[1 - (\lambda_1/\Delta_1)].$$

If, following (10.20), we define

(I.6) $$2\varepsilon = \overline{L_z}/\overline{S_z},$$

we have

(I.7) $$\varepsilon \cong -\lambda/\Delta_1,$$

and

(I.8) $$g = 2(1 + \varepsilon).$$

[5] H. A. Bethe, Ann. Physik **3**, 133 (1929).

J. SEMICLASSICAL DISCUSSION OF
FERROMAGNETIC SPIN WAVES

The Hamiltonian of the system is

(J.1) $$H' = -2J\Sigma S_i \cdot S_j,$$

where S_i is the spin operator in units of $\hbar$ for the ith atom. Each atom has $2S_0$ resultant electron spins. The quantum equation of motion for S_m is

$$i\hbar\dot{S}_m = [S_m, H'] = 2J[(\Sigma S_i \cdot S_j)S_m - S_m(\Sigma S_i \cdot S_j)]$$

$$= 2J \sum_j [(S_m \cdot S_j)S_m - S_m(S_m \cdot S_j)] = -2J \sum_j S_j \times [S_m \times S_m],$$

which becomes, upon using the commutation relation $S \times S = iS$,

(J.2) $$\hbar\dot{S}_m = 2JS_m \times \Sigma S_j.$$

For a simple cubic lattice with lattice constant a we have, by series expansion, treating S_m as the center,

(J.3) $$\sum_j S_j = 6S_m + a^2\nabla^2 S_m + \cdots,$$

where the S's are now considered *classical* vectors, and not as quantum operators. For small distortions we neglect higher order terms in the series expansion; thus we have the equation of motion

(J.4) $$\hbar S = 2Ja^2[S \times \nabla^2 S]$$

for the spin considered a classical quantity.

Let

(J.5) $$S = S_0 + \varepsilon$$

where S_0 is the unperturbed spin vector, and ε represents a spin wave of small amplitude. We look for solutions of the form

(J.6) $$\varepsilon_x = \varepsilon_0 \sin \omega t \sin k_x x \sin k_y y \sin k_z z;$$

(J.7) $$\varepsilon_y = \varepsilon_0 \cos \omega t \sin k_x x \sin k_y y \sin k_z z.$$

Then, from (J.4),

(J.8) $$\hbar\omega = 2S_0 Ja^2 k^2.$$

This is the fundamental relation between the frequency and the wave number of a spin wave. A drawing of a spin wave is shown in Fig. J.1.

The energy of a spin wave is

(J.9) $$W = -Ja^2 \Sigma S_m \cdot \nabla^2 S_m,$$

using (J.1) and (J.3), taking care not to count interactions twice. Using our standing spin waves in a rectangular enclosure we have, after replacing $a^3 \Sigma$ by $\int$,

(J.10) $\qquad W = Jk^2a^2\varepsilon_0^2 \int \sin^2 k_x x \, \sin^2 k_y y \, \sin^2 k_z z \, dV/a^3,$

or, finally,

(J.11) $\qquad\qquad\qquad W = Jk^2\varepsilon_0^2 V/8a,$

where V is the volume of the specimen. The energy is also equal to $n\hbar\omega$, where n is the excitational quantum number. Therefore

(J.12) $\qquad \varepsilon_0^2 = (8an/JV)(\hbar\omega/k^2) = 16S_0 a^3 n/V.$

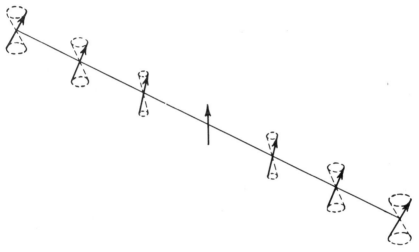

Fig. J.1. Spin wave on a line of atoms.

The next thing to do is to relate the spin wave amplitude to the change in intrinsic magnetization M of the specimen. If the specimen is saturated along the z axis in the absence of spin waves, the component of magnetization along this axis will be reduced by the excitation of spin waves. By geometry

(J.13) $\qquad\qquad M^2 = M_0^2(1 - \overline{(\varepsilon/S_0)^2}),$

which gives

(J.14) $\qquad\qquad \Delta M/M_0 = \overline{\varepsilon^2}/2S_0^2 = \varepsilon_0^2/16S_0^2,$

after the spatial average is carried out. Using (J.12),

(J.15) $\qquad\qquad V \Delta M = a^3 n M_0/S_0 = 2n\mu_B.$

This result shows that the change in magnetic moment of the specimen, as a consequence of the excitation of a spin wave with excitation quantum number n, corresponds to the reversal of n electrons. This is in agreement with the more rigorous quantum theory treatment.

BLOCH $T^{3/2}$ LAW

For thermal equilibrium the average value of the quantum number n for a wave of frequency ω is given by

(J.16) $\bar{n} = (\Sigma n e^{-n\beta})/\Sigma e^{-n\beta} = 1/(e^{\beta} - 1),$

where $\beta = \hbar\omega/kT$. We now want the sum of $\bar{n}$ over all allowed states. The number of states with wave number less than k is, per unit volume, $(1/2\pi)^3(4\pi/3)k^3$, whence the number of states with energy in dE at E is $(1/2\pi^2)k^2(dk/dE)\,dE$, which is equal to $(1/4\pi^2)E^{1/2}/(2S_0Ja^2)^{3/2}\,dE$. Thus the sum of $\bar{n}$ over all states is, per unit volume,

(J.17) $\Sigma\,\bar{n} \cong (N/4\pi^2)(2S_0J)^{-3/2} \int_0^{\infty} \dfrac{E^{1/2}\,dE}{e^{E/kT} - 1}$

$$= (N/4\pi^2)(kT/2S_0J)^{3/2} \int_0^{\infty} \dfrac{(x)^{1/2}\,dx}{e^x - 1}.$$

Here $N = 1/a^3$ is the number of atoms per unit volume. Now by series expansion

(J.18) $\dfrac{1}{4\pi^2} \int_0^{\infty} \dfrac{(x)^{1/2}\,dx}{e^x - 1} = 0.0587,$

so that

(J.19) $\Sigma\bar{n} = 0.0587 N (kT/2S_0J)^{3/2}.$

Therefore

(J.20) $\dfrac{\Delta M}{M_0} = (0.0587/S_0)(kT/2S_0J)^{3/2}.$

This expresses the well-known Bloch $T^{3/2}$ law in the form obtained by Moller for atoms with spin quantum number S_0. For a body-centered cubic lattice,

(J.21) $\dfrac{\Delta M}{M_0} = (0.0587/2S)(kT/2S_0J)^{3/2}.$

If we had included the zero-point motion of the spin system by increasing $\bar{n}$ in (J.16) by adding $\frac{1}{2}$, we should have found that, at $0°K$, $\Delta M/M_0 = \{[S(S + 1)]^{1/2} - S\}/S$. This expresses the fact that the maximum spin component in quantum theory is S, whereas the magnitude of the spin is $[S(S + 1)]^{1/2}$. The transverse spin components appear in spin wave theory as a zero-point motion of the spin wave system.

K. THE BLOCH THEOREM

We now prove that the lowest state of a quantum-mechanical system in the absence of a magnetic field can carry no current, even when interelectronic interactions are taken into account.

The Hamiltonian is, in the absence of a magnetic field,

$$(\text{K.1}) \qquad \mathcal{H} = \sum_n \left[V(X_n) - \frac{\hbar^2}{2m} \nabla_n^2 \right] + \frac{1}{2} \sum_{m \neq n} V(X_{nm}),$$

where $V(X_n)$ is the potential of the nth electron in the field of the ion lattice and $V(X_{nm})$ is the Coulomb interaction energy of electrons n and m. The total current $\mathbf{j}$ is related to the total electronic momentum by $\mathbf{j} = e\mathbf{P}/m$.

Suppose that the lowest state carries a momentum $\mathbf{P}_0$, and that $\psi(X_1, X_2, X_3, \cdots)$ is the exact wave function for this state. Consider the wave function

$$(\text{K.2}) \qquad \phi = e^{i(\delta P/\hbar) \cdot \Sigma X_r} \psi,$$

where $\delta\mathbf{P}$ is very small; this corresponds to a state in which each electron has been given an additional momentum $\delta\mathbf{P}$. Then the total momentum in the state ϕ is

$$(\text{K.3}) \qquad \mathbf{P} = \mathbf{P}_0 + N\delta\mathbf{P},$$

N being the total number of electrons.

The potential energy for ϕ is the same as for ψ, since $\phi^*\phi = \psi^*\psi$. The kinetic energy is, however, changed:

$$(\text{K.4}) \qquad T = T_0 + \frac{N(\mathbf{P}_0 \cdot \delta\mathbf{P})}{m} + \frac{N(\delta P)^2}{2m}$$
$$= T_0 + \frac{m}{e^2} \mathbf{j}_0 \cdot \delta\mathbf{j} + \frac{m}{2Ne^2} (\delta j)^2.$$

We can choose $\delta\mathbf{P}$ opposite in sign to $\mathbf{P}_0$, so that $\mathbf{P}_0 \cdot \delta\mathbf{P}$ is negative. If $\delta\mathbf{P}$ is small enough, the term involving $(\delta P)^2$ can be neglected. Thus the total energy of the state ϕ is less than that of the state ψ; but ψ is the exact ground state wave function and any other function must have a higher energy. Therefore $\mathbf{P}_0$ (and $\mathbf{j}_0$) must be zero for the ground state. This means that at absolute zero the system cannot have a spontaneous current.

Bohm has shown that for *each* solution of Schrödinger's equation with a non-vanishing current there exists another solution with a lower current and a lower energy. Thus, if we have a group of states carrying some current j_i, they cannot have a minimum free energy, because there is always another group of states with the same statistical weight, but with a lower energy and hence with a lower free energy. It is important to note, however, that in the presence of a magnetic field the state of lowest free energy *can* carry current. This observation is central to recent theoretical work in superconductivity.

L. PERTURBATION OF NEARLY FREE ELECTRONS BY A PERIODIC POTENTIAL

Let the perturbation due to the crystal lattice be written as a Fourier series:

$$(L.1) \qquad H' = \sum_{-\infty}^{\infty} V_n e^{-2\pi i n x/a}; \qquad (V_0 = 0).$$

The matrix elements of H' in a plane wave representation are

$$(L.2) \qquad (k'|H'|k) = \sum_n (V_n/L) \int_0^L e^{-ik'x} e^{-2\pi i n x/a} e^{ikx} \, dx;$$

the integral is zero unless

$$(L.3) \qquad k' = k - 2\pi n/a,$$

in which case the matrix element is equal to the appropriate V_n. The first order wave function is

$$(L.4) \qquad \psi_k = \frac{1}{L^{1/2}} \left[e^{ikx} + \sum_{k'} \frac{(k'|H'|k)}{W_k - W_{k'}} e^{ik'x} \right]$$

$$= \frac{1}{L^{1/2}} e^{ikx} \left[1 + \sum_n \frac{V_n}{W_k - W_{k'}} e^{-2\pi i n x/a} \right],$$

subject to $k' = k - 2\pi n/a$. The solution (L.4) is of the Bloch form as required. We have $W_{k'} = \hbar^2 k'^2/2m$. The energy to the second order is

$$(L.5) \qquad W_k = (\hbar^2 k^2/2m) + \sum_n \frac{|V_n|^2}{W_k - W_{k'}}.$$

The assumption on which this calculation is based is that the denominator

$$W_k - W_{k'} = \frac{\hbar^2}{2m} \left[k^2 - \left(k - \frac{2\pi n}{a} \right)^2 \right]$$

is not very small. The demonimator will, however, vanish for $k = \pi n/a$. In this case we must do a more careful calculation.

When k is close to $\pi n/a$, we may take the wave function as

(L.6) $\psi = e^{ikx}(A_0 + A_n e^{-2\pi i n x/a})$,

because the other Fourier coëfficients will be small. The coefficients A_0, A_n are determined by minimizing the energy

(L.7) $W = [W_0 A_0{}^2 + W_n A_n{}^2 + 2V_n A_0 A_n]/[A_0{}^2 + A_n{}^2]$;

here $W_0 = \hbar^2 k^2/2m$; $W_n = \hbar^2 (k - 2\pi n/a)^2/2m$,

and the mean value of V is taken to be zero; we have supposed that $V_n{}^* = V_n$.

At the minimum we have, by taking variations δA_0 and δA_n,

$$2A_0(W - W_0) - 2V_n A_n = 0;$$

$$-2V_n A_0 + 2A_n(W - W_n) = 0.$$

These equations have solutions for A_0, A_n only if

$$(W - W_0)(W - W_n) + V_n{}^2 = 0$$

or

(L.8) $W = \tfrac{1}{2}\{W_0 + W_n \pm [(W_0 - W_n)^2 + 4V_n{}^2]^{\frac{1}{2}}\}$.

The most interesting feature of this result is the discontinuity in energy for $k = \pi n/a$; we have at this point

(L.9) $\Delta W = 2|V_n|$,

so that energies lying between

$$(\hbar^2/2m)(n\pi/a)^2 \pm |V_n|$$

are forbidden.. We note that the Bragg condition for reflection is also $k = \pi n/a$, and this condition also marks the boundaries on the Kronig-Penney model. At the boundary the wave functions are standing waves which do not carry current.

For k just above the first gap we find on expanding (L.8) to the first order in $(W_0 - W_n)^2$ that, letting $k' = k - \pi/a$,

(L.10) $W \cong \dfrac{\hbar^2}{2m}\left[\left(\dfrac{\pi}{a}\right)^2 + k'^2\left(1 + \dfrac{4W_a}{\Delta W}\right)\right] + \Delta W/2$,

W_a being the energy at the gap, so that as far as dependence on k' is concerned

(L.11) $W - W_a = \dfrac{\hbar^2}{2m}\alpha k'^2$; $\alpha = 1 + \dfrac{4W_a}{\Delta W}$, which suggests that the electron behaves as if it had a mass

(L.12) $$m^* = m/\alpha.$$

THREE DIMENSIONS

In a three-dimensional simple cubic lattice

$$\cdot H' = \Sigma V_n e^{-2\pi i \mathbf{n} \cdot \mathbf{r}/a},$$

and the condition for non-vanishing matrix elements is

$$\mathbf{k}' = \mathbf{k} - 2\pi \mathbf{n}/a.$$

A forbidden zone occurs when

(L.13) $$k^2 = (\mathbf{k} - 2\pi \mathbf{n}/a)^2,$$

or

(L.14) $$\mathbf{n} \cdot \mathbf{k} = \pi n^2/a,$$

or

(L.15) $$k_x n_1 + k_y n_2 + k_z n_3 = \pi(n_1{}^2 + n_2{}^2 + n_3{}^2)/a.$$

M. TIGHT BINDING APPROXIMATION FOR METALLIC ELECTRONS

Suppose that the ground state of an electron moving in the potential $V(r)$ of an isolated atom is $\phi(r)$ and that the energy is W_0; suppose further that ϕ is an s state. The treatment of bands arising from degenerate $(p, d, \cdot \cdot \cdot)$ atomic levels is more complicated. If the influence of one atom on another is small, we get a zero order wave function for one electron in the whole crystal by taking

(M.1) $$\psi_k(\mathbf{r}) = \sum_j C_{kj} \phi(\mathbf{r} - \mathbf{r}_j),$$

where the sum is over all lattice points. This function is of the Bloch form if we take $C_{kj} = e^{i(\mathbf{k} \cdot \mathbf{r}_j)}$, which gives

(M.2) $$\psi_k(\mathbf{r}) = \sum_j e^{i(\mathbf{k} \cdot \mathbf{r}_j)} \phi(\mathbf{r} - \mathbf{r}_j).$$

We prove it is of the Bloch form by considering the effect of a translation by a vector $\mathbf{g}$ connecting two lattice points:

(M.3) $$\begin{aligned} \psi_k(\mathbf{r} + \mathbf{g}) &= \Sigma\, e^{i(\mathbf{k} \cdot \mathbf{r}_j)} \phi(\mathbf{r} + \mathbf{g} - \mathbf{r}_j) \\ &= e^{i(\mathbf{k} \cdot \mathbf{g})} \Sigma\, e^{i\mathbf{k} \cdot (\mathbf{r}_j - \mathbf{g})} \phi[\mathbf{r} - (\mathbf{r}_j - \mathbf{g})] \\ &= e^{i(\mathbf{k} \cdot \mathbf{g})} \psi_k(\mathbf{r}) \end{aligned}$$

so that the Bloch requirement is satisfied.

We get the first order energy by calculating the diagonal matrix elements of the perturbation $H'(r)$ expressing the difference between the potential in the crystal near an ion and the potential of an individual atom. We have

(M.4) $$(\mathbf{k}|H'|\mathbf{k}) = \sum_j \sum_m e^{i\mathbf{k}\cdot(\mathbf{r}_j - \mathbf{r}_m)} (\phi_m|H'|\phi_j);$$

writing $\varrho_m = \mathbf{r}_m - \mathbf{r}_j$ and treating all lattice points as equivalent,

(M.5) $$(\mathbf{k}|H'|\mathbf{k}) = N \sum_m e^{-i\mathbf{k}\cdot\varrho_m} \int \phi(\mathbf{r} - \varrho_m) H' \phi(\mathbf{r})\, dV.$$

If now we neglect all integrals except those between nearest neighbors connected by ϱ and write, for a crystal of N atoms,

(M.6) $$\int \phi^*(\mathbf{r}) H' \phi(\mathbf{r})\, dV = -\alpha/N;$$

(M.7) $$\int \phi^*(\mathbf{r} - \varrho) H' \phi(\mathbf{r})\, dV = -\gamma/N;$$

we get

$$(\mathbf{k}|H'|\mathbf{k}) = -\alpha - \gamma \sum_m e^{-i\mathbf{k}\cdot\varrho_m},$$

so that the first order energy is given by

(M.8) $$W = W_0 - \alpha - \gamma \sum e^{i(\mathbf{k}\cdot\varrho_m)}.$$

For a simple cubic lattice the nearest neighbor atoms are at the positions

(M.9) $$\varrho_m = (\pm a, 0, 0); \quad (0, \pm a, 0); \quad (0, 0, \pm a)$$

and

(M.10) $$W = W_0 - \alpha - 2\gamma(\cos k_x a + \cos k_y a + \cos k_z a),$$

so that the energies are confined to a band with limits $\pm 6\gamma$. For small k,

(M.11) $$W \cong W_0 - \alpha - 6\gamma + \gamma k^2 a^2.$$

The energy at the bottom of the band is independent of the direction of motion. The effective mass is

(M.12) $$m^* = \hbar^2/2\gamma a^2.$$

We see that for every state of an electron in the free atom there exists a band of energies in the crystal. We have considered here one state of the free atom and have obtained one band. The number of states in the zone which corresponds to a non-degenerate atomic level is equal to $2N$, where N is the number of atoms. We see this directly: (M.10) is periodic in k, and thus only values of k lying within a certain polyhedron in k-space will define independent wave functions. The gradient of W normal to the planes bounding this polyhedron will vanish, and in the simple cubic case the polyhydron is defined by $-\pi/a < k_x < \pi/a$, etc. The volume of the polyhedron is $8\pi^3/a^3$; now the number of states (counting both spin orientations) per unit volume of k-space is $1/4\pi^3$, so the number of states is $2/a^3 = 2N$.

N. BRILLOUIN ZONES OF GENERAL CRYSTAL STRUCTURES

In three dimensions the requirement that the lattice be periodic is

$$(N.1) \qquad V(\mathbf{r}) = V(\mathbf{r} + n_1\mathbf{a}_1 + n_2\mathbf{a}_2 + n_3\mathbf{a}_3),$$

where n_1, n_2, n_3 are integers; $\mathbf{a}_1$, $\mathbf{a}_2$, $\mathbf{a}_3$ are the basis vectors of the lattice. We expand the potential as

$$(N.2) \qquad V(\mathbf{r}) = \Sigma\, V_n e^{2\pi i \mathbf{n}\cdot\mathbf{r}},$$

where $\mathbf{n} = n_1\mathbf{b}_1 + n_2\mathbf{b}_2 + n_3\mathbf{b}_3$ is a point in the reciprocal lattice (Appendix A).

The matrix elements of the perturbation V in the plane wave representation vanish unless

$$\mathbf{k}' = \mathbf{k} + 2\pi\mathbf{n},$$

and the discontinuities in the energy occur when two states having initially the same energy combine under the influence of V—that is, when $(\mathbf{k}')^2 = (\mathbf{k} + 2\pi\mathbf{n})^2$, or

$$(\mathbf{n}\cdot\mathbf{k}) - \pi n^2 = 0.$$

This defines a plane in the reciprocal lattice. We construct the plane by joining the point $\mathbf{n}$ to the origin by a line, and drawing a plane perpendicular to this line through the midpoint.

Suppose that the structure contains s atoms per unit cell, and that the positions of these atoms in the unit cell are given by u_t, v_t, w_t. The Fourier components of the potential are

$$(N.3) \qquad V_n = \sum_{t=1}^{s} A_{nt} e^{2\pi i(n_1 u_t + n_2 v_t + n_3 w_t)}$$

If all the atoms in the cell are identical,

$$(N.4) \qquad V_n = A_n S_n,$$

$$(N.5) \qquad S_n = \sum_{t=1}^{s} e^{2\pi i(n_1 u_t + n_2 v_t + n_3 w_t)};$$

S_n is the *structure factor*, which is the principal factor determining the relative intensity of x-ray reflection from different crystal planes. Apparent zone boundaries for which the structure factor vanishes do not give rise to energy discontinuities.

EXAMPLE. *Face-centered lattice.* There are four atoms in the unit cell, at $(0, 0, 0)$; $(\frac{1}{2}, 0, \frac{1}{2})$; $(0, \frac{1}{2}, \frac{1}{2})$; $(\frac{1}{2}, \frac{1}{2}, 0)$. The structure factor is

$$S_{n_1, n_2, n_3} = 1 + \cos \pi(n_2 + n_3) + \cos \pi(n_3 + n_1) + \cos \pi(n_1 + n_2),$$

which gives

$$S_{100} = S_{110} = 0;$$

$$S_{111} = S_{200} = 4.$$

Thus the first zone is marked out by the $\{111\}$ and $\{200\}$ planes. The values of the free electron energy at different points on the zone boundary vary by a factor of about 2. Zones for other crystal structures are discussed in the book by Mott and Jones, Chap. 5. Zones for bcc and fcc lattices are shown in Fig. N.1.

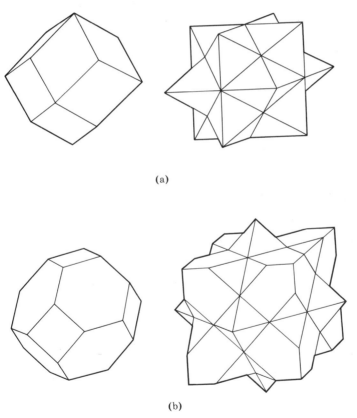

(a)

(b)

Fig. N.1. The first two Brillouin zones in (a) the bcc lattice and (b) the fcc lattice. (By permission from *Modern theory of solids*, by F. Seitz. Copyright, 1940. McGraw-Hill Book Co.)

Hume-Rothery pointed out that particular alloy phases often occur at the same ratio of valence electrons to atoms:

Phase	Electrons/Atom (observed)	Approximate Theoretical Critical Electron/Atom Ratios
α (fcc)	1.36–1.42	1.36
β (bcc)	1.48–1.50	1.48
γ (complex)	1.58–1.67	1.54

In the second column we list the observed concentrations at the boundaries of the α, β, and γ crystal structure phases. In the third column we list the concentrations for that value of the energy of free electrons for which the energy surfaces just touch the boundaries of the Brillouin zones. The energy of electrons in the actual lattice will increase especially rapidly for higher concentrations, so that it is plausible that phase changes might occur when these changes will permit the excess electrons to be accommodated within the lower zone. This is the zone theory of the Hume-Rothery rules.

O. ELECTRICAL CONDUCTIVITY AT LOW TEMPERATURES

At low temperatures the electrons may only be scattered through small angles, so the number of scattering processes needed to reduce the average forward momentum by a given fraction is increased.

The scattering angle at low temperatures is necessarily small because the phonon momentum available for transfer to the electron is small at low temperatures. The momentum of the electron is changed in the scattering process, and the difference appears as a change of momentum of an elastic wave. The phonon momentum P is of the order of kT/v_s, where $v_s \approx a\omega_{max}$ is the velocity of sound. The electron momentum at the top of the Fermi distribution is $p \approx \hbar/a$, so that

$$(O.1) \qquad\qquad P \approx (T/\Theta)p,$$

as $\Theta = \hbar\omega_{max}/k$. Thus for $T \ll \Theta$ we must have $\Delta p \cong P \ll p$. This means that the angle of scattering is $\approx T/\Theta$. The number of collisions in a time equal to the relaxation time is ≈ 1 for $T \gg \Theta$, as here the collisions may be nearly spherically symmetric, but for $T \ll \Theta$ there are $\approx (\Theta/T)^2$ collisions in a relaxation time as $(1 - \cos \phi)$ is the measure of the loss of forward momentum in a collision with scattering angle ϕ.

The number of phonons at low temperatures is proportional to T^3 on the Debye theory. The combined effect of the T^3 temperature dependence of the number of phonons and the T^2 dependence of the scattering angle factor makes the conductivity proportional to T^5.

P. MOBILITY IN INTRINSIC SEMICONDUCTORS

At first sight we might expect the effect of lattice scattering on mobility in semiconductors to be given by expression (13.52) for the electrical conductivity, where p^2 now would be taken as a suitable average over the Maxwellian velocity distribution of the electrons excited to the conduction band. However, in calculating the conductivity in Chapter 13 we made a tacit assumption which is quite good for the fast electrons at the top of the Fermi distribution in a metal, but which is a poor assumption for the electrons near the bottom of the conduction band in a semiconductor. In arriving at (13.46) we performed an operation equivalent to taking

$$(P.1) \qquad \text{grad } \psi = i\mathbf{k}\psi,$$

as for a plane wave. For the Bloch function

$$(P.2) \qquad \psi = u(\mathbf{r})e^{i\mathbf{k}\cdot\mathbf{r}}$$

we actually have

$$(P.3) \qquad \text{grad } \psi = \left[i\mathbf{k} + \frac{1}{u} \text{ grad } u \right]\psi,$$

so that for the small values of k $(ka \ll 1)$ of importance in the semiconductor problem it is a better approximation to take

$$(P.4) \qquad \text{grad } \psi \cong \left[\frac{1}{u} \text{ grad } u \right]\psi.$$

On redefining ψ_i in (13.40) and ψ_s in (13.41), and making other appropriate changes in the previous derivation, we may expect to replace (13.48) by a relation of the form

$$(P.5) \qquad \overline{Q_d} = G^2 d^2 \overline{Q_s},$$

where G is a factor involving something like $|\text{grad } u|^2$. The result (14.16) obtained by more accurate quantum-mechanical methods is more or less consistent with this expression for $\overline{Q_d}$.

Q. DERIVATION OF THE CONWELL-WEISSKOPF FORMULA

In the standard derivation of the Rutherford scattering formula it is shown that the angle θ through which the particle is deflected in a

Coulomb potential $e/\epsilon r$ is given in terms of the collision parameter b by the relation

(Q.1) $b = (e^2/\epsilon m v^2) \cot (\theta/2)$,

where v is the velocity of the incident particle of charge e. The collision parameter b is the distance of the nucleus from the line which would be followed by the particle if there were no Coulomb force. We are interested in the quantity $1 - \cos \theta$ as a measure of the loss of forward momentum on collision. By a trigonometric identity we have

(Q.2) $1 - \cos \theta = 2/[1 + (\epsilon m v^2 b/e^2)^2]$.

We suppose that the effective range of the interaction of an electron with a single ion is d, where d is related to the concentration N_e of ionized impurity atoms by

(Q.3) $d = \tfrac{1}{2} N e^{-\frac{1}{3}}$.

We are in effect saying here that the impurities are arranged on a simple cubic lattice of spacing $2d$ and that each impurity atom dominates the scattering within a sphere of radius d.

The probability that the collision parameter will have a value between b and $b + db$ is $2\pi b \, db/\pi d^2$, so that the average value of $1 - \cos \theta$ is

(Q.4) $\overline{1 - \cos \theta} = (1/\pi d^2) \int_0^d (1 - \cos \theta) 2\pi b \, db$

                          $= 2(e^2/\epsilon d m v^2)^2 \log [1 + (\epsilon d m v^2/e^2)^2]$.

The mean free path is approximately

(Q.5) $\Lambda \approx 2d/\overline{(1 - \cos \theta)}$.

The mobility (14.27), apart from a constant of the order of unity, follows from (Q.4) and (Q.5) after averaging over a Maxwellian distribution and making certain minor approximations.

R. FERMI LEVEL AND THE CHEMICAL POTENTIAL

Using the Boltzmann definition of the entropy,

(R.1) $S = k \log W$,

the variational equation leading to the Fermi-Dirac distribution function may be written as

(R.2) $$\delta\left(\frac{S}{k} - \alpha N - \beta U\right) = 0,$$

so that

(R.3) $$\alpha = \frac{1}{k}\left(\frac{\partial S}{\partial N}\right)_{U,V}.$$

Now the *chemical potential* μ is defined through

(R.4) $$dU = T\,dS - p\,dV + \mu\,dN$$

for a system in which the number of particles is allowed to vary. From (R.4),

(R.5) $$T\,dS = dU + p\,dV - \mu\,dN,$$

and

(R.6) $$\left(\frac{\partial S}{\partial N}\right)_{U,V} = -\frac{\mu}{T}.$$

Comparing (R.3) with (R.6), we have

(R.7) $$\alpha = -\mu/kT.$$

Now on looking back at the derivation of the Fermi-Dirac distribution function in Chapter 12 we see that $\alpha = -W_F/kT$. Therefore

(R.8) $$\mu = W_F;$$

the chemical potential is equal to the Fermi energy.

It is a well-known thermodynamic result[6] that the condition for two phases to be in equilibrium with respect to any chemical species (in this case the electrons) is that the chemical potential of that species should have the same value in the two phases. This result follows on considering the change of the Helmholtz free energy

(R.9) $$dF = p\,dV - S\,dT - \Sigma\mu\,dn$$

on transferring dn particles from phase i to phase j at constant volume and temperature:

(R.10) $$dF = -\mu_j\,dn + \mu_i\,dn.$$

For equilibrium $dF = 0$, whence we have the stated result

$$\mu_j = \mu_i.$$

[6] See, for example, M. W. Zemansky, *Heat and thermodynamics*, McGraw-Hill Book Co., New York, 3rd ed., 1951, pp. 391, 444.

This result has an important application to contact potential problems, for it tells us that in equilibrium the Fermi level must have a constant value in all conductors.

S. STRESSES AROUND A DISLOCATION

The theoretical results are reviewed by Cottrell.[7] For an edge dislocation along the z axis having a Burgers vector d, the stresses in the medium treated as a continuum are

$$X_z = -\frac{Gd}{2\pi(1-\nu)} \frac{y(3x^2+y^2)}{(x^2+y^2)^2};$$

$$Y_y = \frac{Gd}{2\pi(1-\nu)} \frac{y(x^2-y^2)}{(x^2+y^2)^2};$$

(S.1) $$Z_z = \nu(X_z + Y_y);$$

$$X_y = Y_x = \frac{Gd}{2\pi(1-\nu)} \frac{x(x^2-y^2)}{(x^2+y^2)^2};$$

$$Y_z = Z_y = X_z = Z_x;$$

here G is the shear modulus and ν is the Poisson ratio. The region immediately around the dislocation line must be excluded, as the stresses here are too large for linear elasticity theory to apply.

If we take the stress at any point to be the sum of the superposed stresses of each dislocation acting by itself, the elastic energy of two dislocations will be of the form

(S.2) $$(\sigma_1 + \sigma_2)^2 = \sigma_1{}^2 + \sigma_2{}^2 + 2\sigma_1\sigma_2,$$

where σ_i is the stress of the ith dislocation. The cross-product term $2\sigma_1\sigma_2$ is an interaction energy between the dislocations and leads to a force between them. The forces between a positive dislocation at the origin and a negative dislocation at (x_0, y_0) of (R, ϕ), where $\cos\phi = x_0/R$, are found in this way to be

$$F_R = -\frac{Gd^2}{2\pi(1-\nu)} \frac{1}{R};$$

(S.3)

$$F_\phi = -\frac{Gd^2}{2\pi(1-\nu)} \frac{\sin 2\phi}{R}.$$

[7] A. H. Cottrell, "Theory of dislocations," *Progress in metal physics*, Vol. I, pp. 77–126, Butterfields Scientific Publications, London, 1949.

Here the forces are those acting on the negative dislocation, and the general effect is that the dislocations attract each other with a force whose radial component varies inversely with the distance between them. For dislocations of the same sign equations (S.3) are reversed in sign, and the dislocations repel each other.

T. SUMMARY OF RESULTS OF THERMODYNAMICS AND STATISTICAL MECHANICS

We review here some of the central results of thermodynamics and statistical mechanics; for further reading there are a number of specialized texts. We mention among the more elementary texts those by Zemansky[8] and by Gurney.[9]

The first and second laws of thermodynamics lead to the relation

$$(T.1) \qquad\qquad dU = T\,dS + dW,$$

for a reversible process, that is, for a process occurring sufficiently slowly that there is always equilibrium between the system and its surroundings. For a reversible process $T\,dS$ is equal to dQ, the heat flow into the system; here S is the entropy. In (T.1), dU is the change in internal energy of the system and dW is the work done on the system by an external agency.

If the work is done mechanically by the pressure p, we have

$$(T.2) \qquad\qquad dW = -p\,dV;$$

if the work is done by a magnetic field (Appendix G) we have, per unit volume,

$$(T.3) \qquad\qquad dW = \mathbf{H} \cdot d\mathbf{M},$$

while for an electric field

$$(T.4) \qquad\qquad dW = \mathbf{E} \cdot d\mathbf{P}.$$

In what follows we shall use the connection (T.2), as the appropriate changes for the electric and magnetic problems may always be easily made.

It is useful to consider the Helmholtz free energy defined by

$$(T.5) \qquad\qquad F = U - TS,$$

[8] M. W. Zemansky, *Heat and thermodynamics*, McGraw-Hill Book Co., New York, 3rd ed., 1951.

[9] R. W. Gurney, *Introduction to statistical mechanics*, McGraw-Hill Book Co., New York, 1949.

and the Gibbs free energy defined by

(T.6) $$G = U - TS + pV.$$

Using (T.1) and (T.2), we have

(T.7) $$dF = -S\,dT - p\,dV;$$

(T.8) $$dG = -S\,dT + V\,dp.$$

Thus, in an isothermal reversible change $(dT = 0)$ at constant volume

(T.9) $$dF = 0,$$

and at constant pressure

(T.10) $$dG = 0.$$

These conditions for equilibrium are frequently the basis of the applications of thermodynamics to solid state problems.

The central result of statistical mechanics is that in thermal equilibrium the probability of finding a system in a state i is proportional to $e^{-W_i/kT}$, where W_i is the energy of the state. Thus the average value of a quantity x is given by

(T.11) $$\bar{x} = \sum_i x_i e^{-W_i/kT} / \sum_i e^{-W_i/kT},$$

where x_i is the value of x when the system is in the state i, and the sum is over all states.

Defining the partition function Z as

(T.12) $$Z = \sum_i e^{-W_i/kT},$$

the Helmholtz free energy F is given by

(T.13) $$e^{-F/kT} = Z.$$

This result follows from the definition of F and from (T.11).

Using the celebrated Boltzmann definition of the entropy is the best way to get physical insight into the significance of entropy. Boltzmann shows that

(T.14) $$S = k \log w,$$

where w is the number of possible independent arrangements of the particles in the system. Thus a system of spins all lined up has zero entropy, but in random orientations may have a high entropy, as in (9.20).

U. VALUES OF GENERAL PHYSICAL CONSTANTS

Source: J. W. M. Du Mond and E. R. Cohen, "A least squares adjustment of the atomic constants, as of Dec. 1950," published by the National Research Council, Washington, D.C., 1951.

Quantity	Value
Avogadro's number, L	$(6.025438 \pm 0.000107) \times 10^{23}$ g mol^{-1} (phys.)
Electronic charge, e	$-(4.802233 \pm 0.000071) \times 10^{-10}$ esu
Electron rest mass, m	$(9.107208 \pm 0.000246) \times 10^{-28}$ grams
Planck's constant, h	$(6.623773 \pm 0.000180) \times 10^{-27}$ erg sec
(h-"bar"), $\hbar$	$(1.054206 \pm 0.000028) \times 10^{-27}$ erg sec
Velocity of light, c	(299790.22 ± 0.86) km sec^{-1}
Faraday constant, $F = Ne$	$(2.893556 \pm 0.000021) \times 10^{13}$ esu g mol^{-1} (phys.)
Specific charge of the electron, e/m	$(1.758897 \pm 0.000032) \times 10^{7}$ emu g^{-1}
Compton radian length of the electron, $\lambda_{ce} = \hbar/mc$	$(3.8612050 \pm 0.0000516) \times 10^{-11}$ cm
First Bohr radius, $a_0 = \hbar^2/me^2$	$(5.291508 \pm 0.000035) \times 10^{-9}$ cm
Classical radius of the electron, $r_0 = e^2/mc^2$	$(2.817515 \pm 0.000056) \times 10^{-13}$ cm
Atomic weight of hydrogen	1.0081284 (phys.) ± 0.0000030
Ratio proton mass to electron mass	1836.1388 ± 0.0339
Boltzmann's constant, k	$(1.3802565 \pm 0.0000615) \times 10^{-16}$ erg deg^{-1}
Bohr magneton, $\mu_B = e\hbar/2mc$	$-(0.92712031 \pm 0.0000219) \times 10^{-20}$ erg gauss^{-1}
Wavelength associated with 1 ev, λ_0	$(12396.44 \pm 0.174) \times 10^{-8}$ cm
Frequency associated with 1 ev, ν_0	$(2.418357 \pm 0.000032) \times 10^{14}$ sec^{-1}
Wave number associated with 1 ev, k_0	(8066.832 ± 0.113) cm^{-1}
Energy associated with 1 ev	$(1.601864 \pm 0.000024) \times 10^{-12}$ erg
Energy associated with unit wave number	$(1.985742 \pm 0.000054) \times 10^{-16}$ erg
Speed of 1-ev electron	$(5.931099 \pm 0.000055) \times 10^{7}$ cm sec^{-1}
Energy associated with 1° Kelvin	$(8.616562 \pm 0.000357) \times 10^{-5}$ ev
"Temperature" associated with 1 ev	(11605.556 ± 0.480)°K
Loschmidt's number, n_0	$(2.687444 \pm 0.000067) \times 10^{19}$ cm^{-3}

Author Index

Subject Index

Supermalloy, 169, 177
Superstructure lines, 301
Surface states, 289
Susceptibility, antiferromagnetism, 191, 198
  diamagnetic, 134
    measurement of, 139
    table, 136
  dielectric, 94
  magnetic, definition, 134
  metals, 233, 257, 258
    table, 236
  paramagnetic, 143
Symmetry, elements, 8
  macroscopic, 8
  rotation axes, 8
Systems, crystal, 10
Szigeti relations, 99

$T^{3/2}$ law, 164, 362
Taylor-Orowan dislocation, 324, 325, 326
Taylor theory, 331
Temperature, Fermi, 229
  lowest reached, 151
  melting, of metals, 57
Tetragonal system, 9, 10
Tetrahedral bonding, 16
Thallium-activated KCl, 316
Thermal conductivity, alloys, 244
  metals, 243
  non-metals, 81
  superconductors, 208
  table, 86
  theory, 245
Thermal expansion, 78
  table, 79
Thermionic emission, 236
Thermodynamics, summary, 375
  superconductivity, 209
Thermoelectric effects, 247
  in superconductors, 208
Threshold field curves, superconductors, 201
Tourmaline, 113
Transistors, 291
  characteristics, 293
  junction, 296, 297
  mechanism, 292

Transistors, n-p-n, 297
  point contact, 291
Transition, barium titanate, 118, 119
  ferroelectric, first and second order, 126, 127
  ND_4Cl, 104
Transition layer, 183
Transition metals, 258
  band theory, 269
  oxides, conductivity, 299
Transition temperature, superconductors, table, 207, 208
Translation group, 11
Transverse waves, 51, 57
Traps, electron, 319
Triclinic system, 9, 10
Trigonal system, 10
Tungsten trioxide, antiferroelectricity in, 131

U-centers, 313
Ultimate temperature, adiabatic demagnetization, 151
Ultrasonic frequency, 63
Ultrasonic method, 50
Ultraviolet transparency of metals, 242
Unit cell, 11, 13

V-centers, 313, 315, 316
Vacancy diffusion, 341, 342
Valency, connection with conductivity, 261
van de Waals forces, 7
van Leeuwen theorem, 158
Van Vleck paramagnetism, 147, 354
Velocity, electrons at Fermi surface, 240
  group, 69
  phase, 63
  sound, 57

Wagner interfacial polarization, 111
Wall, Bloch, 183
Water, dielectric constant, 100
Wave equation, free particles, 223
Wave functions, Bloch, 249, 251
  tight binding, 366
  weak binding, 364
Wave vector, 61
Weiss constant, 161, 162